D1000297

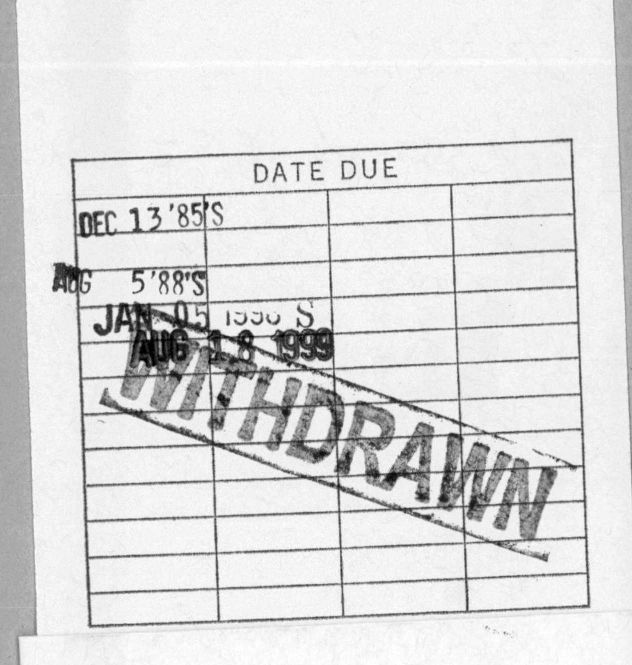
DATE DUE
DEC 13 '85 S
AUG 5 '88 S
AUG 18 1999
WITHDRAWN

STARGAZERS AND GRAVEDIGGERS

ALSO BY IMMANUEL VELIKOVSKY

Worlds in Collision 1950

Ages in Chaos 1952

Earth in Upheaval 1955

Oedipus and Akhnaton: Myth and History 1960

Peoples of the Sea 1977

Ramses II and His Times 1978

Mankind in Amnesia 1982

STARGAZERS AND GRAVEDIGGERS

Memoirs to
Worlds in Collision

IMMANUEL VELIKOVSKY

WILLIAM MORROW AND COMPANY, INC.
New York 1983

Library of Congress Cataloging in Publication Data

Velikovsky, Immanuel, 1895-1979.
Stargazers and gravediggers.

Includes index.
1. Velikovsky, Immanuel, 1895-1979. Worlds in collision. I. Title.
QB601.V443V43 1983 523.2 82-14463
ISBN 0-688-01545-X

Printed in the United States of America

First Edition

1 2 3 4 5 6 7 8 9 10

Book design by Bernard Schleifer

CONTENTS

FILE II

FILE III

STARGAZERS
AND
GRAVEDIGGERS

INTRODUCTION
Eric Larrabee

AN ADMISSION must be made at the outset that when this book was being written, more than a quarter century ago, some of us who read the manuscript believed the author should not complete or publish it. There were questions of confidentiality in a number of the documents quoted and of dignity and appropriateness in responding to criticism which was not at a high level of intellectual discourse. Those who knew Velikovsky appreciated that he had enough work ahead of him as it was without his turning aside to answer people who had so clearly taken leave of their better selves. The readers of the pages that follow will find described (and accurately, as I can testify) a response to Velikovsky's books which, had it not come from distinguished figures in various fields of science and scholarship, would have been unworthy of serious attention. Readers too young to remember will find their credulity strained, but it happened.

On the other hand, why give time or trouble at a late date to such a disagreeable affair? For one thing the chapter is not closed. Velikovsky's work may still be dismissed in many quarters, but its substance has not been so "disproved" as its opponents may wish to think. For another, passions have abated somewhat. Many of the principals are no longer alive, and the extremity of disdain anyone who encountered it will recall has dissipated. More than a few of Velikovsky's proposals which seemed so outrageous at the time are now commonplace. Finally, and by no means least, there is a moral to be drawn.

Scholars and scientists must regularly remind themselves of how fragile their institutions of free and open discussion are unless unorthodoxy is tolerated, if not protected. In this instance, despite repeated protestations of open-mindedness and high principle, it was not. Large numbers of intelligent men and women who prided themselves on their enlightenment and decency behaved very badly. They betrayed the tradition they professed to serve; they undermined the foundation of trust on which intellectual dialogue depends.

My copy of the first (Macmillan) edition of *Worlds in Collision* is inscribed to "the torchbearer," a gesture on Velikovsky's part that gave more credit than I deserved. A considerable amount of accident brought it about that an article of mine in *Harper's Magazine* for January 1950 was the first to expound his thesis in any detail (John J. O'Neill of the *Herald Tribune* was the first, as this book tells, to recognize Velikovsky's coming impact). The *Harper's* article appeared some three months before the book did, so that in the interval the burden of the notoriety it aroused and such defense as could be mustered fell on the magazine and its editors. We must have received thirty or so lengthy letters from angry and offended subscribers, a substantial outpouring as such things go, and we drafted a reply suggesting that any verdict be postponed until *Worlds in Collision* had been published and could be evaluated in its own right. This satisfied no one; we were having our first exposure to the intensity of controversy to come. How *Harper's* had become involved in it therefore needs to be explained.

The editor in chief of *Harper's Magazine* was then Frederick Lewis Allen. The Allens were friends of James Putnam, Velikovsky's editor at Macmillan, and Putnam had told them that a book he was going to publish contained the extraordinary assertion that while the sun stood still for Joshua at midday, there were legends among the pre-Columbian American Indians of a time when the night had lasted too long or the sun had risen slightly above the horizon and stood still. It was one of those arresting items which stick in the mind, and it became a part of the Allens' repertory of bits and pieces of information they delighted in. If true, how come? If the legend had migrated from one place to another, how could it have done so in the later knowledge that the earth is round, that it rotates, and that its circumference is such that midday in Egypt would be late night or early morning in Central America? Another editor at *Harper's*, Merle Miller, had also heard the Allens tell the story. When he saw a prepublication announcement of *Worlds in Collision,* he made the connection and sent to Macmillan for an advance copy of the galley proofs.

We all read them and wanted to publish whatever part or parts we could. I was assigned the job of reducing them, by judicious cutting and trimming, to a usable manuscript of perhaps several installments of 4,000 to 5,000 words each. Shortly I had to report failure. Deprived of its cumulative reinforcing detail, Velikovsky's argument lost much of its persuasiveness and at best was forbiddingly complex for magazine purposes. If we were going to print anything, it would have to be an article *about* Velikovsky's theory, which Mr. Allen thereupon asked me to write since I was the one most familiar with it conveniently at hand. This seemed to me a poor idea. I pointed out that I had no standing as a science writer and no visible qualifications therefor. But Fred, when he badly wanted a contribution to *Harper's,* could be persuasive, and over my reluctance I was persuaded. The unsuccessful cut version of *Worlds in Collision* became the basis for an attempt to describe it.

All this had gone on without Velikovsky's knowledge, as he recorded, for he was out of the country. When he returned, it was clear I should go see him, both to persuade him—against *his* better judgment—that an article in *Harper's* before the book appeared would be suitable and useful and—at least privately, on my part—for me to convince myself that he was what he purported to be, a bona fide scholar. It is pleasant to read now his recollection of that meeting, in his apartment on 113th Street near Columbia University, for I remember it well. I had done a spot check on such of his sources I had access to and took along a list of some twenty questions raised by issues where he was most obviously in conflict with the prevailing wisdom. The readiness of his answers on this occasion, as at many times later in our conversations, more than convinced me that he knew what he was about and that there were depths beneath the surface of this heretic. Then began the process of working toward a text which satisfied us both.

Velikovsky's view, as will be seen, was that any summary which appeared before the book did should not try to tell too much. He did not mind the catastrophes being described, but he would have preferred their agent—the protoplanet Venus—not to be identified. From his point of view he was undoubtedly correct; he well understood that most of us can digest only so much unorthodoxy at one swallow (I was reminded of H. L. Mencken's remark that if

Darwin had published *The Origin of Species* chapter by chapter in obscure journals, he would have been archbishop of Canterbury by the time he finished). But I was necessarily aware, from my point of view, that having read the entire book, I could not very well omit any of the most important elements of it and that, besides, the explication of so many familiar and evocative mysteries—"How art thou fallen from heaven, O Lucifer, son of the morning!"—was among his most impressive achievements. We argued and argued, and if I finally won his consent, it was not wholehearted, as he makes clear. In retrospect I think we both realized it would not have made much difference which course we had taken, so live were the nerves he was about to touch.

More than once since I have been chided for the sin of innocence in taking him at face value. There were many reasons for doing so, and while reconstructing a frame of mind so far back in the past is risky, I should try. Setting aside entirely the force of Velikovsky's contention that human traditions uniformly record overwhelming natural catastrophes within historical times and that numerous physical evidences offer the same testimony, there were also qualities in *Worlds in Collision* favoring its reception that struck me as evident to any dispassionate reader.

First, it was internally coherent. Once the essential premise was accepted (this *might* have occurred), its parts fell into place and did not jar with one another. That is, the overall scheme "explained" the subordinate parts just as a well-formulated hypothesis should.

Second, it in no way involved the supernatural, even by implication. Either Velikovsky's thesis could be proved scientifically or it would fall to pieces. Far from seeking to confirm fundamentalist beliefs (as he was accused of doing), he offered them the most fundamental challenge of all, which was to provide a natural interpretation of "miraculous" events rather than merely to dismiss them as legendary.

Third, it took into account its own conflicts with established theory. Velikovsky's words in this respect were carefully chosen, especially in his epilogue, where he summarized the problems he knew he was presenting for ancient history, the origins of religion, psychology, geology, paleontology, and, not least, astronomical physics. Being aware of these, he made explicit what conclusions must necessarily follow from his, and what would therefore invalidate him if they did not. He was in this sense self-correcting.

Fourth, it illuminated dilemmas which had previously been obscure. Why primitive man was terrified by natural phenomena, which presumably he had been living with for millennia, was unclear. Why mankind identified its gods with planets, and the most powerful among them with two that even today most people cannot identify in the sky, was unaccounted for, let alone why universal tradition told of their warfare with one another and of disruptions in the celestial sphere which caused devastation on Earth. Why was early man so obsessed with the misbehavior of heavenly bodies which, as we assumed, had always pursued their courses before his eyes with infallible regularity? The conventional explanations did not make sense. Velikovsky was the first in our time to face them head-on by proposing an alternative.

Here I must digress and say something of the Velikovskys in a human context. Their household was to any guest invited into it a civilized and familial one, where music and art were routinely at home and where the Western humanist, rationalist, and religious inheritance was held in respect. You knew this from the moment you entered it, whether in New York City or later in the modest house in Princeton where he lived out his days and completed what time allowed him of his task. My wife and I enjoyed their hospitality often. Another inscription, in the flyleaf of *Ages in Chaos*, reads: "To Eleanor and Eric, young but old friends, who are part of myself and my books," and it records something of the affection and respect I had for him.

As an editor I had tried to be accessible to enthusiasts possessed by one or another strange notion and had come to be, I hope by experience, familiar with the characteristics such people have in common. To my mind Velikovsky did not indicate them. By his own description he was "the prisoner of an idea," but after all, why not? What an idea! He was tenacious in discussion when he had an end in view, but he played fair. He was a profoundly traditional man (his copy of the Hebrew Old Testament was well thumbed) and deeply conscious of his origins ("I come of an obdurate race," he said one time). He gave a strong sense of relating to the European academic environment, which is less rigid and formalistic than the American in certain ways. But he was not a fanatic, religious or otherwise. He could step aside and observe his own situation almost objectively, and he took it as given that on many points he might turn out to be wrong (the fact that he repeatedly proposed tests of his theories and sought professional consultation about them reinforces this view). Above all, he had a sense of humor. His manner on first meeting could be patriarchal—as sometimes his writing style is—but on acquaintance he mellowed a lot. I like to think that the longer he lived in the United States and got to know the nonacademic side of our culture, the freer rein he gave to the playful part of his nature, though I doubt that he was ever quite able to accept Einstein's admonition to him that he "enjoy the whole episode from its humorous side."

In the course of things I became Velikovsky's editor for the reply to his critics he prepared for *Harper's* and for his reply to John Stewart's reply to him. Later I drew on his help for a subsequent *Harper's* article (July 1963) attempting to give him credit for validations of his theory it seemed to me were going unrecognized and for a further reply to Donald Menzel's reply to me (I have been wrongly praised for the short shrift Menzel was given; the rebuttal was effective, but it was Velikovsky's doing in my words). As the years passed, our paths diverged. I am not by nature a proselytizer; the role of the Ancient Mariner buttonholing one wedding guest in three is not mine. If an argument is well presented and some fail to perceive this, I tend to think of it as their problem. That is a matter of one's temperament and trust in the scientific process; I still believe that if and where Velikovsky was right, he will prevail. But I know I disappointed him.

An obligation which nonetheless did fall on those of us who had helped put Velikovsky's ideas before the public was to keep track of how they fared. It went without saying that we might have been wrong and that the time could come when this must be acknowledged. There would have to be some forethought given to the means of recognizing that moment if it arrived. One had to be clear in one's own mind, that is, what would constitute proof that Velikovsky was mistaken. That there would be objection was obvious, though none of us anticipated its violence. But the mere statement that Velikovsky did not conform to currently accepted doctrine, no matter how elaborately and firmly asserted, was not enough: It was self-evident. Similarly, the fact that he was not a member of the professional guilds he was challenging, and had disregarded some of their ground rules, was equally in the nature of the situation and did not constitute a compelling objection to what he was saying. But what would be the ways in which he could be *proved* wrong? There were roughly a half dozen I could think of.

We all would have to confess serious doubts if:

—he were shown to have misquoted or misrepresented the data to make them fit his theory,

—there were to exist recorded astronomical observations prior to −687 which conform to retrograde calculations from the present on an assumption of uniformity,

—there were to be found consistent remains (ruins, tree rings, historical records, etc.) which survived the period c. −1500 without any indication of disturbed tranquility,

—carbon 14 dating were to show that the conventional chronology for the New Kingdom in Egypt or the "Hittite" kingdom in Turkey was correct,

—the predictions which Velikovsky himself had proposed as tests of his theory were not to be fulfilled, or

—some other theory were to provide an equally satisfactory explanation of the geological evidence for sudden shifts in climate or sea level, the deposits formed by animals in vast numbers that had died violent deaths, or the many other puzzling anomalies Velikovsky had cited.

At one time or another he was said by his critics to have failed some or all of these tests—or, in the case of his own predictions, his success was discounted as accidental. But on examination the charges against him have again and again proved to be flimsy or worse. He had not misrepresented his data, quite the contrary; his opponents were frequently found to have misread, misquoted, inaccurately transcribed, or distorted their own sources. There are no astronomical observations firmly dated prior to −687 that sustain the assumption of uniformity or remains from c. −1500 which do not testify to convulsions of nature on a massive scale. The tale of Velikovsky and carbon 14 is a tangled one, to be told elsewhere, but there are strong suggestions in the record that laboratory tests have supported his chronology more than once. As for rival theories, there have been many, but none that so combine what he drew from different disciplines to form a unified reconstruction of the buried past.

From its early stages to the present the history of the Velikovsky controversy has seemed to me to be one of continuous retreat on the part of orthodox science. Few of the arguments his early opponents found so impressive are heard any longer from scientists and scholars (though they are tirelessly repeated by popularizers). Even the most conspicuous of his current antagonists says that "there is nothing absurd in the possibility of cosmic collisions" and that the escape of a planet from Jupiter, an interruption in the rotation of the earth, or a shift in the terrestrial axis is possible, if unlikely. None of these was a permissible conjecture thirty years ago, when Velikovsky was ridiculed for giving them credence. But today "collisions and catastrophism"—the same critic speaking—"are part and parcel of modern astronomy."

The same is true of the evolutionary sciences of biology and paleontology, which emerged historically in the nineteenth century by vanquishing their catastrophist adversaries; they still bear the scars of that debate. The uniformitarian or gradualist doctrine as Lyell established it in geology (for subsequent adoption by Darwin) held that no force could be invoked as an effective cause that could not—like erosion, sedimentation, and volcanic activity—be seen at work today. But this was a circular and self-confirming argument; if a unique event had in fact occurred, the rule would prevent it from ever being demonstrated. And in biology the rule was reversed: No one had ever seen a species evolve.

When Velikovsky first proposed a catastrophist version of evolution (in *Earth in Upheaval*), it was again dismissed or ignored, despite the clear possibility that catastrophes generating or accompanied by radiation could cause mutations in a way gradual Darwinian evolution could not. Recent writing on evolution—such as Steven M. Stanley's *The New Evolutionary Timetable* (1981)—emphasizes the myriad species over millions of years that have experienced no evolutionary change whatever; the mass extinctions which repeatedly overcame species, like the dinosaurs, that were wholly "successful" in the Darwinian struggle to survive; and the species, like our own, that emerged abruptly (and quite recently) with all our characteristics intact. Stanley calls the model currently accepted by paleobiologists of his persuasion one of "punctuational" evolution. What might have done the punctuating is what Velikovsky tried to show, calling on the same evidence in the fossil record. The questions he raised are at least now recognized as valid.

Why, if in so short a time his heresies have lost their stigma of the totally unacceptable, were they greeted on their appearance with such antagonism? A number of explanations have been put forward, many having to do with the sociology of science and its "reception system" in actual performance, as opposed to the picture of it as open and value-free which many scientists cherish. Others have noted that in the 1950's scientists (especially those who were politically active) felt themselves to be a beleaguered minority, little listened to by the public; here at last was a matter on which they could pronounce with authority! Still others have argued that science as an institution *must* reject implausibilities (that is, conclusions contrary to current theory), regardless of how convincing the evidence on their behalf, in order to retain its integrity as a functioning system. Velikovsky himself speculated that the extravagance of emotion directed at him was a result of inner doubt he had evoked among those who had hitherto managed to conceal it from themselves. To these I would add only the observation of the Australian David Stove that there was a wide open door in the doctrine of regular, clocklike planetary order on which much of modern science's self-confidence rested, and this unlicensed, presumptuous outsider had had the audacity to walk in through it and announce that the assumption of gradualism, uniformity, and regularity in the solar system was that and no more, an assumption.

A view of the often delayed responses by science to innovation that casts some light on Velikovsky's case was provided by Thomas Kuhn in his influential *The Structure of Scientific Revolutions* (1962). Kuhn saw conventional science as essentially noninnovative, a patient elaboration on the opportunities for investigation created by the successful establishment of a theory, which he called a paradigm. This was an effective instrument for interpreting facts; without it they are, in A. N. Whitehead's word, inert. Given the imperfection of human intelligence, a paradigm would be imperfect. There would be a few facts (anomalies) that had to be left out because they did not fit. The theory could account for most of the facts, hence its success, and it would prove fruitful in the elucidation of more and more of them. At the same time, however, as investigation proceeded, the number of anomalies would increase, until finally they became so numerous that the paradigm itself was cast in doubt. At this juncture there would arise a new paradigm that was able to incorporate not only the previously organized facts but the anomalies as well. In time the sequence would be repeated. This is precisely what has been happening to the paradigm of uninterrupted regularity in the history of the planet Earth during the memory of humans. The anomalies—facts unexplainable under that particular theoretical umbrella—have been accumulating at a lively rate or, rather, since they were always there, have been receiving an amount of attention embarrassingly difficult to ignore. The anomalies are not Velikovsky's fault; they would have been there whether or not he had existed. He merely accelerated the process of their recognition by the decisive and thoroughly legitimate act of offering a new paradigm.

The case against him now principally reduces itself to a question of time. Yes, these things might have happened, but not so recently as 2,500 to 3,500 years ago. Yes, the rocks on the moon might have been molten when they picked up their remanent magnetism, but not recently. Yes, Venus is hot, but not because it is a recent member of the solar system. Yes, Mars is a devastated planet, but not because it was recently involved in planetary near collisions. That is to say, the astronomers with whom so much of Velikovsky's account is concerned have taken a step backward and left the brunt of the contest to the geologists, who are charged with the time scale of the powerful forces which they know all too well have shaped the surface of our planet. Mountain building was recent; changes in sea level and sedimentation on the seabed floor were recent; phenomena we attribute to the end of the last ice age, like the creation of Niagara Falls, were recent. It will be interesting to see how many years pass before the geologists, too, will be willing to say: Yes, it might have happened.

New York City
June 1982

Contra argumenta dictum est
contra testes dicendum est.

—SENECA

file i

FREUD AND HIS HEROES

By the beginning of April 1940 eight months had passed since my wife and I and our two daughters, school-age children, arrived in the United States on July 26, 1939, from the land of Israel, at the time under British mandate. That day, after a few hours on Ellis Island, we traveled by ferry to Manhattan, and on the way I said to a friend, a doctor whom we had known in Europe and who had come to meet us: "We will remain in this country eight months, but if my work on a book should be of greater promise than I can at present anticipate, then we have a longer plan, too: We shall remain in this country for two years." The means we had with us would last that long.

"Do you expect to go back if in eight months the gates of fame do not open before you?" asked my friend. As we gazed at the skyline of lower Manhattan, he added: "Whatever your plans are, expect to be completely obscure in this country after eight months."

It was not fame that beckoned me to these shores; it was the last chance, as I regarded it, to emancipate myself from the daily routine of an overburdened doctor-psychoanalyst and to give my full time to research. Actually I had with me the pages of a manuscript I had begun, "Freud and His Heroes." Free from all other duties, I intended to finish and publish it in the United States. I could not forget that when I was in Paris in 1937, participating in the International Psychological Congress, I had shown an outline of an earlier work on psychology, with biological and philosophical aspects, broadly laid down, to Presses Universitaires, and it had been accepted for publication—but I had never finished it. In December of the same year, 1937, I lost my father. Seeing war approach, I realized that if I did not go to the United States and devote myself completely to the work I had embarked upon, years, away from large libraries, would devour my last chance, and I would remain a busy healer of men all my life.

This new manuscript on "Freud and His Heroes" was inspired by Freud's last book, *Moses and Monotheism.* I disagreed with Freud and saw in the octogenarian a still-unresolved conflict with respect to his Jewish origin and his own father. I turned to his dreams to know more of him than his books could tell. I found that his own dreams, sixteen in number, interspersed among numerous dreams of his patients in his classic *The Interpretation of Dreams,* spoke a language that was very clear but had meaning which Freud did not comprehend—or did not reveal to his readers. All the dreams dealt with the problem of his Jewish origin, the tragic fate of his people, his deliberations on leaving the ranks of the persecuted for the sake of unhampered advancement—or at least in order to free his children from the fate of underprivileged Jews in Christian and anti-Semitic Vienna. From this conflict, in which he struggled with himself, he emerged victorious in the last years before the turn of the century, about the time when, unknown and obscure, he wrote his book on dreams.

To reinterpret the dreams of the founder of modern dream interpretation was certainly a daring enterprise, but I used a method that carried a certain guarantee of objectivity. Besides, having found the same idea in all sixteen dreams, I believed, following Freud's premise, that "those ideas in the dream-thoughts which are most important are probably also those which recur most frequently." This reinterpretation of Freud's dreams would have constituted the part of the book dealing with the psychoanalyst himself. Other chapters were to deal with his heroes: Oedipus, Akhnaton, and Moses. A very unusual idea struck me when I studied the life of Akhnaton: It appeared to me that I had found the historical prototype of the Oedipus legend. About Moses I did not yet have much to say that was new. I hoped an idea would come to me in time.

We arrived in this country five weeks before the war in Europe started. Soon after our arrival I was surprised to hear Stanley Baldwin, former prime minister of Great Britain, speaking in Carnegie Hall at a Convention of Education for Democracy, reply to a question of whether or not there would be a war: "No. If I thought that there was a chance of war, I would not be here now." In a couple of weeks there was war.

In September came the news that Freud had died in England. When, a few years earlier, I had invited him to come to Israel, he replied that he wished very much to come, "I would like to travel and there is no place I would like to go as much—but I am an invalid who with effort subsists in the comfort of his home." Now, an octogenarian, he had had to leave Vienna to die in England. His death was also a personal shock to me, for I was about to mail him my reinterpretation of his dreams when the news of his death came. He, I thought, would have immediately recognized the correctness of my reinterpretation; this I could not expect from his pupils.*

For eight months I worked in the library on Forty-second Street, mainly on books dealing with the Egyptian past—the time of Akhnaton—and with Greek legends, especially of the Oedipus cycle. I saw my ideas substantiated. During that time I made the acquaintance of two distinguished elderly men: Professor Franz Boas, the noted anthropologist, father-in-law of the man who had met us at Ellis Island on our arrival; and Justice Louis Brandeis, whom I met but once, spending a late afternoon in his bedroom that was also his study. A valuable friendship developed with Professor Horace M. Kallen, of the New School for Social Research, whom I can best characterize in the words "humanist and humanitarian." I showed him the chapters of my book on Freud dealing with Oedipus and Akhnaton. He was impressed, and even years later he advised me to put all other work aside and bring out that book. In the early spring of 1940 he offered to help find a publisher for my manuscript. He had published a series of books and could well advise such an inexperienced author as myself. He also was, as his books reveal, well acquainted with the Greek heritage and could evaluate my idea on Oedipus. He took my manuscript and gave it to a publisher of his acquaintance. I scarcely knew who the publisher was; I was told only that he, himself new in New York, had recently had great success with a book by a foreign author.

Now the eight months were over. The children were longing to return to their homeland, from which they had been rather suddenly uprooted; I thought my task was nearly finished after eight

* Cf. Ernest Jones, *The Life and Work of Sigmund Freud* (1955) vol. II, pp. 17, 464; see also Otto Fenichel in *Psychoanalytic Quarterly* (1944), p. 123.

months spent in the library of 4 million books—there is no end to the time one can spend in a library—and I decided to go home. Italy had not yet entered the war, and I had a travel agent cable Rome for plane reservations from there to Tel Aviv. On Friday, April 6, 1940, at ten o'clock in the morning, I went to the agent's office to pick up the tickets for our passage that afternoon on an Italian liner to Naples. The children went to school for the last time, and my wife packed the last pieces of clothing in the valises.

The agent was not yet in his office at the appointed hour. Looking at my list of places to go to arrange things before leaving New York, I found that the closest—just a few doors away from where the travel agent had his office—was the office of the publisher who had my manuscript. Since Kallen had given it to him only a short time before, I did not expect that it had already been read. The publisher's wife met me with these words: "We are very excited about your manuscript. We would like to publish it."

"But I am leaving, and I came to take the manuscript."

"Oh, no, it is a fascinating book. Please stay, and let us publish it."

"But I have passage for myself and my family, and we leave tomorrow. Because it will be Saturday, we are going on board today before sunset."

"Could you possibly arrange for Professor Kallen to sign a contract for you?"

"Yes," I replied, "that is a good idea."

I called my wife from an ice-cream parlor and told her of the unexpected success. "Do we go?" she asked.

"Yes," I answered, "we leave."

I went on to attend to the various affairs on my list. I withdrew the balance of our account from the bank. From Radio City, where I went to get our Italian visas, I called home again and was given this message: "The publisher called here after he spoke to Kallen. He asks you in the name of Kallen to remain in America for two or three weeks and arrange the deal yourself. Kallen says that after you have spent so much effort in this country, it would be unwise for you to leave before settling the matter of the publication of your book."

It was a very hot day for early April. I was already exhausted, and the logic of remaining a few more weeks appealed to me, now that the energy of motion and the heat of the day had drained me of the driving power that is, in Kurt Lewin's law in psychology, the urge to go on by the inertia of a decision.

I called home a little later to say that I had decided to stay. Out of those three weeks grew years; out of an unfinished book grew new books. And I am still at the beginning, if I measure what has been done against what remains to be done.

Is it important to tell what happened to that manuscript? When I returned the following Tuesday, expecting to be offered a contract, I found the publisher, whom I had not seen before, without the exclamations and the enthusiasm of his wife. He said to me: "You must first finish the manuscript. Then we can consider the signing of a contract."

"But was I not asked to remain in this country for that purpose last Friday?"

"We are certainly interested in your book. But if there is a misunderstanding, then it is better that we return the manuscript now."

The publisher's wife was present; she sat apart in the room, listened, chewed gum, and said nothing. I wondered. But I knew that to argue would be of no avail. And after all, it was true that before I finished the book, it could not be published. So I went home, but I did not take the manuscript with me. Some time passed, and the publisher wrote me that he was still considering the manuscript but that its acceptance was not certain.

I never called the publisher again, nor did I write to him. Soon after the incident I became "a prisoner of an idea." A year later the unfinished manuscript came back with no comment.

"Freud and His Heroes" was never finished. The part on Freud's dreams was published by Dr. Smith Jelliffe in the *Psychoanalytical Review* for October 1941 as "The Dreams Freud Dreamed."

Two decades later the chapters on Oedipus and Akhnaton, enlarged, made into a book, and by far more completely documented than was possible in 1940, were published by Doubleday as *Oedipus and Akhnaton, Myth and History* (1960).*

* [Velikovsky completed a draft of *Stargazers and Gravediggers* by 1956; in subsequent years, he made brief additions, of which this passage is one example.]

AGES IN CHAOS

A LITTLE MORE THAN a week passed after the day of our intended sailing, and we had a visit from a scholar of Judaica who brought me greetings from a mutual friend. Our conversation turned to the problem of the remarkable geological formation in the area around the Dead Sea. Shortly after the Arab-Jewish disturbances there in 1929 my wife and I had rather imprudently journeyed afoot through the bare fields between Jericho and the Jordan River. We had also gone through ravines between hills of coagulated lava. These hills, looking like a huge herd of gigantic elephants, stretched for many miles along the Jordan.

"Actually," I said to our guest, "according to the Book of Genesis, the site of the Dead Sea was a plain in the days of the patriarch Abraham—the Valley of Siddim. But when the Israelites under Moses and Joshua reached the area in their flight from Egypt, they found the lake there. Did not some catastrophe take place besides the upheaval in which Sodom and Gomorrah were overturned? That upheaval is described without mention of a sea being formed."

As soon as I said this, an idea came to me: Was there not something here that might be of interest for my unwritten chapter on Moses, one of Freud's heroes?

A few years earlier—I believe it was on my fortieth birthday—my father had given me a book on the Negev (the southern part of Israel) written by Bar-Droma in Hebrew. My father was the first to redeem land in the Negev, and for many years Ruhama—the name he gave to the experimental agricultural station—was the only Jewish development in that part of the country. Though progress was slow and often tortuous, Ruhama and the Negev in general always remained his dominant preoccupation and concern.

When I received the book by Bar-Droma, I was too busy with my psychoanalytical practice to read it. I opened it at one or two places and by chance read that according to some scholar, Mount Sinai must have been a volcano: It rumbled, it threw up smoke, it burned in the night, and people had to be removed from its vicinity in order to be protected from being killed.

Speaking to our guest, I thought of the passage in that book. The next day, if not that very day, I tried to find out the age of the Dead Sea. In an article in the *Geographical Journal* (1923) published in England, W. Irwin compared the salt content (magnesium) of the Dead Sea, which has no outlet, with that of the water brought in by the Jordan, and concluded that the sea is not 1 million years old, as had been thought, but only 50,000 years. But if sodium were taken as the basis of computation and other sources of accretion were reckoned with, the age of the Dead Sea, strangely enough, would be less than 6,000 or even 5,000 years.*

Was it formed in the days of the Exodus, when Mount Sinai erupted and some debacle took place at the Sea of Passage? Was the catastrophe felt also in Egypt? Does any Egyptian document speak of a catastrophe?

I inquired and consulted books, but no book on the history of Egypt mentioned any such catastrophe. Then I came upon a reference to a sage, Ipuwer, who bewailed the fact that the river Nile had turned to blood.

I searched for the source and found it in an edition by Alan H. Gardiner, who had translated the text in 1909. The papyrus is in the Leyden Museum in Holland. I studied the text and came to the conclusion that I had a description of not only a natural catastrophe but precisely the plagues of Egypt:

"Plague is throughout the land. Blood is everywhere," says the papyrus. "There was blood throughout all the land of Egypt," says the Book of Exodus in the Scriptures.

"The river is blood," says the papyrus. ". . . all the waters that were in the river were turned to blood," says Exodus.

"Trees were destroyed. No fruit, nor herbs are found," says the papyrus. ". . . and the hail smote every herb of the field, and brake every tree of the field," says Exodus.

* See I. Velikovsky, "The Age of the Dead Sea," KRONOS, Vol. 4, pp. 40ff.

"Gates, columns and walls are consumed by fire," says the papyrus.

"The fire ran along upon the ground," says Exodus.

"Cattle are left to stray and there is none to gather them," says the papyrus. ". . . gather thy cattle. . . . And he that regarded not the word . . . left . . . his cattle in the field," says Exodus.

In his translation of the papyrus Gardiner used the very words the Scripture used in similar sentences, and it was remarkable to me that neither he nor anyone else had noted the close parallels. ". . . there was a thick darkness in all the land of Egypt. . . ," says Exodus, while "The land is without light," says the papyrus. ". . . there was a great cry in Egypt. . . ," says Exodus, and "It is groaning that is throughout the land, mingled with lamentation," says the papyrus. And so on and on. So similar are the descriptions that once—a few years later—when I sent the parallel texts to Professor John Garstang, the British Egyptologist and archaeologist of Jericho, he answered that the text of the papyrus looked to him like a copy of Exodus. But how could it be a copy if the text of the papyrus is supposed to be much older than the Exodus of the Israelites from Egypt? The latest time the papyrus could have originated was the end of the Middle Kingdom in Egypt. But this was several centuries earlier than the earliest possible date for the Exodus. I tentatively assumed that one of the two histories—the Egyptian or the Israelite—was out of step.

The next clue was in the papyrus. Besides the plagues, it has the story of an invasion by foreigners, the Amu, or Hyksos, coming from Asia into Egypt in the wake of the catastrophe. The Israelites leaving had a definite chance to meet the hordes of the invaders. Actually they met and fought the Amalekites even before reaching Mount Sinai. Were the Amalekites the same as the Amu (Hyksos)?

I was after a book by Theodore Nöldeke about the Amalekites. It was not in the libraries I used, but I found it in the Columbia University library; it was my first visit there. (In a few weeks we moved to the immediate neighborhood of this library, where we lived for the next twelve years.) In his book Nöldeke tells of many medieval (eighth to twelfth century) Arab authors transmitting ancient traditions about the Amalekites, who had suffered plagues in the Hejaz and left for Egypt, which they conquered without meeting resistance and over which they ruled for more than 500 years. Nöldeke did not believe the traditions, but I thought I had found the clue for which I was looking. From the Arab authors—I read them in translation—I also learned that at that time a flood from the erupting sea swept away Arab tribes.

A stone shrine, until the beginning of the present century used as a trough by the Arabs of el Arish, on the Egyptian frontier—and now in the museum of Ismailia—was another Egyptian source that interested me. It told that following a darkness and storm of nine days' duration, when nobody could see the face of the person next to him, the pharaoh Toum went out against his enemies and perished in the Place of the Whirlpool, at Pi-Kharoti. In Exodus the pharaoh of the oppression perished in the sea following a darkness when nobody could see the face of the person next to him at a place named Pi ha-Khirot.* Apparently I had come upon the Egyptian version of the story of which it was always thought that no such version exists (as, generally, no mention of the bondage of the Israelites is found in any Egyptian document). I had also come upon a link between the two histories.

The Hyksos ruled for hundreds of years. If they were the Amalekites, as I became convinced they were, their period must have corresponded with the time of the wandering in the desert and the judges. I discovered much corroborative evidence; the reader will find it in *Ages in Chaos* (1952). The beginning of the Egyptian New Kingdom (Eighteenth Dynasty) must have coincided with the beginning of the period of the Kingdom of Saul and David. But if this was so, then either Egyptian history has six ghost centuries or six centuries are missing from Israelite history. Before this could be maintained with any assurance, I had to ascertain whether or not the correspondence could be followed through in succeeding generations. With their chronologies realigned, the two histories showed invariable and complete correspondence for more than 1,000 years.

The reconstruction revealed Solomon and Egypt's Queen Hatshepsut to be contemporaries. It is said that Solomon was in contact with the rulers of all lands and that they came to his capital. His most illustrious guest was the queen of Sheba. Arabs and Ethiopians vie for her, both claiming her as their queen. Josephus, a historian of the first century, says that she came from Egypt, being queen of Egypt and Ethiopia. I asked myself: Is there any record of Queen Hatshepsut traveling to a foreign country? Such a record is extant.

* The article *ha* is merely the Hebrew *the.* The place is mentioned only once in Egyptian literature and only once in the Bible.

She called the land to which she traveled God's Land and Punt (or Phoenicia), and she brought as gifts from there the exotic animals and plants that Solomon had brought from Ophir. The collation of texts dealing with her expedition reveals many striking details. On her bas-reliefs one can see the Israelites as they looked in the days of Solomon; Solomon's governor at Etzion Geber, the port of entry, is pictured and called by his name, which can be found in the Scriptures.

I remember that day. In the early evening my wife and I walked from the library at Forty-second Street to Central Park and sat down there. The sky was full of light for us. I could not be on a wrong trail.

The Scriptures relate that five years after the death of Solomon a pharaoh came to Jerusalem and took away all the vessels and furniture of the Temple and the palace. Succeeding Hatshepsut on the throne of Egypt was Thutmose III, whose annals tell that he went to Rezenu (the Egyptian designation for Canaan or Israel) and brought from there temple vessels and furniture in abundance; pictures of them are carved on a wall in the Karnak temple. I compared the pictures and the biblical descriptions and found an amazing parallelism in shapes, numbers, materials, down to the most minute details.

My chronological scheme revealed to me that King Ahab of Samaria and King Jehoshaphat of Jerusalem must have been contemporaries of Amenhotep III and of Akhnaton, the great heretic. These two pharaohs exchanged letters with the princes of Rezenu and Syria; a collection of these letters was discovered in 1887 in el Amarna in Egypt. In fact, in one of his letters to the pharaoh the king of Jerusalem almost repeated his biblical prayer, and his generals, mentioned in the Scriptures, signed their letters with the names by which we know them from the Bible: Iahzibada, Ben Zuchru, Adaia. And Ahab left no fewer than sixty-five letters relating the smallest details of his reign as we know them from the Scriptures.

For a while I thought my reconstruction ended with the Babylonian exile, and the original title I had in mind for the book was "From Exodus to Exile." In the summer of 1940 my work was laid out in very broad outlines. But after two or three years of research I extended the reconstruction to the advent of Alexander the Great, the end of the period that I recognized as "ages in chaos." Since both the Egyptian and the biblical time scales are used in the chronologies of other peoples of antiquity, a maze of misconceptions swamped the history of the entire ancient East and had to be disentangled. I worked for more than ten years, strenuously and with enthusiasm, to bring this labor to its completion.

I could not fail to be impressed by the new story of the ancient world. For 2,000 years the question of the date of the Exodus had been debated. No true contact had been established between the two neighboring nations of antiquity, Israel and Egypt. Now there was contact in every century, every generation, almost every year, and between the histories of not just these two nations but among all the nations of the ancient East.

"Because of the disruption of synchronism, many figures on the historical scene are 'ghosts' or 'halves' and 'doubles.' Events are often duplicates; many battles are shadows; many speeches are echoes; many treaties are copies; even some empires are phantoms."

Thus I wrote in the Preface to *Ages in Chaos.*

WORLDS IN COLLISION

ON OR ABOUT October 20, 1940, half a year after I came upon the initial idea for the reconstruction of ancient history, I was sitting at dusk in the dining alcove at a window overlooking the Hudson, reading the Scriptures. I came to the chapter in the Book of Joshua in which the miracle with the sun and the moon is described. I remembered how, in 1912, at the age of seventeen, during my first visit to the land of Israel, I came to the kibbutz Merhavia in the valley of Jezreel—the first, and then the only, settlement in that part of the country, now studded with agricultural settlements. No house, other than the large old mud building that served as the mess hall, was yet standing there, and we slept in the field alongside the tall sheaves. One of the settlers told me that this was the place where Joshua had commanded the sun and the moon to stand still. That night the moon was full and unusually bright, and I looked curiously at the illuminated summer sky and the exultant luminary from my resting place on the ground. However, I do not think that then or at any time thereafter I thought of the story as anything but a poetic metaphor.

Now at the age of forty-five, reading the chapter, I was struck by the fact that only one verse earlier it was said that the Lord cast large stones from the sky. Not knowing the possible relation between a huge train of meteorites and the disturbances it could theoretically cause in the rotation of the earth, the ancient chronicler could only by the rarest chance have brought the two phenomena together unless there was a true relation between them.

I thought: If these were natural phenomena, observed as the standstill of celestial bodies, they must also have been experienced in other parts of the world. The next morning, in the Columbia library, I examined ancient texts of the Chinese in the East and of the Mexicans in the West. I did not find then what I was looking for in the books on ancient Chinese history—in the months and years that followed I came upon many references in ancient Chinese sources to the halting of the sun—but that morning, while making a list of books to read on the Mayas and Aztecs, I was intrigued by the title of a book* by Étienne Brasseur de Bourbourg, a French Americanologist, who pioneered in reading the Mayan calendar, numerals, and other pictorial signs and texts. A day or two later I took out that little book. In it Brasseur tries to prove that in ancient times there was traffic between Egypt and America and that the American continent had repeatedly been subjected to great catastrophes. He expanded on this subject of catastrophes that befell America in another, larger work.†

Mayan documents, such as Manuscript Troano, tell of a cataclysm when earth and sea turned red, the ocean fell on the continent, and a terrible hurricane swept the earth, carrying away all the towns and all the forests. Exploding volcanoes, tides sweeping over mountains, and tempestuous winds threatened to annihilate humankind. In the darkness illuminated only by lightning and burning volcanoes the face of the earth changed: Mountains collapsed, other mountains grew and rose over the onrushing cataract of water driven from oceanic spaces, innumerable rivers lost their beds, and a wild tornado moved through the debris descending from the sky. A world age was brought to its end by unchained elements and a rain of fire, followed by more than two decades of gloom.

About two weeks passed after the day I realized that the earth had traveled through a huge train of meteorites and underwent a disturbance in its rotation, and I was on a new trail. Reading the books on old Mexican history, I was surprised to find the name of the planet Venus mentioned often. One early morning the question crossed my mind: Was not this planet in some way connected with the disturbances?

* Titled: *S'il existe des sources de l'histoire primitive du Mexique dans les monuments égyptiens et de l'histoire primitive de l'ancien monde dans les monuments américains?* (1864).

† Brasseur de Bourbourg, *Histoire des nations civilisées du Mexique et de l'Amérique centrale* (1857).

The Mexican sources, several more of which I had by then read, referred to the first appearance of the planet Venus after the catastrophe; the very darkness, the hurricane, and the burning of the world were ascribed to the action of the star Venus, which had the form of a dragon.

I confided some of my thoughts to Franz Boas. He was rather skeptical, yet he advised me to study Bernardino de Sahagun, a sixteenth-century Spanish authority on Mexico and its ancient literature and beliefs. Soon I found strong support in Sahagun: He related that the Mexican sources called Venus "the star that smoked," and in another place he explained that "the star that smokes" was the Mexican expression for a comet.*

In Brasseur I came across a quotation from Varro, a classical author, thought to have been the most learned of the Romans, who, on the authority of earlier mathematicians, wrote that Venus changed its form and course in the days of Ogyges, famous for the flood that carries his name. In my reconstruction of ancient history I had already synchronized Ogyges, the builder of Egyptian Thebes, with the Amalekite pharaoh Agag, a contemporary of Joshua.†

According to the Mexican sources, there were several cosmic upheavals. Two of them were separated by only fifty-two years, and again the fifty-two-year period was connected with Venus and called by her name. During one of the catastrophes, when the world burned, the sun stood still on the horizon. How, I thought, could the Indians have known the relation between the disturbance in the earth's rotation and the burning of the world—unless such events had really taken place?

I thought of parallels in the Scriptures: Between the Exodus and the day of Joshua at Ajalon about fifty-two years passed. Brasseur, though a clergyman and missionary, had never noticed any similarity between the Mexican and biblical stories; neither had he conceived of a cosmic disturbance in which planets participated; he believed that the continental catastrophe had seismic causes, connected with sudden elevation of mountains, subsidence of land, and ensuing tidal waves and atmospheric phenomena.

Soon I saw my idea substantiated: Every ancient nation referred to Venus as a celestial body that was unlike a planet. "A bright

* Bernardino de Sahagun, *Historia general de las cosas de Nueva España,* Bk. VII, Ch. 4.

† *Ages in Chaos,* vol. I, pp. 71–72.

torch of heaven," it was called by the Chaldeans, who also called it "a stupendous prodigy in the sky that illuminates like the sun." Chinese astronomical texts likewise described Venus as "rivaling the sun in brightness," and Chinese sources referred to the change in the motions of Venus in the past. The Arabs and the Babylonians described the planet Venus as being "with hair," while according to the Talmud, "fire is hanging from the planet Venus" and "the brilliant light of Venus blazes from one end of the universe to its other end."*

Babylonian tablets, sometimes assigned to the early king Ammizaduga, describe the movements of Venus; whereas the present period between eastern disappearance and western appearance is about seventy-two days, in the Babylonian texts the period varies from two months to more than five months.

The early texts of the Hindus and the Babylonians have only four, not five, planets visible to the naked eye, and Venus is not among them. In later texts Venus belongs to the triad Venus, Sun, Moon; subsequently "Venus gives up her position as a great stellar divinity, equal with sun and moon, and joins the ranks of the other planets."†

Human sacrifices were brought to Venus by the Mexicans and, until the nineteenth century, by the Pawnee Indians when Venus "appeared especially bright, or in years when there was a comet in the sky."‡

Should I go on? Should I make the mistake of digesting my book and enabling still more people to discuss its merits and demerits, knowing it only from a condensation? I cannot compress *Worlds in Collision* any more than it is in its present form as a book—there I have not left a sentence that I deemed superfluous.

In it Venus is first mentioned on page 154. The claim that Venus was the extraterrestrial agent of the cataclysm is the third step in my reconstruction. The first step is to show that within human memory global catastrophes shook this world of ours and the second step is to establish that the cause of these catastrophes was extraterrestrial. With these two points proved, many concepts of modern scholarship and science, such as the theory of peaceful evolution,

* Midrash Rabba to Numbers 21, Folio 245a. Cf. "Mazal" and "Noga" in J. Levy, *Wörterbuch über die Talmudim und Midrashim* (2nd ed., 1924).

† A. Jeremias, *The Old Testament in the Light of the Ancient East* (1911), I, 18.

‡ George A. Dorsey, "The Sacrifice to the Morning Star by the Skidi Pawnee," Field Museum of Natural History (Chicago, 1922), p. 3.

are challenged. The participation of a planet in these disturbances puts into question, as we shall see, some notions accepted in celestial mechanics.

After a number of months I became aware that William Whiston, Newton's successor at Trinity College in Cambridge, had advanced a theory of a comet's colliding with the earth. According to him, the collision brought about the Noachian deluge, and he identified the comet of disaster with the comet that appeared in his own time, in 1680. Then I learned that Ignatius Donnelly, an author and a member of the House of Representatives, had theorized (1883) about the origin of till as the result of a collision with a comet; he did not refer to Whiston's work, which he probably did not know, nor did he assign the catastrophe to any particular time. He did not suspect any resulting change in the astronomical position of the earth or of its satellite or in the duration of the day, the month, or the year. Neither of these men suspected the role of Venus or of any other planet generally, nor did they recognize the times of the Exodus, Joshua, or Isaiah as periods of great upheavals.

Studying the ancient sources, I learned that Venus had continued on an elliptical orbit and caused more havoc in the celestial sphere and that Mars, thus disturbed in its path, had become the next menace to Earth. The celestial drama of this later period, the eighth century before the present era, was also the theomachy, or the battle of the gods of the *Iliad.* In years to come a critic from among the astronomers was to comment on my use of theogony or celestial mythology: "These wondrous findings were never made before, because no one realized the benefits to be derived from attributing the mythological activities of the Greek deities to the planets which were named in honor of them."*

With the help of Hebrew, Roman, and Chinese sources I could establish the date of the last great perturbation to the day: March 23, −687.† I became more and more aware that the planet worship of ancient peoples all around the world had had its origin in real and terrible events.

In the course of this research there were many exciting moments. One such came early in my work, when I found in Pliny that Typhon (also called Pallas, by which name Athena was known, too) was a comet called by the name of the pharaoh in whose days it had

* Paul Herget, director of observatory, University of Cincinnati, in Cincinnati *Enquirer,* April 1, 1950.

† *Worlds in Collision* (1950), p. 207ff. particularly pp. 234–37.

appeared; from other sources I knew that Typhon had drowned and been buried on the bottom of the sea. Then I read in Abraham Rockenbach that the terrible comet Typhon had been burning when the Israelites left Egypt. Thus in these two books I found substantiation for some of my surmises. Of Rockenbach's book, *De cometis tractatus novus methodicus,* published in 1602, there is only one copy in the Americas, and before I traced it, I was informed by the Library of Congress that it knew of only one copy in England and another in France. Rockenbach wrote his book relying on ancient undisclosed sources, and I made an attempt to discover these sources.

Almost every day there was something in the books I opened that gave support to some of my points. Morning, afternoon, and evening I returned to the library to read for *Ages in Chaos* and *Worlds in Collision.* The implications of my theory for geology and astronomy drove me to those departmental libraries, too. After a few years I noted with a little surprise that the only library in the humanities and the sciences that I had not visited was the psychology library.

I observed that in the large Columbia University library with its numerous departmental collections of books, I seldom met people who by their age or appearance seemed to be members of the teaching staff. And when I considered that this university has a staff of teachers numbered in the thousands, it appeared to me that not many of them continued their studies after they had attained the professorial chair. Certainly, in their private offices and in their homes they all had selected books; just the same, I could not understand how the process of research could go on without frequent visits to the shelves of a library, the exciting hunt from a footnote in one book to a passage in another, then to some literary guide, again to the card catalog, and once more to the shelves.

In this process I spent days, weeks, months, years, and, finally, a decade, in the same day returning again and again to the library, reading, searching, taking notes, traveling to other libraries, occasionally requesting books from the union catalog if they were not in New York libraries. Daily I climbed the steps of a library, and as I took the stairs to the main floor, I often made a prayer of gratitude that another day was given to me, with all the spiritual treasures of humankind since the invention of print, nay, since the invention of the alphabet, and even from before, as my hunting ground. Could I not today have the society of Plato, and not just Plato but his most sublime hours, and not only listen to what he knows and thinks but at the same time have a transcript of his ideas in his own tongue and in a careful translation placed at my disposal more quickly than the admirably able translators can translate the speeches of the members of the United Nations extemporaneously? Thankful to all those who collected, translated, commented, edited, and published, I felt favored to be able to explore so freely the work of innumerable authors and thinkers and to learn from their findings and from their errors, too.

And around me were young people, who filled the reading rooms, especially before examinations, and deserted them on holidays. Of the professors I knew I met at the library only a few occasionally during the year.

The young whom I met in the general library or in one of the departmental libraries turned from freshmen to sophomores and then to juniors and seniors; new freshmen came in, and I mingled with them, and they, too, became seniors. And some of the freshmen of 1940 became members of the faculty by 1950 or 1952, and they, too, began to use the library only on rare occasions.

THE LONG WAY

IN THE SUMMER OF 1942 I mailed the first two chapters of my historical work to Professor Harry A. Wolfson at Harvard University; he gave them to Professor Robert H. Pfeiffer, an authority on the Old Testament who also read courses in Egyptian and Assyrian history at Harvard. Pfeiffer wrote an analysis of these two chapters in a letter to Wolfson, who referred the letter to me. In Pfeiffer's judgment, "the author shows considerable familiarity with a great variety of ancient sources" and prefers to draw his conclusions from them rather than from the results of modern research. "The main thesis of the paper—the identification of the Hyksos with the Amalekites—is entirely new to me; as far as I know it has never been advanced." He found my arguments "extremely ingenious," but he stressed the resulting conflict with established chronology. "He refrains from giving any dates for the events which he describes. . . . Unless he overthrows the current chronology, he identifies events which in our chronology are separated by more than five centuries."

Pfeiffer properly understood the scope and the implications of my theory. I traveled to Cambridge, Massachusetts, met first Wolfson, then Pfeiffer and gave him the subsequent chapters, as far as they were written. After a couple of days Pfeiffer and I met again and discussed at large the evolving problems. He advised me to try to demonstrate my thesis on ancient art. A month later (August 22, 1942) he wrote me:

> I am delighted to hear that you have made some progress in the plans for the publication of your revolutionary reconstruc-

> tion on ancient history and chronology. I sincerely hope that some University Press or reputable publisher will accept your manuscript for publication. I regard your work—provocative as it is—of fundamental importance, whether its conclusions are accepted by competent scholars or whether it forces them to a far-reaching and searching reconsideration of the accepted ancient chronology.

He himself apparently was shaken but not convinced. The next spring he read two more chapters and wrote (April 17, 1943):

> As usual I have been fascinated by your unheard of identifications and dates and admire your incredible ingenuity. I fear however that there is some truth in the old proverb, "You cannot teach an old dog new tricks." I can only repeat the words of King Agrippa to the Apostle Paul, "Almost thou persuadest me. . . ."

He again expressed his wish to see my work published.

In 1944 I offered my book to a university press. It was in its hands for fourteen months, and the staff certainly was interested in it. After showing it to several readers, the staff sent the manuscript to a historian who advised against its publication.

All this time I worked strenuously to improve and amplify my work. Of great help to me was Dr. Walter Federn, Egyptologist, the son of a well-known psychoanalyst. We exchanged numerous letters discussing many details of my work. He generously placed at my service his incomparable knowledge of hieroglyphic inscriptions and Egyptological literature, and his taking upon himself the role of devil's advocate allowed me to know all the possible objections to my reconstruction of ancient history. My finding in these very problems additional arguments *for* the reconstruction added conviction in my mind that I was not on a stray path.

AT MADEMOISELLE

One day in April 1946 I read in the morning paper that Dr. Harlow Shapley of the Harvard College Observatory would be in town. The magazine *Mademoiselle* was arranging a college forum, and he was scheduled to be the main speaker at the luncheon. For a time I had been thinking of a check on my theory through spectral analysis of the atmospheres of Venus and Mars. Shapley, whose name appeared often in the press, was a popular figure because of his many interests extending beyond his special field in science, and I thought of suggesting this test to him. I give our conversation as I reproduced it in a letter written four years later to Ted O. Thackrey of the *New York Post*, an acquaintance of mine.

April 5, 1950

Dear Mr. Thackrey:

You ask me to describe my experience with Dr. Harlow Shapley.

On April 13, 1946, four years ago, I met him at the Commodore Hotel, where he was a speaker at a college forum discussing world government. I asked whether he would give me a few minutes during the intermission. He graciously agreed. Here is our conversation almost verbatim.

V. Dr. Shapley, I have been working for the last six years on a research and I have written down the results. In this research I came to the conclusion, certainly unorthodox, that in historical times there were changes in the constitution of the solar system. (I was careful not to say what kinds of changes took place, or when; neither did I mention the Old Testament or Joshua. Even in the book [*Worlds in Collision*] I mention Venus for the first time only after page 150.)

S. How did you come to this conclusion?

V. I worked mainly on ancient records, but I arrived at this conclusion also from other materials, geological—

S. (interrupting) Do you realize that we cannot build such a theory on an old record, which may be basically wrong?

V. I did not build it on one record, but on many, from various races, from all corners of the world; from nations as far apart as the Assyrians, Hindus, and the tribes of Mexico. The records corroborate one another.

S. If so, then that is different. But do you realize that if there were, as you say, changes in the constitution of the solar system in historical times, your research must bring you into conflict with Newtonian gravitation?

V. (thinking: My theory can be fitted into the prevailing Newtonian system, yet this Dr. Shapley must have a quick mind, since it is true that while working on my book I wondered how it could be that a purely mechanistic theory survived in astronomy from the seventeenth century when nothing was known of electromagnetism.) (Aloud) Yes, I realize that. But in the present work I do not give any interpretations in terms of physics, of the events described; I only try to establish facts. I wish you would agree to read the manuscript, and if you are satisfied, on reading, that my thesis is supported by sources to an extent that it deserves some laboratory investigation, would it be possible to undertake one or two rather uncomplicated spectroscopic analyses?

S. I would like to read your manuscript, but I am very busy, and therefore, if somebody whom I know would read it first and recommend it to me, I promise you to read it, too. As for the experiments, write to me at the Harvard College Observatory or to Dr. [Fred] Whipple, my assistant, referring to this conversation, and if possible, we will do it for you.

V. I thank you, indeed. Whom would you suggest as the reader of my manuscript?

S. Do you know Professor Lynn Thorndike of Columbia?
V. I do not know him personally.
S. Ask him.
V. If Thorndike will not be able to attend to this, whom would you suggest?
S. You give me some name.
V. How, for instance, would Professor Horrace Kallen do? He has read another manuscript of mine.
S. If Professor Kallen reads and recommends it, I shall carefully read it, too.
V. I appreciate this very much. . . .

I thanked Dr. Shapley for his courtesy and for the time he had given me and, declining an invitation to stay for lunch, went home believing that I had met a great and good man.

ONE WHO READ AND ONE WHO DIDN'T

TWO DAYS LATER, on April 15, 1946, I wrote Shapley a few lines: "In accordance with our conversation of April 13th, when you kindly agreed to test some of the conclusions of my historical cosmology, I offer the following implication of my theory for testing: The atmosphere of the planet Mars consists mainly of argon and neon." Two days later, on April 17, I wrote again asking for another test: "May I offer another test which bears directly upon my reconstruction of historical cosmology? It is my conclusion that the planet Venus abounds in naphtha and its gases; therefore bands of gaseous hydrocarbon should be found in the absorption spectrum of Venus." To have these investigations made was actually the purpose of my seeing Shapley and asking him to read my manuscript. For weeks I heard nothing.

As I had agreed to with Shapley, I telephoned Thorndike, asking permission to bring him a manuscript. He declined, being too busy with his own work. Then, as I would have done anyway, I gave my manuscript of *Worlds of Collision* to Horace Kallen, who at that time was dean of the Graduate Faculty of the New School for Social Research. On May 13 I wrote him:

> I look upon this day as upon a milestone in my work. Quite five years ago I promised to give you the answer as to the nature of the catastrophe of the days of the Exodus—and only today do I fulfill it. During these years of work I gathered material to substantiate my explanation of the events. . . . You

> will read and see the scope of problems involved in *Worlds in Collision.*

Kallen, on our rare meetings, about twice a year, would ask me: "Tell me, what was the nature of the catastrophe that I read about in your *Ages in Chaos*?" And I would answer regularly: "Please wait until I am able to substantiate my thesis with more proofs." Once we met in the subway traveling downtown; it went so fast and made so much noise that it was not easy to hear each other. Instead of answering his old question, I asked Kallen: "Which miracle in the Old Testament do you regard as the most unbelievable?" I expected that he would say, "Joshua stopping the sun," but he said, "Elijah being carried away in a chariot of fire." So I had no point. I could have told him something about Elijah, the man of barometric and electric wonders, but there was too much noise. Anyway, I had not received the answer I had tried to elicit.

But in that spring of 1946 the time had come, and I gave him the first part of my manuscript. After he had read it, he telephoned me and spoke some very encouraging words. Then I gave him the second part—"Mars"—of *Worlds in Collision.* Kallen wrote (May 21, 1946):

> I have now finished the remaining part of your manuscript. The vigor of the scientific imagination that you show, the boldness of your construction fill me with admiration. The implications of the very simple and psychologically correct assumption that prophets and chroniclers could have been reporting experience instead of using metaphors are so developed that one would be hard put for it to challenge their cogency. . . .

In the meantime, four weeks after I had written to Shapley asking for the tests he had tentatively agreed to make, I received a short note dated May 15 and signed by his secretary: "Dr. Shapley asks me to write you that your unelaborated statements or arguments about the atmospheres of the planets are not sufficient grounds for astronomers to examine your claims."

I replied to Shapley eight days later:

> There is nothing I would like better than to substantiate my statements of April 15th and 17th by arguments. In the first

two files of my MS I show that in the second and first millennia before this era changes occurred in the constitution of the solar system and in the position of Earth, Moon, Venus and Mars. Presented in these few words my conclusions may appear strange, but they are built upon an extensive material from diverse fields of science. I have this material ready for you if you would like to read it. Speaking to you on April 13th, I understood you wished some other scholar to read the manuscript first. I gave it to Professor Horace M. Kallen, Dean of the Graduate Faculty of the New School for Social Research.

I added that Kallen's reaction had been favorable.

I wrote this letter on May 23 but postponed mailing it for three days, until the twenty-sixth. In the meantime, Kallen wrote to Shapley. I asked Kallen to do this in order that Shapley might be persuaded to instruct one of his assistants to perform the tests in which I was interested.

Kallen wrote:

May 23, 1946

Dear Shapley:

Dr. Immanuel Velikovsky tells me that he has hinted to you his remarkable theories regarding changes in the structure of the solar system during historical times and the evidence for those changes which he has found in the religious and other literature of the world and in the changes of calendars in areas as far apart as Mexico and Egypt.

He tells me also that one crucial point of his theory involves the content of the atmosphere of Venus which, if his theory is valid, would show petroleum gases, and he has suggested to you a spectroscopic analysis of the atmosphere of Venus for those gases.

I have just finished reading his manuscript. After taking it up, I could not put it down. From the side of the history of ideas and social relations, it seems to me that he has built up a serious theory deserving of the careful attention of scholars—theory and fact showing a kind of scientific imagination which on the whole has been unusual in our times. If his theory should prove to be valid, not only astronomy but history and a good many of the anthropological and social sciences would need to be reconsidered both for their content and explanation. If it should not prove to be valid, it would still be one of those very great guesses which occur far too infrequently in the history of human thought.

I am myself so impressed by what Dr. Velikovsky has had to say and the way in which he has established his hypothesis that I feel as eager as he to have it undergo the crucial test which the spectroscopic analysis he suggests would be.

I very much hope that you can make this test. . . .

Shapley answered Kallen on May 27, apparently before he received my letter:

Dear Kallen:

The sensational claims of Dr. Immanuel Velikovsky fail to interest me as much as they should, notwithstanding his exceedingly pleasing personality and evident sincerity, because his conclusions were pretty obviously based on incompetent data. Throughout the histories and literatures of times past he has assembled unverified observations and claims which modern science has either overlooked or looked at and ignored, or discarded on the basis of more competent observational material.

Shapley had not seen a single line of my manuscript, did not know a single argument or literary source I employed, yet he wrote in such a manner that a reader of his letter could not help thinking that he, Shapley, had examined my manuscript and was writing to Kallen who had not seen it. The actual situation was the reverse. The only information Shapley had had from me was that "in historical times, according to historical and literary material, the structure of the solar system underwent changes."

Shapley's letter to Kallen goes on:

Dr. Velikovsky's claim that there have been changes in the structure of the solar system during historical times has implications which apparently he has not thought through; or perhaps he was unable to convey to me in our brief conversation. If in historical times there have been these changes in the structure of the solar system, in spite of the fact that our celestial mechanics has been for scores of years able to specify

> without question the positions and motions of the members of the planetary system for many millennia fore and aft, then the laws of Newton are false. The laws of mechanics which have worked to keep airplanes afloat, to operate the tides, to handle the myriads of problems of every day life, are fallacious. But they have been tested competently and thoroughly. In other words, if Dr. Velikovsky is right, the rest of us are crazy. And seriously, that may be the case. It is, however, improbable.

Astronomical computations used by modern science are based on a very short observational period, inadequate for the making of sweeping conclusions and their elevation to the status of inviolable laws. In the preface to *Worlds in Collision* I wrote to this effect: "If, occasionally, historical evidence does not square with formulated laws, it should be remembered that a law is but a deduction from experience and experiment, and therefore laws must conform with historical facts, not facts with laws." However, the careful reader of *Worlds in Collision* knows that I have shown how the history of the cosmic changes could comply with the accepted laws. I only intimated at the end of my book that the existing theories in science are based on the postulate that the sun and the planets and the comets are all neutral electrically and magnetically, and the celestial mechanics conflicts not with my history of catastrophes, but with the numerous observations which indicate that the bodies of the solar system are electrically charged.

The end of Shapley's letter to Kallen was more gracious. He explained that the laboratory of the Harvard Observatory had no equipment to perform the tests I required on "this surprising theory that petroleum gases are in the atmosphere of Venus," and he advised that I communicate with Dr. Walter S. Adams of the Mount Wilson Observatory, "who has worked with the best equipment available" on the problem of the atmosphere of Venus, or with Dr. Rupert Wildt of the McCormick Observatory, University of Virginia, who did not have the necessary equipment, either, but who knew about the atmospheres of planets.

Kallen did not send me a copy of Shapley's entire letter, only the last part. But I thought that I should see the beginning, too, so it was arranged that I receive the full text. Kallen answered Shapley by saying again that he was "much impressed both with the data that Velikovsky has assembled and his method of handling them. It makes fascinating reading under any circumstances. The first effect is that of shock, then you get intrigued."

But Shapley did not become intrigued enough to read the book about which he expressed himself so vehemently. Returning the original of Shapley's letter, I wrote to Kallen on June 16, 1946:

> Shapley knows about my work only that "there have been changes in the structure of the solar system during historical times." He does not know what kind of changes I describe, nor does he know anything about my material. His judging my material as "obviously based on incompetent data" and "unverified" or "discarded" is therefore not founded on anything but surmise.

I added:

> Is it not a strange position for the scholarly world that "we are all crazy" if one of the planets changed its orbit because of a contact with a comet or another planet? If the Newtonian law and astronomy and mechanics are built on a presumption that there could not have been in historical times a large perturbation, though small perturbations are observed daily, then astronomy and mechanics dictate to historians what they are allowed to discover in the past. In my opinion a historical fact cannot be denied because of a physical theory, and if such a fact is established, the physical law must suit the fact, not the fact the law. As you know, I made my effort to establish the historical facts, not upon one or two evidences, as Dr. Shapley imagines, but on many corroborative ones from all corners of the world.

It seemed that the Shapley chapter was closed. Despite his promise to read the manuscript after it had been read and approved by a reader of scholarly standing, he was not interested. In the future, accusations emanating from the Harvard College Observatory were to be leveled against the author and his publisher claiming that they had failed to show the manuscript to scientists before publication. Of course, Shapley was not the only scientist, and as the story will bring out, other scientists did examine and discuss the book, and precisely its physical parts, before it was published.

As I was writing this eight years later, in the summer of 1954, in our garden in Princeton, I received a visit from a young professor of aeronautics at Princeton University. I inquired of him what was the basis of Simon Newcomb's mathematical proof (1903) that no airplane that would carry a pilot could be constructed. My guest answered: "Most probably he based himself on the erroneous ideas of Newton concerning the effect of air resistance." And he added: "I will send you a paper by Kármán."

Theodore von Kármán of the California Institute of Technology was the foremost authority on aeronautics. In his article "Isaac Newton and Aerodynamics" (1942),* he wrote:

> It has often been stated, and it is true to a certain extent, that the common belief in the correctness of Newton's theory of air resistance was an impediment in the solution of the problem of mechanical flight. In fact, the strict application of Newton's theory gave a pessimistic prognosis for the feasibility of practical flying machines.

Kármán showed the extent of Newton's misconception, which "explains the tremendous discrepancy as far as the magnitude of the lift is concerned." He went on to state:

> The discrepancy was discovered by experiments soon after the publication of the *Mathematical Principles*. . . . However, Newton's formula for the air on inclined surfaces was repeated in hundreds of books and official specifications. . . . In building codes of several countries, and states and counties, the wind pressure on inclined roofs was specified according to Newton's formula as late as the last decade. This is really a remarkable proof of the inertia of official specifications, since, according to experimental evidence and also the modern theory, the wind might exert a lifting force on a roof consisting of two slightly inclined surfaces, whereas Newton's theory yields a downward directed force.

The force with which a wind lifts a roof is about five times stronger than the force with which it presses the roof down; Newton took into consideration only the latter force. Built according to his mechanics, many roofs were lost in hurricanes, lifted off by the air pressure. The same error delayed the solution to the problem of flight. Newton "could not see that the pressure propagation increased tremendously the normal force."

* *Journal of Aeronautical Sciences*, vol. IX, no. 14.

This error of Newton by itself had no relation to my theory since I had not questioned his mechanics. Even if Newton's mechanics of air resistance were without fault, it would have proved nothing against my theory. What matters here was not Newton's error, but Shapley's error in writing to a layman in physics that my idea of changes in the celestial order could not be right because Newton was proved right in an area where actually he was proved wrong.

Oceanic tides, according to Shapley, follow precisely Newton's formula, another proof that Velikovsky could not be right. How precisely do they follow the formula?

> The ancients knew that the ebb and flow of the tides varied with the phases of the moon. So complex is the real earth as compared with the idealized earth assumed by the astronomers and physicists that we have, as yet, no general theory that permits tidal forecasts for any point on an ocean. Tides are, of course, predicted with great accuracy for all principal ports; these are not computed from general theory, however, but from analysis of tidal records over a long period of years at the particular port concerned.*
>
> [The Newtonian scheme] fails to explain fully the vagaries of the local tides. For example, many ports have but one tide in a lunar day; in others the lag is many hours from the time the moon is at zenith; in still others the two daily tides are of greatly different heights. They also vary with the seasons. These and many other facts make it clear that the tides are not a simple direct response to the vertical component of the moon's gravitational pull, which is really far too small for effective lifting of the water masses anyway.†

The authors of the textbook on geology from which this last quotation is borrowed did not express any doubt concerning the Newtonian theory of tides; they showed only that there exist many irregularities that require explanation, that the force of the moon's gravitational pull is insufficient, and that no theoretical prediction of tides is possible. Therefore, to refer to the tides as providing support for the Newtonian theory is once more a statement in contradiction with the observed facts.

* James Gilluly, Aaron C. Waters and A. O. Woodford, *Principles of Geology* (1951), p. 396.

† *Ibid.*, p. 398.

JOHN J. O'NEILL

UNTIL THAT TIME in 1946 the only reader of the complete manuscript of *Worlds in Collision,* as it was then, was Kallen. One day, in the summer of that year, I thought: Should I show my work to John O'Neill of the *Herald Tribune*? I felt the need to hear the reaction of an experienced man who, as science editor of that newspaper, had certainly dealt for many years with all kinds of sound and unsound theories. I had read a review of his biography of Nikola Tesla; I liked what I read, and I marked in my memory the author and his book. O'Neill recognized the greatness of Tesla, whom he knew as intimately as Tesla would allow anyone to know him. Tesla, who developed the use of alternating current, stood up for many years under the attacks of Edison, who announced in the press that alternating current was injurious to health and its use should be forbidden.

I called the *Herald Tribune.* It happened to be the day of the week O'Neill was there, and he told me to come that very day. I sat in a leather chair in the waiting room of the editorial floor. After a few minutes a slightly built man with white hair and an immaculate linen collar came to me with a briefcase in his hand. I had my manuscript in two folders. I asked him to read it. He told me in his friendly but businesslike manner: "My desk is piled high with papers to read. I shall take your manuscript, but do not expect me to read it for two or three months." I was a complete stranger and was satisfied with this answer.

That month my wife and I went for a seven-day rest in a tourist house near Lake Mahopac, one hour from New York, the only time we left the city that hot summer. During the week I went to New York for one day. The apartment telephone rang. It was a private secretary of O'Neill, who was happy to have reached me. She said that for some days she had called many times, from morning till night, so as not to miss me, because Mr. O'Neill wished very much to talk to me. I remained in town, and we met. O'Neill told me that he had taken my manuscript, planning to spend no more than five minutes on it while sitting on a bench in his garden, but he had not set it aside until he finished reading it. "It is a whale of a book," he told me. "I have never read anything comparable." We talked far into the night, and I listened to O'Neill's many ideas on scientific progress. He expressed his belief that a new fact or set of facts may well compel science to reconsider its basic postulates.

I returned to spend my last day or two at Mahopac. Soon after I was back in town, I received another call from O'Neill. "I want your permission to refer to your book in my next column." I would have liked to have known what he was going to reveal of the content, but I felt it would be insulting to show distrust of his judgment, so I simply agreed.

On August 11, 1946, my theory was for the first time mentioned in the press. This preview in the *Herald Tribune* opened a few doors for me. In it O'Neill wrote:

> . . . We are living on a planet on which events can be terribly exciting. The fact that the period covered by what we may call modern history has been a relatively quiescent era has lulled us into a state of false security and into a totally misleading philosophy concerning the earth and its possibilities.
>
> Our misleading philosophy is the result of a period of relatively quiet cosmic activity. . . .
>
> . . . There has been built up in the minds of the people a belief that life, the world and the universe are on an extremely orderly basis, that there is no possibility of disastrous events of first magnitude taking place. . . .
>
> All major scientific developments of the last half century indicate that this complacent attitude is entirely unwarranted. . . .
>
> . . . The planets may not be occupying permanent positions. . . . The failure to observe such changes in a period of a couple of thousand years would not preclude the possibility of

such events taking place frequently in the longer time scale. . . .

The probability that events of such magnitude have taken place within historical time is presented in researches now completed by Dr. Immanuel Velikovsky. . . . He has assembled into a monumental work evidence from all the early civilizations that in the first and second millenniums before Christ tremendous terrestrial cataclysms took place. . . .

In a magnificent piece of scholarly historical research he has correlated Sumerian, Chaldean, Hindu, Chinese, Mayan, Aztec, Icelandic, Egyptian and Hebrew records showing that the times of cataclysms described in all of them correspond. In the light of this record and the data he has assembled about the cataclysms, there unfolds a most exciting picture of terrestrial events that raises world history to a level of superlative interest. Obscure allusions to events in classical and sacred literature become crystal clear as he fits together the jigsaw puzzle of history.

"World-shaking events" is no figure of speech in Dr. Velikovsky's work. The earth, on at least two occasions, was shaken to such an extent that the prevailing calendar was thrown out of gear . . . [and] its axis [was tilted] so that the latitude of places was changed by a wide arc of circle producing extensive climatic changes, according to the historical evidence. . . .

Some different interpretations undoubtedly will be assigned to causes and effects by astronomers and physicists than are contained in the early records and conclusions drawn from them. Dr. Velikovsky's work, as yet unpublished, presents a stupendous panorama of terrestrial and human history which will stand as a challenge to scientists to frame a realistic picture of the cosmos.

IN SEARCH OF A PUBLISHER

IN JUNE 1946 I started to make the rounds of the publishers with the manuscript of *Worlds in Collision*. The first I offered it to was Appleton-Century. In my memory was the fact that Appleton was the original publisher of Darwin in America, and I thought that this fact spoke for the vision of this publisher in the past. I saw only the lady receptionist. Not very long afterward I received a letter in which the editor advised me that my book would not fit into its program, but he thought that Macmillan, which has a very large list, would be the right publisher for it.

When two months later O'Neill's article was printed, it seemed that it should not be too difficult to find a publisher for my book. I offered it to several other publishers, but none of them kept it for more than a few days, indicating that hardly any of them gave it to an outside expert. A few glances through the manuscript by an editor or an editorial assistant sufficed for the conclusion that this was not a book for the general reader. The many footnotes and references to old books, papyri, and the like scared all of them off. Each of them decided that there was no chance of enough public interest in it, that this was a book for some foundation or university press to publish.

The editor of one of the most vigorous publishing houses in America wrote:

> It is a disappointment to me to say that ours is a negative decision. This, of course, in no way detracts from our tremendous

> respect for the vast scholarship and originality of your manuscript. Our basic reason for not going ahead is that we do not believe *Worlds in Collision* to be a book for the general public, and we are publishers of quite a small list aimed wholly at this market. The admirable erudition displayed in your discussion of Egyptian, Assyrian, Greek, Babylonian, Chinese and Mayan records does not seem to us in any way designed for the general reader but wholly for specialists. It seems to us that in its present form, the book would be an admirable one for the Smithsonian Institute [*sic*] or some university press to publish. A popular version would require almost literally a translation directed at the minds and emotions of the laymen.

A celebrated editor of another important publishing house wrote similarly:

> I could not fail to be impressed by the vast erudition with which you describe the cataclysms recorded by man. The astronomical, geological and meteorological phenomena which you describe and document so thoroughly are almost frightening. . . . Perhaps the real significance of your book is that it rationalizes what always has passed for the miraculous and inexplicable. I keep wondering whether so formidable an array of citations does not obscure the reader's interest in the ever-recurring motif of cataclysms, and I am forced to the conclusion that your book would be too special for the general reader who is unequipped with any scholarly apparatus. That is why I think your book should be brought out by a noncommercial house, say, a university press. I don't believe that we could make it a book of sufficient general interest to warrant our undertaking it. It is with genuine humility, in the face of your wide scholarship, that I must render this adverse decision. . . .

Between June and the latter part of October eight publishers saw the manuscript. Only once did I have a little different experience. I mailed a publishing house a clipping of O'Neill's article together with an inquiry whether it would like to see the book. I received the answer of its president: "By all means." An editor called me and asked me to come over. I left my manuscript in the hands of a very affable editor. Then, not hearing from him for quite a while, I asked to see him. He was changed. Yes, he had seen the piece, and it looked very much like a book for study in colleges; it was too serious, too dry, and too long. If I agreed to shorten it or, better, to take some interesting section and print it alone as an essay, then possibly . . .

Here I interrupted him to tell an anecdote I had read somewhere: "When Charles Darwin submitted his *The Origin of Species*—or was it another work of his?—to a publisher, the publisher, who felt an obligation to the person who had sent Darwin, not to reject the manuscript, made a compromise offer: 'Your book is dry and long. Could you possibly take one chapter and develop it interestingly? For example, the chapter about butterflies. Ladies love to read about butterflies.' "

With this story I once more warmed up the editor, and he promised to do something about the book. But after a while, perhaps two weeks, he informed me, a little triumphantly, that the book had been read for the house by a reviewer and been rejected. I answered that I myself would come to acknowledge the rejection if only I were given the opportunity to know the criticism that led to it. So I went to the publishing house and soon was called into the editor's office. Covering the name of the reviewer, he gave me the piece to read. After telling briefly something of the contents of the manuscript, the receiver went on to say that I could not possibly be right, because I propound catastrophism, and science knows positively that there must have been millions of years of uninterrupted evolution in order to transform the three-digit foot of the ancient horse into the one-digit foot of the modern horse.

I asked the editor: "Would you please do me a favor? Promise me that you will preserve this criticism. There will come a day . . ." I went away, the manuscript in my briefcase having been turned down because of the three-digit horse.

After eight publishers had rejected the manuscript, I decided to follow the neglected advice of Appleton's editor and phoned Macmillan for an appointment.

A MANUSCRIPT BECOMES A BOOK

IN THE MORNING of the day when I had my appointment with Harold Latham, chief editor of Macmillan, I was called by telephone and told that he had to leave town on some assignment and that I could meet him on another date or see James Putnam, an associate editor, at the agreed hour. I felt a little disappointed but chose to see Putnam. For him it was a fateful switch.

Putnam proved to be an enthusiastic editor and reminded me in his eagerness of a hunter who goes after game in the fall. He gave the manuscript to an outside reader—I do not know who he was—and a few weeks later he told me that the reader was definitely for the publication of my work but suggested that I give in one volume the story of a single great cataclysm, leaving the rest of my story for future books; the manuscript as submitted to Macmillan contained also the description of earlier world catastrophes. This was good advice. In years to come, after having elaborated in separate works on the historical, geological, and astronomical aspects of my theory, I shall return and print the part of *Worlds in Collision* that was then left out, dealing with the Deluge and other early events. I even have reason to believe that we have not followed the advice far enough. The first volume should have contained the story of Venus only; the part about Mars, or the catastrophes that occurred in the eighth to seventh centuries before the present era, less spectacular but closer to our time, should have been published as a book by itself, on the heels of the first book.

Rather soon, in December 1946, Putnam wrote me a very encouraging letter, which almost meant that the manuscript was accepted. But additional readers had it—one of them was O'Neill; the other was Gordon Atwater, the curator of the Hayden Planetarium and the chairman of the Astronomical Department of the American Museum of Natural History in New York. Having read O'Neill's article, he became interested in my theory, especially as a subject for dramatization in the Hayden Planetarium. The planetarium was presenting a few dramatizations of astronomical subjects during a year, each program running for a month or two.

Putnam supplied me with the report he received from Atwater in order that I might follow some suggestions it contained. It said, *inter alia:* "The theories presented by Dr. Velikovsky are most unique and should be presented to the world of science in order that the underpinning of modern science can be reexamined with respect to these theories."

He referred to the physical and philosophical concept of convergent and divergent phenomena, with the idea that the events I described belong to the latter category and then advised:

> The author should not summarize with such finality at the end of each argument. He should not attempt to grip science in a steel trap, leaving it with no avenue of escape. Science is a product of honest research and sincere personal endeavor. The true scientist is receptive to new relationships and will work hard to establish their firmness or weakness.

By this method, he assumed, I would "enlist the cooperation of the brilliant minds in science today."

In May 1947 Macmillan and I signed an optional contract which was not binding for it beyond the small amount that it paid as a sign of serious intention. So the manuscript was kept for more reading and checking. It is hardly necessary to add that I dealt with the trade book department, not the textbook department, though in later years a number of critics from the ranks of the scientists accused Macmillan of offering a heretical book as a college textbook, which was an ungrounded accusation. In its catalog of 1950 it was listed as a "general interest" book.

From the time the article of O'Neill was printed, there were efforts made by Jerome Ellison and then by Clifton Fadiman to have my story told for a magazine, and several letters were written to O'Neill and to me, but I was not responsive. Finally, I agreed to meet Fadiman, but not for the purpose of a magazine article; I wished his opinion on the presentation of my books. I left my *Worlds in Collision* with him. The next time we met, he told me that he had read it till the light of morning, when he finished it; then he read *Ages in Chaos*. He found that the language needed much polishing.

I was fortunate in finding a copy editor very close to where I lived, a young woman, a graduate of Smith College, stricken in childhood with polio and confined to a wheelchair. After a while Miss Marion Kuhn learned my preferences and idiosyncrasies—simple words, short sentences, abhorrence of clichés and avoidance of any newly invented terms; no exclamations, no italics, no sarcasm. She soon realized that I wished to have my English corrected, but not my style changed. We developed into a team. She started with *Ages in Chaos* and worked with me many months on it, editing and typing—while I was simultaneously filling in the footnotes and endlessly checking my sources. Then, seven months after signing the optional contract, I started to bring Miss Kuhn my *Worlds in Collision*.

Years later Fadiman would write that Velikovsky "writes about fifty times better than his critics." I was glad that I had not listened to the advice of those who, since 1940, tried to persuade me that it would have been preferable for my work if I had written in one of the languages I knew better and then let it be translated, but that I persisted in writing in English, after already having had to change the language of my writing twice in my life, from Russian to German to Hebrew.

In the beginning of 1948 I put aside *Ages in Chaos* and in a few months brought *Worlds in Collision* to completion.

In May 1948, a year after the optional contract, after so much more careful study, Macmillan and I signed a regular contract, replacing the optional.

That month the state of Israel came into being, and dramatic developments followed. Since the fall of the previous year, I had been writing for the editorial page of the New York *Post* a series of over fifty articles on the Middle East, signing them "Observer."

When, several months later, my manuscript was finally given to the printer, my wife and I boarded the *Mauritania* on the first leg of a journey to Israel. In our cabin we found a large fruit basket with a card from Putnam, wishing us bon voyage. We went to Israel in order to meet our daughter Shulamit, who, more than two years earlier, in 1946, had left her graduate studies in the Physics Department of Columbia University and returned to her homeland. When the UN voted (in November 1947) for a Jewish homeland on a small partitioned part of what had been promised by the British mandate, the armies of seven Arab countries crossed their borders and attacked the overwhelmingly outnumbered defenders, in cities and *kibbutzim*, and the world watched the outcome of the struggle.

We traveled by a roundabout route: by ship to France, then to Tunis by air, then to Athens, and finally by a small plane to Haifa.

During my stay in Israel signs of fatigue showed themselves after nine years of strenuous work without a day of rest. We returned on February 9, 1949, to New York and found the galleys of *Worlds in Collision.* I was approaching the decisive day when the unconventional, even heretical, views to which I had come in the course of long years of painstaking research would stop being my private thoughts and the conviction of a single person. I did not try to calm myself with the thought that I would be spared some violent opposition, even ridicule, yet the violence of this opposition, when it came, surpassed my expectation.

"THE DAY THE SUN STOOD STILL"

ON MARCH 18, 1949, one year before the publication of my book, Frederick L. Allen, editor in chief of *Harper's Magazine,* a century-old journal of great tradition, wrote to the author of *Worlds in Collision,* whom he had never met:

> Dear Dr. Velikovsky:
>
> Two or three years ago when I first heard Jim Putnam tell about the thesis of your book, I was fascinated; and a few months ago when I heard that the book was in proof I asked Mr. Putnam if we might see a set of galleys here at *Harper's* with the idea that possibly this Magazine might be able to publish some of the material serially before this book came out. Mr. Putnam let us look at the galleys; our editors here were fascinated and one of them, Mr. Larrabee, prepared one of the two excerpts which we hoped to publish in a sort of condensed version of part of the book.
>
> Then we heard from Mr. Putnam that your return to this country had been delayed and then that you were ill, and accordingly we marked time waiting till you might be ready to consider this project. Now I'm told that Mr. Putnam has gone abroad for a brief stay and therefore take the liberty of writing you directly.
>
> We think it should be possible, by eliminating some of the details in your account of what happened, to get out of the book two rather long articles—of something like six to eight

thousand words apiece—which would demonstrate your thesis while not attempting to introduce all the evidence that is produced in the book. For the right to publish two such articles, if approved by you, we should be glad to pay $600.00, or $300.00 for each one. Our hope would be to bring out these articles just before book publication and it is our experience that the serial publication in such cases helps rather than hinders the sale of the book, as I think Mr. Putnam will agree. The main question is whether we can prepare these condensed versions of your material in such a way that they are entirely satisfactory to you as well as to us.

I hesitate thus to approach you while Mr. Putnam is away but I'm wondering whether we might show you the first of the two articles as we have worked it out and see whether it is satisfactory to you; and also whether you approve of this general idea. If you prefer to wait for Mr. Putnam's return and consult him, that is of course quite all right with us. I simply hate to postpone this whole matter any longer than we need to.

Sincerely,
Frederick L. Allen

From this letter it is evident that the author of *Worlds in Collision* was not the initiator of the article in *Harper's* that broke the story of his book to the public in January 1950. The editors of *Harper's* were so eager to present the theory that they even prepared an article without the knowledge of the author, and they approached the author without the knowledge of his editor at Macmillan, who had gone abroad. It so happened that I did not even answer this letter from Frederick Allen. I was not eager to have my story retold in condensed form with all its documentation omitted. Only by presenting all my evidential material could I make acceptable the strange story of what happened to our world thirty-four and twenty-seven centuries ago.

Not until the summer had passed, in September or October (or half a year later), did I agree to see Eric Larrabee, one of the editors of *Harper's.* He came together with James Putnam. When I opened the apartment door, I saw the very inquisitive eyes of this young man who became my first previewer, not counting O'Neill, who had written his article in 1946. Larrabee was full of respect and humility. He told me that he had read my book a number of times. He had obtained from Clifton Fadiman his notes about my book. Larrabee had a series of questions to ask about some problems that were raised in his mind on reading *Worlds in Collision.* I answered all the questions, and I could read pride and satisfaction on Putnam's face. Larrabee had written a piece about the book, but he did not feel that he should read it to me, saying that I would not like it and that he wanted to write a different piece. He would read the book still another time. I asked him not to disclose the content of my book in his preview beyond revealing that there were global catastrophes in historical times caused by strong perturbations among celestial bodies, not even mentioning the planet Venus—the *dramatis persona* of that volume—and to limit his article to indicating the problems raised by my book.

When he returned after a week or two, he had a new version, and again he was certain that he had not succeeded in explaining my theory properly. I listened as he read his piece. I found that he had not heeded my request not to reveal the content of the book; but he disarmed me by his eagerness, and I felt that it would be ungracious if I rejected his effort. So I let the story go through as he told it, only suggesting several factual corrections. Since it was entirely his piece, there was no remuneration in it for me.

The article was published as the leading piece in the January 1950 issue of *Harper's,* when it started its hundredth year as a magazine. An editorial comment to Larrabee's article said: "For almost a year we have been waiting for the chance to tell you about 'The Day the Sun Stood Still.' . . ." It was explained that the theory would be expounded in several volumes. "There is scarcely a branch of human knowledge which is not touched upon in the course of Dr. Velikovsky's argument. . . . It is obviously preposterous to attempt to explore the implications of the Velikovsky theory without a careful study of the entire book, to say nothing of the volumes still to come." However, it went on, "No one who has read Mr. Larrabee's article can ever again read the Old Testament prophets with the same blind piety, or the same blind skepticism, that he felt before."

Thus the magazine warned its readers not to be hasty in judging my theory by the content of the article. Similarly, Larrabee cautioned his readers:

> This article is an attempt, necessarily condensed and incomplete, to offer a preview of Dr. Velikovsky's findings. It is impossible to give here any idea of the extent of the material he

> has assembled to substantiate his argument. . . . Philosophy, science, religion—there is scarcely an area of knowledge or conviction invulnerable to Dr. Velikovsky's detailed and documented denial that the earth's history has been one of peaceful evolution.

Larrabee disclosed that the theory "invites skepticism as to the infallibility of the Law of Gravitation," reckoning as it does with the probability that electromagnetic forces also play a part in celestial mechanics, at least under the conditions of a close approach or near collision between two celestial bodies. It happened that he said more than the book actually contained, for he incorporated ideas discussed with me but not included in the book.

The article in *Harper's* caused immediate reverberations all around the country, as if it had caught the imagination of the people expecting something unusual at the midcentury point. In several states the magazine was sold out in a few days. Newspapers quoted the article and even reproduced it in full, displaying it and illustrating it with pictures on biblical themes; abroad, too, several publications, among them *Paris-Match,* printed large articles based on the *Harper's* story.

On the newspaper stand on my way to the library I saw that "Sun Stopped" was also displayed in another sense: The old New York daily the *Sun* had been absorbed by another newspaper.

Only a few days after I bought my copy of *Harper's* at the stand, there took place a phenomenon that was not immediately made public. An astronomer in faraway Japan observed an enormous mushroom cloud rising on Mars. Two months later it was interpreted as the first collision of celestial bodies observed in modern times: The body that struck Mars must have been a rather large planetoid.

This interpretation, by E. J. Öpik, a prominent Irish (originally Estonian) astronomer, was in the making when clouds began to gather quickly in the book world: The first rumbling, as we shall see somewhat later, was wrapped in an envelope and mailed to Macmillan.

DAMNED TO FAME

When *Harper's* was preparing the piece by Larrabee for the January 1950 issue, I was reminded by James Putnam that according to the Macmillan contract, the serialization rights before the publication of the book belonged to the author and that if I wished to make use of this right, I had to do so in time. I decided to approach a literary agent and was referred to one who had recently moved his office to my neighborhood. He was out of town; a young secretary took care of the business. I gave her two chapters of my book in galley sheets and asked her to investigate whether there was a serious magazine that would like to serialize a portion of my book on the basis of the samples, explaining that *Harper's* would have a preview. The secretary called me several days later to say that she had an offer from *Reader's Digest,* and, a day or two after that, that she had had another offer, from *Collier's.*

I was reluctant to accept the latter offer, being concerned that the work on which I had spent so much effort should not be presented as a sensation. I telephoned Horace Kallen, told him of the offer, of my reluctance, and asked his opinion. He said: "By all means agree. If such an offer should come to me, I would be only happy. Don't be a snob; it is un-American. President Roosevelt also printed a piece in *Collier's.*"

Before agreeing, I wished to be assured that the serialization would be given to my control since magazines usually cut texts at their discretion. I was promised this.

The articles in *Collier's* turned out to be not a serialization, but a condensation. The difference is that in the first case it would be some of the sections of my book printed as they were, only with some omissions of details; in the second case, it is a story told in different language, with the intent to cover the entire book in a few articles. According to the agreement, the magazine was to use the material in three issues.

The secretary of the literary agent gave the galleys of the section that she received from me to an associate editor of *Collier's*—there are many of these, and they have little power to make decisions. When the associate editor approached the chief editor of nonfiction, the latter looked through the material and announced to his subordinate that he himself would write the three pieces—something that is not usually done.

The two editors came with the first article, and I, being late, found them waiting on the dark staircase before the door of my study. I apologized and was prepared to be as uncritical as possible. However, I found the version offered me so inaccurate that it was unacceptable. It was not only full of errors, but also showed an inability to discern the main issues from secondary details. I reminded the gentlemen that they had acquired the right for serialization under the condition, agreed to in writing, that I must consent to the version prepared by them. So I offered to do the rewrite job and to present my story in an authentic way. They left, and I put my other work aside and condensed a large part of my book into one article. When the two gentlemen came again in a few days, the editor of nonfiction gave only a glance at my condensation—he could not have read more than two sentences—and told me that it was not written in a manner that they could use. The deadline—a very rigid affair in the world of magazine publishing—had to be met: It was five weeks before the date of the issue, and no postponement was possible.

They decided to revert to their own piece. I could not agree to the manner in which they chose to represent my ideas. They insisted that I should correct it, but I could not see how I could make the article satisfactory. They were pressed by their deadline the very next morning and told me that I had to point out to them the inaccuracies, which they would eliminate, but if I did not make use of this prerogative, they would be compelled to publish the piece as it was. I insisted that they had obtained only the rights for serialization; the story they wrote I could not make authentic merely by the elimination of numerous inaccuracies.

I regretted that I had followed Kallen's advice. As much as I tried, I could not convey to my visitors the idea that I must be exceedingly careful to be presented in a scholarly way, without sensationalism, and that ten years of strenuous work must not be jeopardized because of the hurt ambition of a journalist.

I had to leave for a reception at Putnam's house near Washington Square—he insisted on my coming—and I agreed with the *Collier's* editors to meet them later in the evening to try to iron out our differences. At Putnam's—the affair was for a writer who had published a novel—I met for the first time Frederick Allen, who had written me almost a year earlier and had been so eager to have the story in *Harper's.* I told Putnam of the situation with *Collier's,* and returning to my study, I called the *Collier's* people and asked them, instead of coming to me, to go to Putnam, whose social affair was by then over. The conference there went on past midnight, and several times Putnam talked with me over the telephone. Finally, it was agreed that at six the next morning the associate editor would come to my study and that I would do the editorial job—at my discretion—on their piece; nine in the morning was the deadline. A few times the editor, unable to agree to my changes, tore his coat from the hanger in order to go away, but finally, we finished the revision of the piece, as satisfactorily as was possible under the circumstances. Later we had a hard time with the second installment, and the third installment was never written or printed, though *Collier's* had rights to three and also paid me for three as agreed, without my asking it to do so.

The articles were printed five and nine weeks later, in the issues of February 25 and March 25, 1950 embellished by frightening drawings in color and introduced each time with a note by the *Collier's* editor. My name was displayed, so that the reader was led to believe that I was the author of the articles, since the name of the editor, whose condensation I had corrected as well as I had been able, was printed in small type.

I had earlier tried to assert my desire that *Collier's* not advertise the article in newspapers and was assured by the people whose names were at the top of its masthead that no advertisement would be printed, unless the text was first shown to me. But on the evening of February 16 I bought *The New York Times* and *Herald Tribune* of the next day, and in both was a full-page ad with a gravure from Doré showing the passage of the Israelites through the sea. Across the page large letters said: "YOU WILL BE ARGUING ABOUT THIS FOR

YEARS!" This was the only true thing in all this sore experience. The advertisement concluded: "Be sure to read 'The Heavens Burst' by Dr. Immanuel Velikovsky." The name of the editor was omitted.

My experience with *Reader's Digest* was different. One December evening, following an invitation, I went to see Fulton Oursler, a senior editor of the *Digest,* in his studio on Central Park South. After some compliments, especially to the poetic qualities of my book, Oursler began to read with great animation the article he had prepared. It, too, turned out to be not a serialization but a piece of original writing. He started it with a reference to the Scopes monkey trial when Clarence Darrow asked William Jennings Bryan whether, believing in everything written in the Bible, he believed also in Joshua's stopping the sun. The answer was: "I do," and this made Bryan the laughingstock of all enlightened people. Now my book proved that a natural phenomenon was behind the biblical story.

I corrected a number of details and advised Oursler on some changes, but in general let him present the story from the angle he had chosen, so that it remained his own subjective piece, signed with his name. However, I expressed my desire to see the corrected version in order to be sure that no errors of fact would be included. When Oursler came to my studio, bringing with him his eight-year-old son, to whom he had probably promised a meeting with some man of revolutionary ideas in science, I thoughtlessly made a number of factual remarks in the presence of his son, so that Oursler asked me: "Is there not one page where I was correct?," to which his son answered, "Daddy, on the first page Dr. Velikovsky made no remarks." We parted friends.

WRITING THE EPILOGUE

THE SO-CALLED FRONT MATTER, including the preface, is usually sent to the printer after the book has been set and the proofs read. In the case of *Worlds in Collision,* I deliberated with myself about the last pages of the Epilogue, set and proofread: whether to include them in, or omit them from, the book. They dealt with celestial mechanics.

In the Epilogue I discussed the problems solved and the new problems that presented themselves in the fields of history and chronology, Bible criticism, development of religion, mass psychology, geology, paleontology, astronomy, and physics. I wrote:

> Having discovered some historical facts and having solved a few problems, we are faced with more problems in almost all fields of science. . . . Barriers between sciences serve to create the belief in a scientist in any particular field that other scientific fields are free from problems, and he trusts himself to borrow from them without questioning. It can be seen here that problems in one area carry over into other scientific areas, thought to have no contact with each other.
>
> We realize the limitations which a single scholar must be aware of on facing such an ambitious program of inquiry into the architectonics of the world and its history. In earlier centuries philosophers not infrequently attempted a synthesis of knowledge in its various branches. Today, with knowledge becoming more and more specialized, whoever tries to cope with

such a task should ask in all humility the question put at the beginning of this volume: *Quota pars operis tanti nobis committitur*—Which part of this work is committed to us?

So I finished my book. Originally I had written another chapter and had let it be set. I foresaw the arguments of the astronomers, and I intended to meet them. The phenomena I described were deduced by me from ancient literature and folklore. I could, of course, remain in my domain, offer no physical solution at all, and allow astronomers to take over where I left off. This would probably have been the way that any other historian or folklorist would have chosen in a similar situation. Or I could try to reconcile my findings with the conventional tenets in astronomy. But there was a growing conviction on my part that it was justifiable to question the exclusive role in the celestial mechanics of a law established in 1687, a time when electromagnetic forces were not known and not reckoned with.

In January and February 1950 I consulted with a few physicists. I engaged several instructors in the Physics Department at Columbia University to calculate the rate of decrease with distance of the magnetic field created by a rotating charged body (the sun) in which field electrically charged bodies revolve. I received most divergent answers.

Then I visited Lloyd Motz, professor in the Astronomy Department at Columbia University, and showed him the pages intended as the concluding chapter of my book. There I gave a long series of physical phenomena unexplainable in the framework of existing theories. He went through the chapter carefully.

I found Motz to be a man of clear thinking, good heart, and high principles. In order to protect him from later being accused of cooperating with a heretic, I suggested that his help take the form of paid private instruction. We discussed various aspects of the problem; he always adhered to the conservative notions, yet he explored the possible actions and counteractions in the event that the sun and planets are charged.

Motz read with me the foundry proofs of the pages dealing with celestial mechanics. My own feeling against their inclusion in my book was dictated by two factors: I had no quantitative solution to the problem, and though I wished to meet the arguments of astronomers by showing where their concepts conflict with facts, I did not wish to make *Worlds in Collision,* a book of humanistic studies, into a book upon which, because of these additional pages, astronomers would declare themselves supreme arbiters. But this they did anyway, as we shall see.

I heard of the brilliant impression a young German physicist, Carl Friedrich von Weizsäcker, had made at the annual meeting of the American Physical Society that convened at Columbia University. I contacted him by telephone, and he agreed to meet me on February 6 at Pennsylvania Station in New York. We met, went together to Grand Central Station, and while we rode on the train as far as New Haven—he was going to Boston to visit at Harvard University—he kindly discussed with me some points of the problem that occupied my mind. His own theory in cosmogony was a revival of the Kant-Laplace nebular theory. Between 1900 and 1950 this teaching was considered discarded and was supplanted by the catastrophic theory of T. C. Chamberlin and F. R. Moulton, according to which planets had been born from the sun disrupted by a passing star in a gigantic near collision or—in a later variant—from a companion star of the sun shattered by a passing star. Weizsäcker claimed that the old Kant-Laplace nebular theory could be freed of the mechanical impossibilities inherent in it.

Weizsäcker calculated the strength of the magnetic field necessary to stop the earth, and it was not exceedingly great.* But he advised me not to include the section in question in my book because all we can say at present is that *if* the sun is a charged body to the extent that it can influence the planets and comets on their paths, then celestial mechanics is faulty. However, he did not believe that such is the case.

He indicated also that theoretically the Earth could be stopped by the mechanical action of a thick cloud of dust, but the earth in such a case would be entombed under a mountainous stratum of dust.

I returned to Professor Motz and told him of my conversation with Weizsäcker. I replaced the chapter with a few sentences in the Epilogue, which can be read on page 387 of *Worlds in Collision* (American edition). Motz agreed with this formulation. He read pages 384 to 388, the part of the Epilogue dealing with astronomical matters, and corrected what needed correction. This did not imply that he agreed with my theory or shared my skepticism concerning the accepted notions, but actually there was not a state-

* A much smaller magnetic field would be required merely to tilt the terrestrial axis.

ment with which a most conservative astronomer would not agree. For Motz's protection I repeat that he remained a follower of accepted notions in science, yet his unshackled mind could comprehend other solutions that might claim attention if they could explain as much as the old theory and something else besides.

In Motz's judgment, if the terrestrial globe were retarded in its rotation, or stopped, or even reversed, it would not necessarily be destroyed, depending on the time element involved, though civilizations would be destroyed. And this was what actually happened, according to the sources that served me in writing *Worlds in Collision.*

I have not abandoned my idea of presenting the problems of cosmology which, in my opinion, require reexamination of the fundamentals in the kinetics of the universe. Not being a physicist, I intend to tackle the subject in the framework of the history of science, showing the development of the theory of celestial motion from the time of Aristarchus; explaining the mechanism Gilbert and Kepler had in mind (the sun as a magnet), the theory of Descartes concerning vortices or fields of force in motion, the argument Newton put forth against Kepler (a magnet cannot be hot and preserve its quality), the opposition of Leibniz to Newton, the role Voltaire played in the victory of Newton over Descartes, and much more, carrying the problem into the light of modern discoveries. I still hope to complete this book, "The Orbit."*

* [Several essays of this incomplete manuscript will be published posthumously.]

"WAVING THE RED FLAG"

SOON AFTER THE publication of Larrabee's article in *Harper's* (January 1950) and before the publication of the previews in *Reader's Digest* (March issue) and *Collier's* (February 25 and March 25), an unusual correspondence took place between Professor Shapley and the Macmillan Company. One afternoon early in February James Putnam came to my apartment to see how work was progressing. I was already in the process of preparing the index, a task undertaken after the last set of proofs had been read. Putnam had with him two letters from Shapley and his own reply to the first letter. He appeared to be concerned. Glancing at the letters, I said that communications of this sort deserved no answer and went to Marion Kuhn to fetch the index. Upon my return, I proceeded to discuss a more important problem: I had not yet decided whether to keep the last chapter, already set in type, or to omit it, and I was to meet Weizsäcker in a few days, as I mentioned earlier.

The following are the letters from Shapley and the answers to him by Putnam and George Brett, president of Macmillan. Putnam did not show me Brett's letter, but he mentioned that Shapley's second letter would be answered by President Brett. At the time Shapley could not have seen anything but the *Harper's* article.

HARVARD COLLEGE OBSERVATORY
Cambridge 38, Massachusetts

January 18, 1950

Editorial Department
The Macmillan Company
60 Fifth Avenue
New York 11, N.Y.

Gentlemen:

I have heard a rumor from a source that should be reliable that possibly Macmillan Company will not proceed to the publication of Dr. Velikovsky's "Worlds in Collision." This rumor is the first item with regard to the Velikovsky business that makes for sanity. What books you publish is of course no affair of mine; and certainly I would depend on your expert judgment rather than on my own feelings in the matter. But I thought it might be well to record with you that a few scientists with whom I have talked about this matter (and this includes the President of Harvard University and all of the members of the Harvard Observatory staff) are not a little astonished that the great Macmillan Company, famous for its scientific publications, would venture into the Black Arts without rather careful refereeing of the manuscript.

The Velikovsky declaration or hypothesis or creed that the sun stood still is the most arrant nonsense of my experience, and I have met my share of crackpots. The fact that civilization exists at the present time is the most profound evidence I know of that nothing of this sort happened in historic times. The earth did not stop rotating in the interests of exegesis.

This note, of course, is not for publication or any further use than to report that to one reader of Macmillan's scientific books the aforementioned rumor is a great relief.

Sincerely yours,
Harlow Shapley

THE MACMILLAN COMPANY

Professor Harlow Shapley
Harvard College Observatory
Cambridge 38, Mass.

January 24, 1950

Dear Professor Shapley:

Thank you very much for your letter of January 18 which has been referred to me, as I have been working with Dr. Velikovsky on his book, WORLDS IN COLLISION, for several years. I am afraid that the rumor which you have heard is unfounded, as the book is about to go to press and we plan to publish it on March 28.

As I am sure you realize, we are publishing this book not as a scientific publication, but as the presentation of a theory which, it seemed to us, should be brought to the attention of scholars in the various fields of science with which it deals. Obviously it is a most controversial theory, and we have long since faced the fact that there will be a great diversity of reaction to the book. As to Dr. Velikovsky's scholarly attainments, you will perhaps be interested in the brief summary of biographical data regarding him, which I am enclosing.

As you probably know, the publication of the article by Eric Larrabee in *Harper's* has created a wide-spread interest in the book. When you see the book itself, in which, I may add, many changes have been made in the final proof, I shall be very much interested to know whether or not your feeling about it remains the same. I shall be glad to see that a copy is sent to you as soon as stock is available, which will probably be early in March.

I appreciate very much the spirit in which your letter was written, but I cannot believe that our publication of this book, which is presented by us as a theory, will affect your feeling toward our publications in the scientific field.

Sincerely yours,
[signed] James Putnam

HARVARD COLLEGE OBSERVATORY
Cambridge 38, Massachusetts
January 25, 1950

Mr. James Putnam
The Macmillan Company
60 Fifth Avenue
New York 11, N.Y.

Dear Mr. Putnam:

Thanks for your full letter of January 24.

It will be interesting a year from now to hear from you as to whether or not the reputation of the Macmillan Company is damaged by the publication of "Worlds of Collision." Possibly you already have published similar "theories" and know that the reaction of the public is not professionally or financially undesirable. My chief interest now in your publication of the volume is just to see if the reaction is favorable—an experiment in the psychology of scientists and the public.

Larrabee is probably too little to judge by, but from where I sit the celestial mechanics of Dr. Velikovsky is complete nonsense. Perhaps in the book he follows through some of the consequences that must result from the celestial manipulations he describes.

If I remember correctly, several years ago (perhaps only three or four) Dr. Velikovsky, with an introduction from Horace Kallen, or some other acquaintance of mine, met me in a New York hotel. He sought my endorsement of his theory. I was astonished. I looked around to see if he had a keeper with him. He declined to participate in the tea or cocktail; but he was a very attractive individual in manner and vocabulary. I tried, but rather futilely, to explain to him that if the earth could be stopped in such a short space of time it would overthrow all that Isaac Newton had done; it would have wrecked all life on the surface of the planet; it would have denied all the laborious and impartial finds of paleontology; it would have made impossible that he and I could meet together in a building in New York City less than four thousand years after this tremendous planetary event.

Dr. V. seemed very sad. But somehow I felt he was feeling sorry for me and the thousands of other American physical scientists and geologists and historians who have been so, so wrong.*

You cannot wonder that I looked for a keeper. But of course if he and Macmillan are right, I should rather be looking for the million keepers who should be in charge of the million of us who are not willing to change the facts and careful recordings of nature, in the interests of exegesis.

Naturally you can see that I am interested in your experiment. And frankly, unless you can assure me that you have done things like this frequently in the past without damage, the publication must cut me off from the Macmillan Company. But this is a triviality.

One of my colleagues by request is writing a commentary on Larrabee's article, and, being also a classicist, will probably have a good time. I don't suppose there would be any chance that you would send to me for this colleague an early copy of the proof sheets so that it will be Dr. V. who is discussed and not Mr. Larrabee?

Yes, it will be an interesting experiment. Incidentally, I suppose you have checked up on the references of Dr. V. He certainly has had a brilliant and varied career, and is remarkably versatile. It is quite possible that only this "Worlds in Collision" episode is intellectually fraudulent.

Sincerely yours,
[signed] Harlow Shapley

* You may be able to report that Dr. V. has never been in New York and that my consultant was another planet handler.

I would make a short comment on this last letter. Shapley's memory of our meeting differs from my recollection and notes. At our meeting in the spring of 1946 I disclosed to Shapley—as is obvious from my correspondence with him and with Professor Kallen following that conversation—only that "there were changes in the constitution of the solar system in historical times." I mentioned neither Joshua, nor the stopping of the sun, nor the stopping of the earth, nor Venus, nor the kinds of changes I describe in my book. I did not name a single literary or historical source that served me as evidence. I asked Shapley, not to endorse my book, but to read it in order to understand my reason for requesting that two definite spectrographic tests be conducted. I was not sad but elated at the prospect of the tests' being made.

THE MACMILLAN COMPANY

February 1, 1950

Professor Harlow Shapley
Harvard College Observatory
Cambridge 38, Massachusetts

My dear Professor Shapley:

Your letters of January 18 and January 25 with reference to Velikovsky's WORLDS IN COLLISION have just been referred to me. Normally, presumably, they would have been handled by the vice-president in charge of our Trade Department, the department which has contracted for the publication of WORLDS IN COLLISION. But as Mr. Latham is in England, the correspondence has been referred to me.

At first glance it would seem that we owe a debt of gratitude for waving the red flag. Mr. Latham presumably knows all about this publication, but as he is not here and I only have available to me the documentary evidence from our files, I am taking your cautionary note to heart and am insisting that just as soon as the proofs can be made available—they are in the process of being corrected—we get the opinions of three scholars on the book as a whole.

I take it you yourself have not had an opportunity of reading the book. I think it would be a little unfair to ask you to do so at this time. But I do appreciate your having taken the trouble to flag us down, because it enables me to get three additional opinions on my own count to back up or to refute the opinions of those critics who reviewed the manuscript for Mr. Latham.

It isn't often that scholars take the trouble to caution a publisher as you have. I am most grateful to you for your kindness.

Sincerely yours
[signed] George Brett
[President of the Macmillan Company]

CENSORS APPOINTED

THUS MY PUBLISHER submitted to the pressure or listened to the warning. An unusual procedure was established. For more than three years—from November 1946—the book had been in the hands of Macmillan. During that time it was examined extensively and in detail by expert readers. Now, after the fourth set of proofs had been drawn and the actual printing was about to begin, the book was turned over to the censorship of three persons. Putnam did not tell me this in so many words, nor did I then see Brett's reply, but I felt that they would ask the opinion of some additional experts.

Knowing the role of czar that Shapley played among the astronomers on the East Coast, and seeing the violence of his opposition to the publication of my book, I was concerned for Atwater and his position at the planetarium, especially in view of the fact that *This Week* magazine (a weekly supplement to the *Herald Tribune* and numerous other newspapers in this country) had invited Atwater to write an article on the forthcoming book, to say nothing of his plan to stage *Worlds in Collision* at the planetarium. I went to see him to tell of the new developments, so that he would not act blindly when his own position might be endangered. I found him in his office at the planetarium; he had already been informed by Putnam, who had naturally turned to Atwater, his astronomer reader, when Shapley wrote his letters. Putnam had even read him the letters over the telephone, and by this time Atwater knew that probably three prominent scientists would be approached to censor the book.

He was calm and gave me the following explanation of the fury that had caused Shapley and certain other astronomers to lose their sense of propriety.

"You see," he said to me, "Shapley must have some mental reservation that all is not perfect in the established teaching about the universe. He must fortify his inner insecurity by implacability. This mental reservation is his Achilles' heel. You have wounded him just there."

Gordon Atwater is an unusual example of a human being: open face, trained body of an athlete, simple and strong as the Greeks thought their heroes to be, and neither shrewd nor scheming.

The book was given to the censors a few weeks before the publication date. I was not informed of what was going on. As I heard from O'Neill at a much later date, in 1952, two of the three censors were for the publication of the book, and one against.

In 1952 O'Neill also disclosed to me the name of one of the censors who passed the book—I have never met him. It was the chairman of the Department of Physics at New York University. O'Neill happened to speak with him on the subject and so found this out. The physicist did not necessarily subscribe to any of my views, but he may have found in my book a serious and sincere effort to solve some important issues.

Two men said to the book, "Live," and one said, "Die." How close my book came to being scrapped a few weeks before the publication date, after *Harper's* and *Reader's Digest* had already previewed it.*

During the time that the page proofs of *Worlds in Collision* were in the hands of censors, efforts were made to keep the ranks closed and to stamp out the revolutionary doctrine before it could permanently impress the minds of men. *Science News Letter,* in its issue of February 25, published the opinions of Shapley and a few other specialists. The article carried the heading "Theories Denounced," the subject being "Velikovsky's Statements." However, none of those who "denounced" could have seen the book, with its authentic statements and evidence, for one simple reason: The book had not yet been printed. Denouncing a theory not yet printed and examined in detail is like writing a criticism of a performance by an actor before it has actually taken place.

* [Later still Velikovsky found out that four scientists had been asked to read and comment on the book. All were for publication, though one of the four expressed some reservations. Copies of the four letters are in the Velikovsky archive.]

Those who were asked their opinion could offer only trivialities or generalities. Nelson Glueck, of the Hebrew Union College in Cincinnati, declared that with biblical verses one could prove anything at all; Carl Kraeling, director of the Oriental Institute of the University of Chicago, concluded that my book was "another example of the apologetic procedure"; Dr. Henry Field, anthropologist and archaeologist, said that the book was wrong because the Israelites did not cross the Red Sea, but almost certainly the shallow sea of reeds. (I did not locate the Sea of Passage, and in any case, what matters was that in my book I gave many sources showing that "The water of all oceans and seas was divided.")

Dr. David Delo, of the American Geological Institute, asserted that all mountains were "formed millions of years ago," and no new mountains had sprung up since then. Therefore, Velikovsky "appears to be by-passing all the sound scientific observations of a multitude of geologists made during the past 100 years."

The last remark is incorrect because for more than thirty years there has been hardly any other geologist in the Old or the New World who would contradict the fact established by explorers on all major mountain chains of the world—the Himalayas, the Alps, the Rocky Mountains, the Andes—that great upthrust of mountains took place in a time "almost unbelievably recent.*

Such was the dissonant choir of "denouncers"—none of them vicious—who assented to say something for *Science News Letter* against my forthcoming book. The real attack was made by Shapley.

> Although most men of learning, when informed that Dr. Velikovsky's work is actually to be published in several volumes, appear to be amazed, it is the astronomers who express their thoughts most definitely.
>
> Dr. Harlow Shapley, director of the Harvard Observatory, who said that he was speaking for his fellow astronomers, called Dr. Velikovsky's theory that Venus, in the guise of a comet, had made the earth stand still for a few days, "rubbish and nonsense."

In support of such an annihilating statement Shapley offered only two brief sentences: "There are written records of the obser-

* This material is presented in my *Earth in Upheaval* (1955), pp. 70–92.

vation of the planet Venus 500 to 1000 years before the Exodus," and "Venus has a mass approximately a million times greater than any comet." We shall meet both these arguments again, and then we shall discuss them in detail.

By way of generalization, *Science News Letter* announced at the beginning of its piece that "Using such phrases as 'nonsense and rubbish,' top astronomers, geologists, historians, archaeologists and theologians denounced statements by Dr. Velikovsky. . . ."

Science News Letter prints a list of its officers; Harlow Shapley was at that time its president.

The great displeasure with my forthcoming book, not yet read or seen, was the natural consequence of my being unorthodox. Anybody who resolutely steps off the beaten track and walks uncharted trails trespassing the fields owned by congregations of specialists, must be disciplined; his ideas must be invalidated before their scent poisons the good thinking and the loyal behavior of the rest of the camp.

I quote from a speech, "Running in Trails," given two decades earlier by a scientist at commencement exercises at the University of Pennsylvania:

> There exist in many parts of the world various species of a subfamily of ants, the *Dolichoderinae,* whose individuals characteristically run in trails, in well established paths, maintaining the same highways throughout many generations. . . . These species of ants are essentially blind; they run by scent; the nest odor is maintained along the trails through the constant passing to and fro of the hundreds or thousands of members of the colony. . . . The inherited social habits suffice year after year, generation after generation.
>
> When a new brood of ants is hatched and passes through its preparatory larval stages, it is impregnated automatically with the colony odor. . . . The young ants become adults, and then, dressed up with caps and gowns or the analogous vestments of the formicine world, they start the endless patrolling to and fro, saluting each other with twiddling antennae, maintaining the status quo, keeping alive the social smell that has been established by their forerunners. . . . They too go through their training to adulthood, and, with diplomas under their arms, start out along the well-established path, saluting each fellow

in passing, checking up that he too is conforming to the colony's customs and is in good odor.

Occasionally, by accident or by some psychic aberration, a trail runner gets off the beaten path and ventures out alone. Usually he becomes wholly lost or, after random wanderings, stumbles back on to the good old trail. Occasionally one of these vagrants is followed by a fellow or two, but the new divergent trail with its slight and uncertain odors has relatively little appeal; devoid of vision these timid adventurers hurriedly smell their way back to the well scented customs and go on running to and fro, twiddling antennae with those who do likewise, happy apparently to keep clear of those realms that have not the proper social fragrance.

If a natural calamity disturbs the aromatic trail of the *Dolichoderinae,* consternation and helplessness ensue. If a strange insect appears, blind fighting results—then back to patrolling out and in; a sudden obstruction on the path, brief excitement follows, and the trail is reestablished with as little diversion as possible from the former path, and on they go as before; . . . back to the beaten path, no matter how circuitous or absurd it may be, back to the saluting, the twiddling, and the maintenance of the old social aroma. . . .

It is clear that the universe of knowledge is expanding at a terrific rate—expanding in all directions, while the *Dolichoderinae* and similar organisms, unchanged in size and outlook, continue to twiddle their antennae along familiar trails.

The commencement speaker whom I have here quoted was Harlow Shapley.

"IT IS HARD TO QUARREL WITH NUMBERS"

THE PERSON WHOM Professor Shapley described in his letter to Macmillan as "one of my colleagues," who is "also a classicist" and would have "a good time" rebutting Velikovsky and his theory, was Cecilia Payne-Gaposchkin, an Englishwoman married to a Russian, both astronomers at the Harvard College Observatory. Her piece was written for *The Reporter,* at that time a new magazine, published by Max Ascoli, looking for sensational material. Weeks before the article appeared in print it was distributed in mimeographed form, bearing the title "A Thing Imagination Boggles At." The scope of distribution in this form was probably very extensive. Professor Vasili I. Komarewsky, a chemist at the Illinois Institute of Technology and a classmate of mine in the *Gymnasium* in Russia, told me that he received a copy from the Harvard Observatory, though he had no interests that were in any way related to that topic or that institution. John J. O'Neill also received a copy, and T. O. Thackrey, publisher and editor of a New York daily newspaper, received one directly from Shapley.

In this seven-page mimeographed article Professor Payne-Gaposchkin made all kinds of assumptions about the book, which she judged on having read only Larrabee's article in *Harper's.* She wrote of her "amazement, consternation, incredulity, and derision. . . . Let us suppose that we are dealing neither with hoax nor with science fiction . . . we shall find that it is rubbish." Of course, the most outrageous point was the suggestion that the earth stopped in its rotation.

> If the biblical story which Mr. Velikovsky seeks to establish is to be accepted at its face value, the rotation of the earth must have been stopped within six hours. All bodies not attached to the surface of the earth (including the atmosphere and the ocean) would then have continued their motion, and consequently have flown off with a speed of 900 miles an hour at the latitude of Egypt.

This astronomer "of highest standing" in Shapley's appraisal set out to destroy Velikovsky's assumption with the weapon of the exact sciences. But exact science requires exact figures. If the earth stopped rotating suddenly or in a very small fraction of a second, unattached objects would move away at a velocity of 900 miles an hour at the latitude of Egypt since that is the linear velocity of terrestrial rotation at that latitude. But if, as Professor Payne-Gaposchkin says, the earth decelerated within the space of six hours, or 21,600 seconds, the inertial push experienced by objects on its surface would be 500 times smaller than their weight. A man weighing 160 pounds would experience a forward push equal to 5 ounces. Of course, he would not fly off into space, for his weight is much greater than the push. Nonetheless, atmosphere and oceans would be set in motion. *Worlds in Collision* describes erupting oceans and swirling hurricanes on many pages.

When a reviewer receives a statement from a Harvard College Observatory professor, on the letterhead of that institution, he takes the figures seriously. This statement was sent out in advance of the publication date of *Worlds in Collision* and thus of the reviewing date, with the unconcealed purpose of influencing the reviewers.

When the article was printed in *The Reporter*, some changes were made. The passage in question reappeared in the following formulation:

> Let us assume, however, that Dr. Velikovsky is right—that the earth did stop rotating. In that case, all bodies not attached to the surface of the earth (including the atmosphere and the ocean) would have continued their motion, and would have flown off with a speed of nine hundred miles an hour at the latitude of Egypt.

Here I question the good faith of the author. Mrs. Payne-Gaposchkin must have been made aware of her error and of what the correct calculation would be. Dropping "six hours," she should have dropped the entire argument. She allowed the unwary reader to believe that the element of time is unimportant, whereas it is all that counts. An airplane that is stopped suddenly on hitting a rocky mountain disintegrates, but one that is slowed down in the course of twenty minutes does not. Even planes traveling with the velocity of the earth's rotation are brought to a stop without disintegration. Besides, I have not offered the stoppage of the earth's rotation as *the* solution of the phenomenon observed. Each time the phenomenon of the disruption in the day's length is mentioned, another solution is offered: "If rotation persisted undisturbed, the terrestrial axis may have tilted in the presence of a strong magnetic field, so that the sun appeared to lose for hours its diurnal movement."*

As her chief geological argument Payne-Gaposchkin asserted in the published article that "there is no evidence of a wholesale disturbance of ocean level near 1500 B.C.," or 3,500 years ago, and this alone suffices to show that no global catastrophe could have occurred then.

Professor Reginald Daly, of the same Harvard University, dean of American geologists, was world famous for his observation that "a recent world-wide sinking of ocean level" of twenty feet took place "about 3,500 years ago."† This noted geologist brought together observations from many parts of the world. "Similar emergence [of coast]," according to Daly, "is found along the Atlantic Coast from New York to the Gulf of Mexico; for at least 1,000 miles along the coast of eastern Australia; along the coast of Brazil, southwest Africa, and many islands of the Pacific, Atlantic, and Indian Oceans." Philip H. Kuenen, of Leyden University, in his *Marine Geology*, confirmed Daly's claim: "In thirty-odd years following Daly's first paper many further instances have been recorded by a number of investigators the world over, so that this recent shift is now well established."‡ As for the time of this sudden drop of the ocean level, Kuenen wrote, "The time can be fixed as roughly 3,000 to 3,500 years ago [i.e., 1000 to 1500 B.C.]." Mrs. Payne-Gaposchkin took a risky chance by asserting, without inquiry, that "there is no evidence of a wholesale disturbance of ocean level near 1500 B.C." She proceeded:

* *Worlds in Collision*, p. 44.
† Reginald Daly, *Our Mobile Earth* (1926), p. 179.
‡ Philip H. Kuenen, *Marine Geology* (1950), p. 538.

> Is this scientific age so uncritical, so ignorant of the nature of evidence, that any considerable number of people will be fooled by a sloppy parade of the jargon of a dozen fields of learning? Evidently a great national magazine [*Harper's*], and a publisher who has in the past handled great works of science, believe that they will.

She compared *Worlds in Collision* to the Great Moon Hoax, which was published a century ago as a story of intelligent beings presumably observed on the moon by Sir John Herschel, through a telescope in South Africa (he had nothing to do with the hoax), and expressed her fear that it would have a similar monetary success. "The road to fame and fortune for the twentiety-century scholar is clear. Never mind logic; never mind the precise meaning of words or the results of exact research." And having stated for some reason that "the most insidious part of the argument is the appeal to Biblical sources" and having mixed up Ovid and Hesiod, she finished with a seven-line verse from *The Cock and the Bull* to make the piece as derisive as possible:

> Excuse me, sir, I think I'm going mad.
> You see the trick on't, though, and can yourself
> Continue the discourse *ad libitum,*
> It takes up about eighty thousand lines,
> A thing imagination boggles at;
> And might, odds-bobs, sir! in judicious hands
> Extend from here to Mesopotamy.

The Reporter placed large ads in *The New York Times* announcing the publication of Payne-Gaposchkin's "Nonsense, Dr. Velikovsky!" Under this title the article was published in the issue of March 14, 1950, twenty days before the publication of the book on April 3. Thus the reviewers of the country were supplied with an analysis by an astronomer from Harvard. In order that this article not pass unnoticed, *Science News Letter* for March 25 (nine days before the publication of *Worlds in Collision*) presented "Retort to Velikovsky." It begins: "With the title, 'Nonsense, Dr. Velikovsky,' the first detailed scientific answer to Dr. Immanuel Velikovsky's theory that the sun stood still a couple of times around 1500 B.C. appears in the issue of *The Reporter.*" *Science News Letter* reproduced the 900-mile sentence: "Assuming for a moment that the earth did stop rotating, Dr. Payne-Gaposchkin points out that all bodies not attached to the surface of the earth, including the atmosphere and the oceans, would have continued their motion, and would have flown off with a speed of 900 miles an hour in the latitude of Egypt." And it ended with the quotation "Never mind logic; never mind the precise meaning of words or the result of exact research."

Four weeks after the publication of the article in *The Reporter,* and eight days after the publication of my book, a new issue of *The Reporter,* that of April 11, printed a letter from Larrabee in which he took Professor Payne-Gaposchkin to task for "not having read the book which she believes to be 'a sloppy parade of jargon' . . . so far she has demolished nothing but a journalist's condensation of a formidably documented argument."

The same issue carried a letter from Cecilia Payne-Gaposchkin in answer to Larrabee's letter. It begins: "I have obtained an advance copy of *Worlds in Collision,* have spent the weekend in reading it, and should like to report to you that my opinion of the 'theory' is in no way modified by having done so. The book is better written and more fully documented than the popularizing previews, but is just as wrong."

Neither from the mimeographed copies of the Payne-Gaposchkin preview nor from her article as it appeared in *The Reporter* could the public or the reviewers have known that Cecilia Payne-Gaposchkin had not read *Worlds in Collision.* Though attacking the substance of the book and even its style, she made no mention of the fact that her sole source of information about it was the Larrabee article in *Harper's.* The item in *Science News Letter,* characterizing the Payne-Gaposchkin article as a "detailed scientific answer to Dr. Velikovsky," also failed to reveal this fact. And the ads in *The New York Times* announcing the Payne-Gaposchkin piece were equally reticent about it.

"SOMEBODY HAS DONE YOU DIRT"

TED O. THACKREY, who a year before had left the position of chief editor of the New York *Post* and was publishing the *Compass*, a progressive newspaper that often presented the political views of Henry Wallace, reprinted in its issue of February 19, 1950, Larrabee's *Harper's* article. Thackrey also wrote an editorial in which he made a very generous evaluation of the place in science he expected my work to occupy in years to come.

On February 20 Harlow Shapley, whose political views were close to those of the *Compass*, wrote a letter to Thackrey, and their correspondence went on until June 6. On February 20 my book had not yet been published, not even printed. Obviously many things happened during the time of that correspondence, and there were many participants in the events, scientists and others. But in order to present the correspondence without interruption in its sequence, I shall quote these letters, and the story of those days will follow.

HARVARD COLLEGE OBSERVATORY
Cambridge 38, Massachusetts

February 20, 1950
(Not for publication. HS)

Mr. Ted Thackrey
The Compass
New York City, New York

Dear Ted:

Somebody has done you dirt. They got you to republish Larrabee's article from the January Harper's Magazine. Collier's also has given this crank a great run, and several other presumably reputable publications have handled the stuff with a flat pen.

In my rather long experience in the field of science, this is the most successful fraud that has been perpetrated on leading American publications. To me the article seems so transparent that I am surprised that Harper's and Macmillan would handle it. I am not quite sure that Macmillan is going through with the publication, because that firm has perhaps the highest reputation in the world for the handling of scientific books.

A representative of Max Ascoli's magazine, The Reporter, called me up a few weeks ago and asked me to write a refutation or comment. My colleague Mrs. Cecilia Payne-Gaposchkin has written such a paper for The Reporter, and I suppose it will be forthcoming soon. I enclose a copy. It occurs to me that The Compass might like to republish (with permission) this comment from an American astronomer of the highest standing.

A few years ago this Dr. V. sent me a copy of his pamphlet "Cosmos Without Gravitation." I filed it away with the other crank literature that comes to a scientific laboratory. We could dig out several equally plausible writings, mostly published at the author's expense. We have the publications of the Flat Earth Society—desperately sincere. We have the theories on the origin of the solar system by the Fuller Brush man of Florida. We have the writings of the men who unfortunately were unable ever to go to school, but have herewith overthrown the theories of Einstein (as Dr. V. has overthrown Darwin and Newton and all the rest).

A number of astronomical groups have talked about this business, and their sad conclusion generally is that we are in an age of decadence where nonsense stands higher than experiment and learning.

Of course one should not pay any serious attention to these matters, and I certainly would not have done so if The Compass had not reprinted, apparently with a straight face, the Larrabee article.

This man Dr. V. came to me in New York several years ago and asked me to endorse his work so that he could get it published. I pointed out to him that if he were right then all that Isaac Newton ever did was wrong. Nevertheless we seem to have built up a civilization, and the hotel in which we were standing, on account of the contributions of Newton and others of his kind.

You know, of course, that I personally am a sympathetic friend of the thwarted and demented, and have no high respect for formalism, and none at all for orthodoxy. But this "Sun stood still" stuff is pure rubbish, of the level of the astrological hocus-pocus, except that Dr. V. has read widely as well as superficially and can parade a lot of technical terms which apparently he has not mastered. But if he had mastered them, who would want to publish his stuff!

Sincerely yours,
Harlow Shapley

To this letter Shapley attached a mimeographed copy of Payne-Gaposchkin's article containing the entirely erroneous calculation discussed in the preceding section. My book was not yet printed, and Shapley could not have seen it. He apparently did not abide by the prospect of the proofs' being examined by three unnamed scientists, as had been broached to him by Mr. Brett twenty days earlier.

March 7, 1950

Dr. Harlow Shapley
Harvard College Observatory
Cambridge 38, Mass.

Dear Harlow:

I have delayed an answer to your letter of February 20 until I felt reasonably recovered from my initial reaction to its content.

I could not feel that our friendship was worth retaining if I were not as frank in my reply as you undoubtedly were being with me.

In the first place, I feel that I must take with you as sharp an exception to your series of wholly unwarranted and unfounded characterizations of Dr. Velikovsky, as I have had occasion to take in another field when your political views have led to nearly as unwarranted an assault upon your own integrity.

I am genuinely shocked, in rereading your letter, at the epithets you have seen fit to use in characterizing Dr. Velikovsky, a man of unusual integrity and scholarship, whose painstaking approach to scientific theory is at least a match for your own. . . .

. . . You further suggest that, evidently through your efforts, there is now some question about whether Macmillan will go through with the publication, thus not only confessing to do direct damage, but to provide some evidence of having successfully damaged Dr. Velikovsky's work. . . .

. . . I have had ample opportunity to verify from a wide variety of unimpeachable sources Dr. Velikovsky's scholarship and high integrity as an individual. His claims as to his studies, his background and his degrees have consistently, and without exception, been on the modest side.

It seems to me that you are making both a personal and professional mistake—a gravely serious and dangerous one—by the totally unscientific and viciously emotional character of your attack upon Dr. Velikovsky and his work.

I am writing this advisedly, since it is obvious that you have seen fit to unleash a series of attacks, by no means directed to me alone, both against Dr. Velikovsky and against his work, without ever once having taken the trouble to examine his work or even to glance at the evidential research with which it has been accompanied.

I submit that, at the time of writing your letter, you had neither read the manuscript of Dr. Velikovsky's "Worlds in Collision," nor a single piece of evidence in its support. At the most, it is possible that you had examined superficially a popularization of a very small portion of this work by Eric Larrabee of Harper's Magazine.

It would be totally presumptuous of me to make the slightest effort to maintain the scientific validity of the conclusions which Dr. Velikovsky has stated as tentative theses, growing out of the historical evidence which he has amassed. But I think it is equally evident that you are at the present time, despite your scientific attainments, in an even less valid position to quarrel with Dr. Velikovsky's evidence or his conclusions, since you have not taken the trouble to examine either. In fact, it is impossible for me not to be alarmed at the intensity and character of the attack, particularly from an individual of your scientific attainment, which is based so completely on hearsay and emotional reaction. I am sure you would yourself hesitate to reach a conclusion about the nature of a planet without having examined with care all of the available evidence. And yet, you have had no hesitancy in proclaiming a distinguished scholar an impostor, a charlatan and a fraud and characterizing his work as pure rubbish.

That your course of action is, on its face, both morally and criminally slanderous and libelous, would have been perfectly evident to me, even had I not made a most thorough study of the law in relation to slander and libel. . . .

Certainly, it is possible that the evidence adduced by Dr. Velikovsky is scientifically inconclusive, but to maintain that it is rubbish merely because of a possible (though by no means certain) conflict with another working hypothesis, without even having bothered to make an examination of the evidence is, it seems to me, clearly nonsense, even when the nonsense is uttered by one who has achieved such an eminently responsible position in the field of astronomy as yourself.

I beg of you, in all earnestness, to consider your course of conduct in this matter and contrast it with the high standards you set before your students, before proceeding further in your campaign to destroy a man whom you do not know and to damn a theory about which you obviously know nothing.

I did take the trouble to read the article which you had prepared by Mrs. Cecilia Payne-Gaposchkin. Again, I have no presumption of scientific knowledge in her field and no basis for accepting or rejecting the scientific theories expounded in her article. I do, however, have a criticism of the main tenor of the article itself, which is as follows:

1. The article is an attack upon a book which the writer has not read.

2. In at least two instances, the article sets up strawmen and then proceeds to demolish the strawmen. In other words, the article attributes to Dr. Velikovsky statements which are not made either by him or in his manuscript, and then proceeds to quarrel with those statements as though they were authentic. This is, to say the least, a most unscientific method of criticism. . . .

Although it has no bearing whatever upon the case under discussion, except that it was a minor point raised in your letter, I feel that I can scarcely refrain from twitting you on the patronizing and blanket references to the unschooled and informally educated (Dr. Velikovsky is, of course, neither). Surely, it should not require a layman like myself to remind you, for example, of such contributors to the field of scientific knowledge as Leeuwenhoek, the untutored church janitor who discovered and proved the existence of microbes, to the annoyance of the then existing practitioners of medicine.

Sincerely,
Ted O. Thackrey

cc. Dr. Immanuel Velikovsky

"FOLLOWING THE PRECEDENT OF ONE GALILEO"

HARVARD COLLEGE OBSERVATORY
Cambridge 38, Massachusetts

March 8, 1950
Confidential

Mr. T. O. Thackrey
The Daily Compass
164 Duane Street
New York 13, New York

Dear Ted:

I apologize immediately for having written such disparaging remarks about an acquaintance of yours. My astonishment stands, but so does my apology. . . .

Last week's Science News Letter, incidentally, included statements on the Larrabee article from men in other fields—all of distinction, I believe—and they seem to be unfavorable. "Time" of this week also takes a dim view.

I myself am not writing anything in response to Dr. Velikovsky or Larrabee or anyone. In fact, the only hot communication I have made was this letter to you. I certainly wrote it to the wrong person!

In half a dozen groups, chiefly of Harvard University professors (and they are not all ill-mannered, injudicious, or dumb), without exception I have found no one whose views about the Reader's Digest survey of the volume, to say nothing of Larrabee's article, were other than mine. Many, like Ickes in the New Republic, took the whole business as a joke. Wasn't Larrabee a Lampoon editor?

Perhaps I wrote you that a vice-president of the American Astronomical Society thought that the Council of the Society should send a protest to Macmillan, the famous publisher of highly reputable scientific books; but I said immediately, and so did many others, that such an action would merely give greater publicity to Dr. Velikovsky's contributions. Freedom to publish is a basic freedom. . . .

Our trouble about the Macmillan Company and Harper's, if you call it trouble, was that such publications seem to throw doubt on the care with which they referee other manuscripts on which we want to depend. There was no fear whatever of being misled by Dr. Velikovsky's views. . . .

In conclusion, I remember that Dr. Velikovsky was a very nice personality, quiet, modest, and apparently genuinely sorry that I and the likes of me had been so misled by Isaac Newton, Laplace, Lagrange, Simon Newcomb, the great national observatories in all the leading countries. He was, in fact, quite charming, as I remember him. No doubt, from what you say, he is a deep scholar in some fields. I have not yet seen statements from scholars to this effect, and possibly you would not value them highly if they should speak adversely. They squabble among themselves—these philosophers of the ancient times and of the fragmentary records. But it is hard to quarrel with a differential equation, or with numbers; and therefore the trained astronomers and physicists, almost to the last man, will insist on the fallacy of Dr. Velikovsky's celestial mechanics. Even the planetarium lecturer, who is almost totally unknown to astronomers, was evasive in his not unfavorable comments.

In signing off I again apologize for the vigor of my language; but following the precedent of one Galileo, I stand fast on the evidence and assertions that Venus did not participate in the stopping of the rotating of the earth some fifteen hundred years B.C. One cannot be dishonest in such matters and remain a scientist.

But I insist on remaining your friend. Neither Dr. V. nor the planet-comet Venus should get between us.

Sincerely yours,
Harlow

To this letter Shapley added two long postscripts. In one he referred Thackrey to Dr. Gerald M. Clemence, director of the *Nautical Almanac,* or to Dr. Jan Schilt of the Columbia University Observatory. In the second he wrote: "... it seems more than reasonable that it would be better to tackle hard mathematical problems with mathematics rather than with scripture." He also referred to his correspondence with Kallen and inquired whether I had gotten in touch with Walter Adams of the Mount Wilson Observatory or Rupert Wildt of Yale, as he had suggested to me through Kallen four years earlier in 1946.

Three hundred and forty years earlier, on the night of January 7, 1610, Galileo directed his telescope toward Jupiter and saw three stars around it; the next night he found that they had moved; on the thirteenth of the month he saw the fourth moon of Jupiter. Since these bodies revolved around Jupiter, an illustration of the Copernican concept of the planetary system was discovered; Galileo saw in the motions of the Jovian moons proof of the correctness of the Copernican theory.

Astronomers and philosophers declared that these moons were a fraud. Clavius, the celebrated Jesuit mathematician of the Roman College, "laughed at the idea of the four new planets that one probably had to stick in one's telescope to see. May Galileo persist in his opinion and be happy. I persist in my opinion."* And his opinion was that Galileo arranged these planets in his telescope to cheat the credulous and to earn undeserved fame. Professor Clavius was not a man without erudition. As a matter of fact, he was the chief author of the Gregorian calendar reform.

Professor Francesco Sizzi, an astronomer in Florence, declared that there could be but seven planets because seven is a holy number; therefore, there could be no moons around Jupiter. "We have only seven windows in our heads," he said, "two nostrils, two eyes, two ears, one mouth."

Libri, a philosopher, refused to look into Galileo's telescope.

* Hermann Kesten, *Copernicus and His World* (1945–46), p. 367.

When he died, Galileo wrote in a letter to a friend that the deceased philosopher might perchance see the moons of Jupiter on his way to paradise.

Can we believe that this was the behavior of philosophers and astronomers—to declare something a fraud that one refuses to examine?

The level of the arguments raised against Galileo and the Copernican system of the world may be also illustrated by the opinion expressed by Scipio Chiaramonti, professor of philosophy at the University of Pisa, the Harvard of those days, who in 1632 published a book against the Copernican system: "Animals that are capable of motion have joints and limbs: the earth has neither joints nor limbs, therefore it does not move."

And in order to meet the counterargument that in the Ptolemaic system the sun and the planets move, though they, too, have neither limbs nor joints, the professor prepared a reply: The sun, the planets, the stars are of a heavenly substance and can move. "It is to the last degree unseemly to place among the celestial bodies, which are divine and pure, the earth, which is a sewer full of vile filth."

If, in matters of science, the opinion of the majority decides where truth lies, then the Earth was the center of the universe until about 300 years ago.

In rehabilitation of the opponents of Galileo, it must be said that in 1611, a year after Galileo had published his *Sidereus Nuncius* with the description of his discoveries, Christopher Clavius, and other Jesuits of the Roman College, repeated the telescope observations and confirmed them; Galileo received a triumphant welcome from Clavius and his mathematicians.*

* Joseph Needham and Wang Ling, *Science and Civilization in China*, vol. 3 (1959), p. 444: "John Adam Schall von Bell, later to be the first European director of the Chinese Bureau of Astronomy, was present as a young man in the hall of the Roman College in May 1611 when Galileo received a triumphant welcome from Clavius and his mathematicians after their confirmation of his discoveries."

MISLED BY LAPLACE

A READER OF THESE PAGES may start thinking, if he has not done so already, that the truth of *Worlds in Collision* depends on revision of the theory of celestial mechanics. Now, if the mechanics of the solar system—and of the entire universe—was understood completely in the years before man knew anything, not only of atomic energy but even of electromagnetism, that lights our houses, moves trolley cars, and carries our voices, is then *Worlds in Collision* a chimerical invention?

Not necessarily so. And whose authority to support this assertion can be greater than that of Laplace, the creator of the idea of the permanency of orbital motions, the author of the celebrated *Mécanique céleste*? Only very recently I came across a passage of his, first in a book by Kenneth Heuer; then I looked it up in the original source, in the sixteen-volume edition of Laplace by L'Académie Française.*

In his *Exposition du système du monde,* Laplace discussed the effects of a meeting of the Earth with a large comet. He said that for his own generation the chances of such an encounter must be very small, but "the small probability of such an encounter must accumulate during many centuries and will become very great [*très grande*]. It is easy to visualize the effect of such a shock on the Earth." From here I follow Heuer's translation of Laplace:

* *Oeuvres complètes de Laplace* (1884), vol. VI, p. 234. Also see vol. VII, pp. cxx, cxxi; vol. VI, p. 346.

> The axis and the movement of rotation would be changed. The seas would abandon their ancient positions, in order to precipitate themselves towards the new equator; a great portion of the human race and the animals would be drowned in the universal deluge, or destroyed by the violent shock imparted to the terrestrial globe; entire species would be annihilated; all monuments of human industry overthrown; such are the disasters which the shock of a comet would produce, if its mass were comparable to that of the Earth. [The mass of Venus is almost equal to the mass of Earth.]
>
> We see then, in effect, why the ocean has receded from the high mountains, upon which it has left incontestable marks of its sojourn. We see how the animals and plants of the south have been able to exist in the climate of the north, where their remains and imprints have been discovered; finally, it explains the newness of the human civilization, certain monuments of which do not go further back than five thousand years. The human race, reduced to a small number of individuals, and to the most deplorable state, solely occupied for a length of time with the care of its own preservation, must have lost entirely the remembrance of the sciences and the arts; and when progress of civilization made these wants felt anew, it was necessary to begin again, as if man had been newly placed upon the earth.

The possibility of such a catastrophe, even its probability in the past, was maintained by Laplace, who, for the entire population of modern observatories, was the greatest authority that ever lived. Did not Shapley, in his letter to Thackrey, joke about a visitor who pitied him for having been misled by Laplace? Would not such an encounter with a large comet and the change in the position of the axis and "the movement of rotation" of the globe be the very same blasphemous things for which the academicians hurriedly carried my book to the stake of public derision?

They and their leader were misled not by Laplace but by a defective knowledge of their gospel and by an exaggerated sense of their own infallibility.

"HOW YOU MISJUDGE ME"

BY THE TIME the next letter was written *Worlds in Collision* had been published and reviewed in very many places and was in the center of public discussion, as it had already been since the beginning of the year.

April 10, 1950

Dr. Harlow Shapley
Harvard College Observatory
Cambridge 38, Massachusetts

Dear Harlow:

I have delayed an answer to yours of March 8th until I could examine carefully some of the material to which your letter refers, and examine, as well, the circumstances under which it was written.

You refer to Science News Letter and to Time Magazine as evidences of unfavorable views of Dr. Velikovsky's work coinciding with your own, but unless I mistake certain reasonably clear indications the chief inspiration for these adverse views stems from Dr. Harlow Shapley of the Harvard College Observatory!

You note that you yourself are not writing anything in response to Dr. Velikovsky or Larrabee, and that, in fact, the only hot communication from you was your letter to me.

On the other hand, Mrs. Cecilia Payne-Gaposchkin's article was directly inspired by you, and I am informed by Mr. Gorden A. Atwater that two communications to Dr. Velikovsky's publishers, The Macmillan Company, from you, are so sizzling that your letter to me might seem tepid by comparison!

I do not doubt that many groups, including groups of Harvard University professors, who are by no means ill-mannered, injudicious or dumb—to quote you and agree with you on that score—hold views which coincide with your own; but I should be astonished to find that they had reached their conclusions completely independently of discussion with you.

There is, of course, a further elementary factor which continues to perplex and dismay me; at the time your views were expressed, at the time *their* views were expressed; at the time Dr. Gaposchkin's article was written, not you, nor Dr. Gaposchkin, nor the professors you cite—not one—had read the manuscript or the book. At most, they have read comment upon it, or digests of sections of it, without benefit of reference notes or complete treatment.

I am more than a little puzzled at your paragraph mentioning that "a vice-president of the American Astronomical Society thought that the Council of the Society should send a protest to Macmillan, the famous publisher of highly reputable scientific books; but I said immediately, and so did many others, that such an action would merely give greater publicity to Dr. Velikovsky's contributions. Freedom to publish is a basic freedom."

The reason for my bewilderment, in view of the foregoing paragraph, is that I have been assured that you yourself wrote on two separate occasions to Macmillan in an effort to frustrate publication of Dr. Velikovsky's work, and that in doing so your language was as severe as that in your original letter to me on the subject.

Would you please assure me that this report is wholly false; or if it is not, let me know how you would reconcile the paragraph I have quoted from your March 8th letter, and would you let me have copies of your letters?

I have, I believe, at least one advantage in this correspondence; and it is, indeed, not only an advantage in the exchange with you, but with Dr. Gaposchkin. . . . The advantage is that I have read the book in question, while I seriously doubt if you or the above named have actually done so as yet.

In your own case, I am certain.

After analyzing Gaposchkin's unfortunate statement in *The Reporter* concerning the Venus tablets from Babylonia,* Thackrey proceeded:

> . . . it would definitely appear that the criticism that Dr. Velikovsky's book ignores the tablets except in a footnote could not have been written by anyone who read the book.
>
> All this shows that you and Mrs. Gaposchkin made extensive and successful efforts to suppress the book, and damage it by statements not warranted by the text of the book. Into the same category belongs Gaposchkin's statement that Velikovsky confused Ovid and Hesiod. The confusion is hers. . . .
>
> There is another matter about which I am curious: I am informed that Atwater has been asked to resign as curator of the planetarium here. Is it possible that your own reaction to his mild support of Dr. Velikovsky's right to publish could have influenced that decision?
>
> I did note with interest that you feel that you are following the precedent of one Galileo; but I wonder if you would feel it unfair of me to remark that Galileo was advancing the thesis that the accepted science of his time was not yet perfected. I had thought it more likely that Dr. Velikovsky might fairly claim Galileo as a precedent!
>
> Sincerely,
> Ted

Shapley did not answer Thackrey's letter of April 10 until after I had parted with Macmillan. This goal having been achieved, Shapley wrote on June 6, when this parting was supposedly known to only a few persons:

* [These tablets preserve a year-by-year record of the appearances and disappearances of Venus. See the later section "Are the Venus Tablets Missing?"]

Harvard College Observatory
Cambridge 38, Massachusetts

June 6, 1950

Mr. T.O. Thackrey
The Daily Compass
164 Duane Street
New York 13, New York

Dear Ted:

To my letter of March 8 you replied on April 10. I should have written you again on May 12, but I was then at our western observing stations.

I wonder if there is much point in writing further about Dr. V. and his remarkably successful writings. Certainly you and he and his publishers should be quite satisfied with his leadership of the best sellers for week after week, and I ought to be satisfied in that I have not yet met an astronomer, or in fact a scientist or scholar of any sort, who takes "Worlds in Collision" seriously. Some referred to the clever promotion; some referred to the rather charming literary style; and some, while fully exonerating Dr. V. (who should do as he pleases in this free country), are unrestrained in their condemnation of the once reputable publisher. This point is made in many of the reviews.

In the annual address to an important scientific foundation, a distinguished American physiologist on Saturday bemoaned the rather bleak future, and obvious decadence of our time. We have failed completely in our scientific teaching, he stated, or the "Worlds in Collision" atrocity would not have caught on the way it has. It seemed to him that Dr. V. and Senator [Joseph] McCarthy are symbols of something dire and distressful. But I do not worry about it. Time has curative properties.

One thing did worry me a bit in your letter—your intimation that in some way I was carrying on a crusade against Dr. V. Of all the astronomers from whom I have heard comment, I am the mildest and most forgiving. You suggest directly that I am back of various hypothetical crusades, and that my letters to the Macmillan Company were scorchers. How you misjudge me! I enclose copies of the letters, also a copy of the letter from the President of the Macmillan Company. In rereading, it seems to me that I am sad, but not savage.

Sincerely yours,
Harlow

Shapley's letters to Macmillan are found on earlier pages, reproduced from copies supplied by him to Thackrey. For more than three years Thackrey withheld permission for me to use this correspondence. Then, in the fall of 1953, he gave his consent, realizing that it was a matter of fairness.

These letters from Shapley to Thackrey were not intended for publication when written; the first was marked "Not for publication," and the second "Confidential." But whether sooner or later, they belong to history.* They do not contain any personal or intimate matter that the writer could possibly regard as of a private nature, which ought to remain behind a veil. Their writer considered himself to be performing a public service by writing them. Since they were ostensibly a public service, they are, therefore, a public affair.

* [See below, the chapter titled "A Lawyer's Advice." In 1972, in Shapley's lifetime, Horace Kallen published an article in the journal *Pensée,* entitled "Shapley, Velikovsky, and the Scientific Spirit." In it he described the controversy and his own role in it and included excerpts from the letters Shapley wrote concerning Velikovsky in 1950 and later. Shapley did not react. The article also appears in *Velikovsky Reconsidered* (1976).]

THE BOOK IS LAUNCHED, ATWATER THROWN OVERBOARD

It was the tenth of March. Ten years had passed since the spring of 1940, when I started a work, the first volume of which was now printed, bound, and wrapped in a shiny dust jacket. I was waiting on the main floor of the luxurious Macmillan building for my wife to come see the book. Through the open door of the adjoining room I saw many copies of *Worlds in Collision*, but I did not approach to look at any of them. I wished to live this moment together with my wife. Then she arrived. After her came an elderly woman clerk, an employee of Macmillan, who asked that I autograph a book for her son. While I was signing it, there appeared more clerks, salesmen, and editors of Macmillan, all asking me to sign copies of the book for them. I found out later that they had bought their copies; they had not received them gratis.

It looked like the messengers' scene in the Book of Job, in reverse. First came one salesman, who, on asking me to sign his copy, told me he had that day sold 1,000 copies to Brentano's. Then arrived another who said he had sold 1,000 copies to Macy's. Still another said he had just sold 500 to Scribner's. A festive air pervaded the place.

Virginia Patterson, the publicity director at Macmillan, said to me: "I can't remember anything like this ever happening to any other author in this building. As you can imagine, we have seen many authors, but never have so many people come from every floor to ask for an autograph."

As she said this, James Putnam arrived and told us that the nine complimentary copies of the book that had been sent that day to the trustees of the Museum of Natural History had been returned. There would be no show at the planetarium. Putnam observed: "When Atwater's article is printed in *This Week,* I have a feeling he will be fired."

The show *Worlds in Collision* was scheduled for later in the spring and had been announced in the yearly program of the planetarium. Gordon A. Atwater's article was to appear in *This Week* in the issue of April 2, the eve of the publication date of the book. This magazine section was published by the *Herald Tribune* for itself and for many newspapers all over the country as a weekly supplement.

Putnam was right. Between that day, March 10, and the day his article was printed, Atwater's fate was sealed. In the last week of March he was dismissed on a day's notice from both his positions, chairman of the Astronomy Department of the American Museum of Natural History and curator of the planetarium. Shortly before, he had received a letter from Professor Otto Struve in which, I was told, he was asked if it was true that he adhered to Velikovsky's heresy. Atwater, possibly unaware of the grave significance of this question, replied by letter—none of these letters did I see—in which he explained that he believed that science must investigate unorthodox ideas calmly and with an open mind. Thus he gave himself away. His salary was paid until October, but he had to clear his desk immediately; he retained no functions and no office space.

In the meantime, *This Week* was also under pressure not to print Atwater's article. In their confusion the editors of the magazine called O'Neill at his desk as science editor of the *Herald Tribune* and asked his opinion. He showed them the mimeographed article by Professor Cecilia Payne-Gaposchkin ("amazement, consternation, incredulity, and derision") that he had received and advised them to publish Atwater's article. A Californian, Chesley Bonestell, known for his astronomical illustrations, prepared a series of colorful pictures for the article. One of the drawings adorned the cover of *This Week.* In his article Atwater, fellow of the Royal Astronomical Society, wrote:

> By now practically everyone has heard about "Worlds in Collision," and the provocative theories of Dr. Immanuel Velikovsky, its author. Even before the book's publication it has been the subject of a storm of controversy that has swept across the nation.
>
> You may have heard that Dr. Velikovsky's astronomy is

> rubbish, his geology nonsense and his history ridiculous. You will be hearing those things again and again.
>
> I do not intend to say that all Dr. Velikovsky's findings are correct—in fact, I disagree with many of them. But I do contend that, looking at it from an over-all point of view, the author has done a tremendous job, the effect of which is to link science and religion. His book will have an explosive effect in the world of science.
>
> The greatest value of "Worlds in Collision" is this: it sets up an unusual approach to some of the world's great problems. While Dr. Velikovsky's procedures may not be new, his attempt to apply them to modern scientific thinking is revolutionary. However, to many scientists his efforts will seem presumptuous.
>
> But it will happen that while "Worlds in Collision" is being condemned by large numbers of professional scientists, many other groups will welcome the book as a broadening influence in scientific, religious and philosophical fields. While it tends to bridge the present gulf between science and religion—a gulf that modern scientists have made little effort to cross—this is accidental.

Then Atwater told the story of the book's content. He expressed his doubt that Venus had been ejected from Jupiter. "If there was a comet at all, it is likely to have come from outer space—possibly from behind Jupiter." Speaking of the catastrophes that overtook the earth in historical times, he wrote: "Compared to the blows it had received, a thousand hydrogen bombs would be but a flicker. It is hard to conceive a greater tragedy short of complete disintegration."

Atwater explained my method:

> "Worlds in Collision" is the result of a laborious research job in many fields. For years its author studied old manuscripts and records before he was ready to weave them together in this book.... In assembling these proofs Dr. Velikovsky has plunged headlong into a dozen different sciences and has dug deeply into the roots of many. Frequently he has ignored modern authorities and conventional procedures and by-passed the work of years to get at the originals for his own investigation....
>
> Dr. Velikovsky, realizing the impact of his thesis, has gone

> to very great lengths to reveal his method so that it may be searched in detail. While he draws his own conclusions from the evidence, he presents it so others may draw their own. . . .
>
> The scientist has always been receptive to new ideas. If one new contribution is found buried in this mass of evidence, the scientist will be the first to credit it. Although the opening impact of this theory—due to its sensational nature—is certain to arouse violent hostility, even this feeling will be set aside as it is searched and probed for errors and truths.

Under Atwater's name appeared his qualifications—curator, Hayden Planetarium, and chairman, Department of Astronomy, American Museum of Natural History—although a few days earlier he had been dismissed from these posts.

Only a few months before, the preceding December, Otto Struve, in his role as retiring president of the American Astronomical Society, at the conclusion of his year of service in that position, admonished the astronomers assembled in Tucson, Arizona, with the following words: "The [third] danger lies within ourselves. It is all too easy, step by step, to relinquish our freedom of scientific inquiry. . . . Fear of political persecution and of social ostracism is cropping up in unexpected places. . . . We should reaffirm our belief in the freedom of science."

These words were reprinted in *Science* for June 30, 1950, when Atwater was being ostracized for taking them too seriously.

"COPERNICUS? WHO IS HE?"

JOHN O'NEILL, too, received a letter from Struve, which I did not see. It was to the effect that the science editor should refrain from supporting me. O'Neill wrote an angry reply and then, having given vent to his feelings, tore it up the next day. He wrote a series of articles for the *Herald Tribune* on *Worlds in Collision* but was told that this time it was considered preferable to assign the review of the theory to an outside person. On Sunday, April 2, the eve of the publication date of the book, the *Herald Tribune* carried a review of my book by Otto Struve headed "Copernicus? Who Is He?"

Struve assured his readers that the book belongs in the category of "mysticism." Velikovsky has cut "the laborious and often dreary process of logical thinking" and turned to "supernatural phenomena. . . ."

The review announced that I discarded the findings of Copernicus, Galileo, and Kepler (in reality, I discarded nothing of their teachings) and that in my book the earth was stopped in its rotation "without apparently causing a more serious disaster than 'collective amnesia.' "

Struve cut the "laborious and dreary process" of reading the book he reviewed in that article. He was led to believe that he did not need to read it because Cecilia Payne-Gaposchkin, who had reviewed it in *The Reporter*, apparently had done it for him and for his colleagues. "It is a pity . . . that it was necessary for readers to wait until a recent issue of *The Reporter* to learn, through Mrs. Cecilia Payne-Gaposchkin of the Harvard Observatory, that the observations of Venus extend back to five hundred years before the Exodus, thus refuting the absurd story of a comet that turned into a planet." A week after this review by Struve, Payne-Gaposchkin, in a letter to *The Reporter,* acknowledged that she had not read the book when she wrote her article for the periodical. The Venus tablets were used in my book to establish precisely the point that Venus moved as a comet, not as a planet.

The title of Struve's review, "Copernicus? Who Is He?," was intended to convey to the readers the idea that the author of *Worlds in Collision* had never heard of Copernicus. How could anybody so disregard the accepted view of mathematicians over many centuries, and even common sense, as to maintain that the positions of the planets in the solar system are not fixed from everlasting to everlasting and to offer an absurd theory of collisions among the members of that system?

Reading that review, I thought of a few sentences in Copernicus's Preface to his book *De revolutionibus:*

> I can easily conceive . . . that as soon as some people learn that in this book which I have written concerning the revolutions of the heavenly bodies, I ascribe certain motions to the Earth, they will cry out at once that I and my theory should be rejected. Accordingly . . . when I considered in my own mind how absurd a performance it must seem to those who know that the judgment of many centuries has approved the view that the Earth remains fixed as center in the midst of heaven, if I should, on the contrary, assert that the Earth moves; when I considered this carefully, the contempt which I had to fear because of the novelty and apparent absurdity of my view nearly induced me to abandon entirely the work I had begun. . . . How did it occur to me to venture, contrary to the accepted view of mathematicians, and well-nigh contrary to common sense, to form a conception of any terrestrial motion whatsoever?

Actually Copernicus did not publish his book until he was on his deathbed. One hour before he died, the first copy of his book arrived from Nuremberg, where it had been printed, and was placed in his hands. He looked at it but probably did not recognize his work.

"When he died he had a dubious name among experts and a farcical reputation among laymen."*

In the beginning of his review Struve said that for thirty years he had consigned to a special shelf, politely called "Paradox," books on astrology, the flat earth, and flying saucers, and that in those thirty years he had not removed one book from that shelf to a more honorable place. To this shelf he assigned my book, never again to be taken from there into his hands.

Nine months will pass and Struve will take *Worlds in Collision* from the shelf called "Paradox" and write a survey of astronomical theories and observations for the year 1950. It will appear in *Sky and Telescope,* a journal published by the Harvard College Observatory, in the issue of February 1951. Struve will begin with an observation of the Japanese astronomer Saheki: "At about 4:30 [A.M.] on January 16, 1950, the Japanese astronomer Tsuneo Saheki noticed an enormous yellowish-gray cloud extending over the southern limb of Mars and reaching an elevation above the planet's surface of more than 100 kilometers, with a horizontal extent of about 1,500 kilometers." Struve will quote from an article by E. J. Öpik in the *Irish Astronomical Journal* of March 1950 this explanation of the phenomenon: It was a collision between Mars and another celestial body, probably a planetoid.

It so happened that when this phenomenon occurred and was observed, *Harper's Magazine* with the Eric Larrabee article, the first to tell the story of the forthcoming book, was just on the stands. The timing of this first collision in the solar system claimed to have been observed by modern scientists, with the appearance of the article, took on the quality of a strange coincidence. Struve will write:

> Once again we have the question of "worlds in collision" and the resulting fragmentation of planetary and meteoric bodies. It is a bizarre coincidence that 1950, which produced the much-discussed Velikovsky book of science fiction, also produced a deluge of sound papers on various problems connected with collisions within the solar system.

To this "deluge," according to Struve, will also belong a paper by Fred Whipple and Salah Hamid describing two real collisions between a comet and swarms of planetoids in *historical times* as

* Kesten, *op. cit.* p. 234.

well as the work of G. P. Kuiper, a distinguished astronomer, who will offer a theory that would explain "the origin of the present ring of minor planets as the result of collisions among several larger bodies." David Brower will apply Kuiper's collision theory of the Hirayama family of minor planets (planetoids) and find it consistent with observations. E. J. Öpik will read before the Royal Irish Academy in Dublin a paper, "Collision Probabilities with the Planets and the Distribution of Interplanetary Matter." Finally, in several articles in the *Astronomical Journal* of the Soviet Union, V. G. Fessenkoff, the leading Russian astronomer, will discuss his hypothesis of the formation of particles that produce zodiacal glow as the result of collisions between minor planets and meteorites.

Struve will reflect: "All of these theories have one thing in common. They assume that there existed, and even now exist, solid bodies in the solar system whose orbits intersect in such a manner as to produce occasional collision."

In the months ahead more theories and observations will indicate, and even establish, the occurrence of cosmic collisions in the universe.

ARE THE VENUS TABLETS MISSING?

One of the newspapermen who came to interview me before the publication of the book was Harvey Breit of the *The New York Times Book Review.* According to his article printed on April 2, the eve of the publication date of *Worlds in Collision,* I said: "What I require from my reader is courage. Courage in what? Courage to trust in his own ability to think. He should read the book and look into references and make his own conclusions. He must remember that science is not licensed."

Breit, after spending an hour or two with me, became very sympathetic. With an evident inner effort he said before leaving: "I wish Dr. Kaempffert could meet you." Then, after another effort, he went on: "He is writing a review. He met Professor Neugebauer. I wish he could hear your explanation. I would like you to meet both of them."

I soon heard again of Dr. Waldemar Kaempffert's endeavor.

On the occasion of an additional consultation I had with Professor Motz, he told me that Kaempffert, who wanted to check several points concerning my theory with an astronomer, had called at Columbia University and chanced to come to Motz. The latter could tell him only that he had gone carefully through the pages of the Epilogue that dealt with celestial mechanics and that he could not tell him of anything methodologically wrong with my hypothesis, as expressed in the Epilogue. Kaempffert left without finding a useful point to attack and therefore omitted the astronomical side of the story in his review. Traveling home, he met with an accident and broke a rib.

For historical information on my work, Kaempffert dutifully met Professor Otto Neugebauer of Brown University, whose specialty is the ancient astronomy of Babylonia and Greece.

The editor of *The New York Times Book Review* decided that Kaempffert should not speak with me personally, and thus the meeting with Kaempffert, Neugebauer, and myself, proposed by Breit, in which I could have answered the questions in their minds, did not materialize.

On Sunday, April 2, the leading review of the *Book Review* was by the paper's science editor, Waldemar Kaempffert. A picture of a medieval astronomer adorned the front page. The title across the width of the page read: "The Tale of Velikovsky's Comet."

Kaempffert's main argument was this:

> If Venus did not become a planet until 1500 B.C. and therefore in historic times, ancient records should bear out Dr. Velikovsky. . . . The rising and setting of the planet was recorded systematically in the reign of King Ammizaduga, who ruled Babylonia in the sixteenth century B.C., and priestly astrologers undoubtedly observed Venus generations before. The records are discussed by Langdon and Fotheringham in *The Venus Tablets of Ammizaduga*. . . . Dr. Velikovsky refers to these tablets in a footnote but does not indicate their content. In fact, systematic observations of Venus are at least as old as 3000 B.C. Ancient Babylonians and Egyptian watchers of the skies saw the planet exactly as we see it.

Kaempffert ended his article with angry words about a theory that requires the rewriting of every textbook on astronomy, biology, geology, cultural anthropology, and ancient history. If not for the years that must have been needed to collate the hundreds of citations and footnotes, one might have thought the book a hoax.

These Venus tablets of Ammizaduga, which "disproved" my theory completely and which I had omitted to consider, made the rounds and were often mentioned by people who had not read the book but had "read all the reviews." Kaempffert, like Struve, apparently took over from Gaposchkin, who had not read the book either. Kaempffert corrected Gaposchkin's date for the tablets by reducing the age of Ammizaduga, in compliance with the modern revision of Babylonian chronology, from 2000 B.C. to the sixteenth century B.C., or only a few decades before my date of the Exodus.

I wrote an answer to my critic and brought it personally to the editor of *The New York Times Book Review,* Francis Brown. Harvey Breit, on seeing me, came over to say a few kind words.

My answer and Kaempffert's rebuttal were printed with the heading "Dr. Velikovsky vs. Mr. Kaempffert: A Collision of Author and Reviewer" (*The New York Times Book Review,* May 7, 1950).

After quoting Kaempffert, I proceeded:

> I refer to "The Venus Tablets of Ammizaduga" not only in one footnote but dedicate to them a few pages beginning with p. 198, actually the major part of the chapter "Venus Moves Irregularly."
>
> I describe the finding of the Venus Tablets by Sir Henry Layard, the publication of them by H. Rawlinson and G. Smith, by Sayce, and by Langdon and Fotheringham; the work of Schiaparelli who ascribed them to the eighth–seventh century; the finding of the year-formula of Ammizaduga on one of the tablets by Kugler, who, therefore, referred them to an earlier age; the objection of F. Hommel, who insisted that the year-formula was inserted by a scribe of Assurbanipal in the seventh century. Then I say: "If the tablets originated in the beginning of the second millennium, they would prove only that Venus was even then an errant comet," and go on to quote from the tablets as translated by Langdon-Fotheringham, five extensive passages showing how Venus moved in five consecutive years of observation. So in the first year, "On the eleventh of Sivan, Venus disappeared in the west, remaining absent in the sky for nine months and four days, and on the fifteenth of Adar she was seen in the east." In the fourth year, "Venus disappeared in the east on the ninth of Nisan, remaining absent for five months and sixteen days, and was seen on the twenty-fifth of Ulul in the west."
>
> Then I quote from Langdon-Fotheringham, M. Jastrow, and A. Ungnad, all of whom are very perplexed by these figures. "The invisibility of Venus at superior conjunction is given as five months, sixteen days instead of the correct difference of two months, six days." "Obviously, the days of the months have been mixed up. As the impossible intervals show, the months are also wrong."
>
> Is it correct that I refer "to these Venus tablets in a footnote but [do] not indicate their content"? Is it correct to say that the Babylonians "saw the planet *exactly* as we see it"?
>
> I could add that the Babylonians described Venus as "one

> with hair" (comet), and asserted that it rivaled the sun in brightness, and later gave it the appellative, "The great star that joins the planets. . . ."
>
> And as to the Egyptian sources from 3000 B.C. describing the movements of Venus, exactly as they are today, I would like to be instructed: Where can I find such document?

What would be a fair answer on the part of my reviewer-distorter? To admit that he had noticed the footnote to Langdon and Fotheringham's book on page 334 but had not chanced to read page 198 and following, dedicated to these tablets. Instead of this, Kaempffert wrote:

> To bolster his absurd contention that Venus in ancient days was an "errant comet" Dr. Velikovsky quotes on two pages five very short passages from Langdon and Fotheringham's elucidation of the Venus Tablets—hardly an adequate presentation of the content of a scholarly work that commands respect of historians of ancient astronomy.

Rather than acknowledge in direct terms his erroneous statement of a few weeks before, Kaempffert, using abusive language, said that I quoted only five short passages of elucidation. These five passages are not elucidation; they are the text of five consecutive years in the Babylonian tablets.

Altogether twenty-one years of observations are preserved, and I quoted verbatim five of those years, or almost a quarter of the text as translated by Langdon and Fotheringham, in addition to all the authorities mentioned in my reply.

He should have acknowledged that the tablets do not prove, as he had written, that the Babylonians in the sixteenth century saw Venus moving exactly as we do now. He did not do this.

Pinned down on the question about Egyptian sources according to which in 3000 B.C. the Egyptians saw Venus moving exactly as we see it, he acknowledged: "I was wrong in saying that the oldest known Egyptian astronomical records include the movements of Venus." He had been informed by the Oriental Institute of the University of Chicago that "the earliest known Egyptian astronomical observations are of Sirius." He was also told that these observations of Sirius were made in the nineteenth century before the present era. But he concluded on his own that they were based "on still earlier observations that go back at least to 2800 B.C. or roughly 3000 B.C." Not Venus, not 3000 B.C., and not 2800 B.C. So he said: "However, it is inconceivable that priestly astronomers who selected Sirius for observation were unfamiliar with the five planets known in ancient times." To add to the confusion, he quoted Alexandre Moret as saying that observations of the five planets "are attested at least as early as the New Empire. . . . In other words, at a time when according to Dr. Velikovsky Venus was colliding with the earth and wreaking havoc, ancient Egyptians saw her just as we do." However, in my book on various pages I have shown that the Exodus took place at the end of the Middle Kingdom, hundreds of years before the beginning of the New Kingdom, and the catastrophic events I describe preceded the New Kingdom by a very long stretch of time. And again, where is the authority for a renewed "Egyptians saw her just as we do"?

The logic of his answer on this point runs thus: True, it was not Venus, but Sirius, that was seen; it is also true that it was not 3000 B.C., but 1900 B.C. But if the Egyptians saw Sirius in 1900 B.C., they must have seen Venus, too, because it is presently as visible as, and even more so than, Sirius. And if they saw it in 1900 B.C., in all probability they must have seen it also in 3000 B.C. or, say, 2800 B.C. Thus we can affirm that the Egyptians in 3000 B.C. "saw her just as we do" and Velikovsky is disproved.

A FLY AND A RAISIN

TWO DAYS AFTER my rejoinder to Waldemar Kaempffert and his answer were printed in *The New York Times Book Review* I inadvertently had another debate with him.

The Graduate English Society at Columbia University asked me to deliver a lecture at an open meeting on May 9, 1950. The Harkness Theater, the second largest auditorium in the university, was full, and people stood along the walls and sat on the steps. Young and old were there.

When I finished, questions came from many sides, and I answered one after another. The chairman apparently did not see an arm that was being raised repeatedly, so I drew his attention to the futile efforts of the distinguished-looking gentleman, who was then given the floor. He had spoken only a few words—not even a complete sentence—when I injected: "I make one guess; the speaker is Mr. Kaempffert of *The New York Times.*" In his opening words I already heard something of his argument. He did not say who he was, nor did he contradict my guess. When it became clear that my guess was right, the audience cheered. He spoke of Babylonian tablets, and at that point I decided to evaluate his answer to me of two days before. I cited from memory the issue, the sources, book, year, and page. After further exchange of words, back and forth, in order to characterize Kaempffert's way of acknowledging his guilt, I told a little story: A little girl came to the baker and said: "My mother sent me to tell you that in the raisin bread I bought from you this morning there was a fly." Answered the baker: "Bring me the fly; I shall give you a raisin."

I felt the audience was on my side, and it let me know this by cheers and applause. When the heated debate was over, I went to Kaempffert, who stood, downcast, with a few people. In a spirit of good sportsmanship I reached for his hand and exchanged a few friendly words with him. I inquired if it was true that he had broken a rib, and he said yes, when he was trying to see an astronomer about my book.

The next day the *Columbia Spectator*, the student paper, carried on its front page an account of the event. It reported:

> [An] overflow Harkness Theater crowd . . . listened attentively last night while Dr. Immanuel Velikovsky discussed his recently published, highly controversial book, *Worlds in Collision*. Then, as they had expected, fireworks broke loose. Challenging the basic scientific doctrine of gradual evolution, Dr. Velikovsky insisted, as he does in his book, that "within evolution, there must be revolution." . . .

After further details on the content of the lecture, the account went on:

> Relying heavily on wit and an amazing memory for minute historical details, the doctor beat back all comers in the question period. His most outspoken critic, Waldemar Kaempffert, science editor of *The New York Times*, found the going rough, although he had come armed with reams of challenging data.
>
> The audience sat back for the remainder of the evening to enjoy the verbal duel of the two sharp-tongued scholars.
>
> Dr. Velikovsky, who has spent each day for ten years preparing his thesis in Butler Library, was brought back to the campus by the Graduate English Society.
>
> He expressed optimism over the eventual success of his theories, though realizing that "it may be several years before my theory becomes text book material."

file ii

"WITHOUT A PRECEDENT"

ON MAY 25, 1950, while I was at my dentist's, I received a telephone call from home. George Brett, president of the Macmillan Company, had tried to reach me and wished me to contact him immediately. I could expect some dramatic development. I called him, and he asked me to come to his place as soon as possible. I returned home briefly and then went to his office on the fifth floor of the Macmillan building on Fifth Avenue. Only a week or two earlier I had met Ruth Gruber of the *Herald Tribune* in a small café across the street and expressed to her my admiration for Macmillan because it was standing so firmly behind me, especially in view of the fact that my book might cause many of their textbooks to become outdated.

I was seen immediately. I had never met Brett. He was one or two years older than I. He tried to be very pleasant; but he had something extraordinary to say, and he began as soon as we sat down. As well as I can remember, he said the following:

"Believe me, in my thirty-three years in the publishing business, many of them as president of this organization, this situation is without precedent. I have to ask the author of a national best seller, number one on the best seller lists, to release us from our contract. Tremendous pressure is being exerted against our company by a group of scientists. We have secured for you an offer from another publisher, as large as we are, some say even larger. It has no textbook department and cannot be hurt." Then he went on to defend the action he was about to take.

"You see, the general conception is that I and my immediate family own this firm. This is incorrect; my family's interest is perhaps no greater than ten percent. Seventy percent of the business of this company is in textbooks; it is the real backbone of our firm. Therefore, we are vulnerable. Professors in certain universities have refused to see our salesmen. We have received a series of letters declaring a boycott of all our textbooks. Please realize how it works." Here Mr. Brett picked up a pencil and drew some circles. "Academic circles are not isolated groups; they are united in local organizations or in professional associations that are incorporated or represented in larger national organizations." And he drew larger circles: the American Association for the Advancement of Science in Washington, the American Philosophical Society, and the National Academy of Sciences, groups of national importance in which scientists in many fields are represented. "In this way the academic pressure may become widespread."

"You should not be frightened if you believe that this book of mine is good. Have you read my book?" I asked.

He said he had not, but feeling a little discomfited by this admission, he added that he was going to Europe and would read it on the way.

This seemed strange to me. As president of the publishing house he personally had answered Shapley, thanked him for "the red flag," then arranged a three-man censorship panel; he had seen the book climb to first place on the best seller lists; he had observed it discussed on the front pages of national magazines and elsewhere, a discussion into which he must have been drawn more than once; he had been confronted with the efforts to suppress the book and had already negotiated the transfer of rights to another publisher. Yet he had not found time to acquaint himself with the book's contents.

"What do your editors think?" I inquired.

"Our editors in the trade department, as always, think very highly of the book. Mr. Latham [chief editor] has not changed his opinion about it. But while in the trade department they are enthusiastic, in the textbook department they are alarmed by the violence of the opposition to your book."

"Have my opponents among the scientists read my book? I am afraid they have not."

Brett replied that in a number of instances they admitted that they had not read the book. He gave me a letter from a folder containing about eight letters. It was dated May 20, or five days earlier, and was written by Professor Dean B. McLaughlin, astronomer at the University of Michigan, Ann Arbor. It was a very emotional letter. It accused the author of *Worlds in Collision* of charlatanry. On the third page near the top were the words "*Worlds in Collision* is lies and only lies," and on the same page toward the bottom, if my visual memory is correct, Professor McLaughlin wrote: "No, I have not read *Worlds in Collision* and shall never read it," adding a remark to the effect that in order to know that an apple is wormy, it is not necessary to eat it all, and the articles in the press sufficed for him to judge. On the last page he issued an ultimatum, calling on Macmillan not only to cease publishing the book but publicly to confess having made a grave mistake.

Mr. Brett substantiated his words about the refusal of some professors to see the representatives of the firm to discuss the textbooks to be scheduled for the next term and mentioned, among others, a physicist at Columbia University (Polycarp Kusch). The dossier also contained two letters from Shapley, of earlier dates; Mr. Brett gave them to me to read. However, I did not see his answer to the second Shapley letter, in which he promised the accuser that he would submit the book, already on the press, to the last-minute censorship of three prominent scientists. Had I seen this reply, I would have asked Brett to tell me the conclusion of the three censors.

I asked him to give me copies of the letters he had shown me. He told me that if he were in my place, he would sue the writers because of what they had done and would subpoena the letters. Then he agreed to give me copies of them if we should part amicably. Mr. Brett did not give me the copies because we did not part entirely amicably; but I had copies of the correspondence between Shapley and Macmillan, which were made on a typewriter in Shapley's office and mailed by him to Thackrey.

Continuing our conversation, I reminded Mr. Brett that the manuscript had been at Macmillan for a very long time, that an optional contract had preceded the final one, and that several readers had passed on the manuscript. Then I said: "Even if I am wrong in my theory, no suppression of my book should be allowed because science grows by trial and error. How many theories are published and discarded later as erroneous?" Here I stood up and continued: "And now, what if my theory is right? What if it is, as many reviewers have said, a great step forward? How will your publishing house look in years to come? And maybe my detractors will be best known for this, their action."

But Brett, though very polite and trying to be pleasant, was definitely committed to his decision to free his house of a book that was arousing wrath among the powerful of the textbook world, and he began again to draw a pattern of circles to show me how the scientific groups are interlocked, how they are centered, and how they can damage a publishing house. It appeared to me that he was thinking of his shareholders but was not giving a thought to me. I told him that I would consider the matter during the next two weeks and would then give him an answer on whether or not I would release Macmillan from the contract. Brett said that up to then (it was, as I now see, fifty-four days after the publication of the book), including prepublication, some 54,000 copies had been sold. He said also that there would be no promotion in the interim and asked me to come to my decision earlier, if possible, since he was about to leave for Europe and this matter was holding him back. He informed me that only four people in his company and four in Doubleday knew about the decision, that James Putnam was not one of them, and that I should not discuss the matter with him. I took the letter of offer, signed by Mr. Douglas M. Black, president of Doubleday, for consideration but did not promise to release Macmillan from the contract or, if I did, to sign with Doubleday.

After we had conversed for more than an hour, Brett invited me to his apartment. Having passed through now deserted offices on the same floor, we came to a door leading to his apartment in the next building. There a servant gave us tea and tidbits, and we continued our talk. I told Brett a story of a man who was found guilty of having committed a misdeed. The judge offered him a choice of punishment—to be beaten or to pay a fine. The man preferred to be beaten, but before he took the last few lashes, he changed his mind and asked to be allowed to pay the fine.

We returned for a while to Brett's office. Only his secretary was waiting in the adjoining room; otherwise, the place was empty. After we had again left the room and were standing in the hall, he suddenly cried out: "Take me off the hook!"

Brett went down the stairs with me, the elevator man having already left. On the way down I asked him if he had served in the war. He told me in what service and how long. To this I remarked: "Then why are you so afraid?" At the street door we parted with a handshake.

I returned home with the feeling that I could hardly have carried myself any better.

From a magazine article I learned later that the decision to give up *Worlds in Collision* was taken by Macmillan at a stormy meeting of the board of directors, this body being divided. Since a concession had been made to the suppressors in submitting the book to three prominent scientists for censorship and it had passed that censorship, I imagine the people of the trade department had a strong argument for not giving the book away. But what really occurred there, I do not know. I was in the unique situation of being then the most read and discussed author, with clippings arriving by the hundreds, having to leave Macmillan, which had had my manuscript for three and a half years from the fall of 1946, and having to make up my mind where to go next. Brett's opinion that the transfer of the book would pass unnoted—who would notice that the name of the publisher at the bottom of the title page had changed?—appeared very unrealistic to me.

A few days passed. Seeking to have a few points clarified, I telephoned Mr. Latham since I had been asked not to divulge the matter to Putnam. I was told that Latham would call me back. Instead came a call from Mr. Brett. Probably he was hurt by my attitude at our meeting. Possibly he had not met this air of independence before. Certainly I was holding up his trip to Europe. He shouted very angrily: "If we are forced to keep the book, it will die on our hands!" I reminded him that we had agreed that I was to have two weeks to decide. He curtly conceded that this was so but told me without his previous courtesy to come to my decision sooner, if I could. Now I knew that, for the sake of my book, I had to move.

A quarter or half an hour later I had a call from Ken McCormick, editor in chief of Doubleday. He told me he and his colleagues thought very highly of my book, and he would like to see me. We agreed to meet in my studio in a day or two.

Now, with more experience behind me, I must admit that a different course of action was hardly open to Brett. He would have ruined his textbook department—and for what? For a book that, if right, would make many books in his textbook department obsolete. As we shall see, the fury did not abate even after the transfer. And certainly Brett did the very correct and even noble thing in securing for my book another publisher of great repute and great possibilities. This was also stressed by one newspaper when, several weeks later, the transfer took legal form; the press generally joined in criticizing the firm. In the meantime, despite absence of promotion, the book stayed at the very top of all national best seller lists.

CHANGING HORSES IN MIDSTREAM

I HAD TWO WEEKS to decide. Although I had tried my luck with publishers before I went to Macmillan three and a half years earlier, I actually did not know too much about their programs and activities. After all these years I stood again in an open field, thinking about which way to go. I was reluctant to go over to Doubleday, for the very reason that this was an arrangement made by Macmillan. I imagined also that Doubleday, being publishers of very many books, would be unable to pay sufficient, or particular, attention to my book.

Ken McCormick came to my studio. He assured me that his firm would be highly honored if it obtained the rights to my book. He also said that Walter Bradbury, its managing editor, knew my book well and not long before, prior to the new turn of events, had spoken with great excitement about it, and if I should choose his firm, it would promote the book with pride and with vigor, too. I did not give a definite answer, promising only to think over the offer.

One or two days later I had a call from McCormick, requesting me to meet Mr. Black, president of Doubleday. They came together to my studio, and Mr. Black, realizing my apprehension for the fate of my book, explained to me the great care with which the firm handles its books. We discussed conditions and royalties, the rate of which would be increased over those in the Macmillan contract. It was Friday, and they asked me to give my consent by the next day. McCormick volunteered that he would be in the office on Saturday awaiting my telephone call. My father never made a deal on Saturday, and since my youth I honored this tradition. I said that I would decide by Monday. They left.

On Monday I called, and when I said, "Doubleday is my publisher," McCormick several times repeated how happy and pleased he was.

Certain formalities had to be attended to in order to conclude the transaction of parting with one publisher and going over to another, and these were arranged in the office of Abraham Tulin, a prominent New York attorney, who shortly before had sought and made my acquaintance, being impressed with what he called in a letter to me the "evidence, logic, and presentation" of my theory. Walter Bradbury represented Doubleday. *The New York Times* called Tulin's office to find out whether it was true that the book was being transferred from one publisher to another. Macmillan was tight-lipped. "What should we say?" asked Bradbury. I quipped: "Well, I would say that since a group of scientists have attacked me for saying that in the days of Joshua the sun stood still and the day became double [Joshua 10:13], I naturally went to Doubleday." But we said nothing. After a week of negotiations, the contract was signed on June 8, 1950. During this time I heard from Tulin many reminiscences about Justice Brandeis, whom he knew well.

Ten days later, on June 18, *The New York Times* wrote:

> The greatest bombshell dropped on Publishers' Row in many a year exploded the other day. [It referred to the] untold—and officially unadmitted—story of pressure against Macmillan by an important segment of its customers—outraged scientists, teachers and textbook buyers. . . . Dr. Velikovsky himself would not comment on the change-over. But a publishing official admitted, privately, that a flood of protests from educators and others had hit the company in its vulnerable underbelly—the textbook division. Following some stormy sessions by the board of directors, Macmillan reluctantly succumbed, surrendered its rights to the biggest money-maker on its list. Was it censorship? . . .

A SECOND MAN THROWN OVERBOARD

VICTOR GOLLANCZ WAS a British publisher who looked for the extraordinary. *Worlds in Collision* and, even more, the campaign to suppress it were extraordinary. He was interested in my book. James Putnam had only shortly before explained to me that Gollancz selected just a few books a year and promoted them vigorously. I agreed to this choice of a publisher for the British edition, and Macmillan prepared a contract for me to sign. Soon thereafter Gollancz came to the United States on a business trip. Before his departure for England in the first week of June, we were to meet at a luncheon arranged by Putnam.

I heard that Gollancz had a few days earlier paid his parting visit to Doubleday, and I thought it probable that he had been told that Macmillan had transferred the rights to my book to it. Putnam still did not know what had taken place between Brett and me, and nothing as yet was in the press. The day before the luncheon—or it may even have been the same day—I called him and told him that dramatic developments had occurred and that before we decided whether or not to keep our luncheon appointment, I wanted him to inform himself of these developments through Harold Latham, his chief. I added that he could be sure of my devotion and friendship to him whatever he heard. I did not wish to embarrass him in case Gollancz was informed and he was not, and it would not have been fair for me to tell him the story since Brett had told me only four persons at Macmillan knew about the situation and Putnam was not one of them.

A few hours later I had a call from Jim Putnam, who told me: "Now I know everything. I think we should still have the meeting with Gollancz." The whole affair must have been a great blow to him. For more than three years he had worked on the book, which was now at the top of the best seller lists. But he took this blow like a man. I repeated my promise: Now that he knew where we stood, he could count on my friendship in all circumstances. I felt that he was quickly approaching a personal drama and that Atwater's fate would overtake him.

I stipulated that I, not Macmillan, should be the host at the luncheon because I did not wish to be a guest of my former publisher. Mrs. Gollancz and my wife were present. Gollancz may have wondered how much Putnam knew since whatever he himself may have heard would have been told him only under a pledge of secrecy. I allowed the first course or two to go by, and then, in order to relieve the situation, I said, in referring to Putnam, something about "my former publisher." Gollancz's face brightened in a broad smile. Now we could speak openly, and we had a lively chat. My wife found that Mrs. Gollancz belonged to the Bentwich family; two sisters of that family, cousins of Mrs. Gollancz, played in the professional string quartet of which my wife was the leader.

On his return to England, Gollancz prepared the book for print, and in the first week of September, less than three months after our meeting, it was on sale. It was set anew and carried a jacket with the story of the book and its suppression on the front and back flaps and even on the inside of the jacket. Its author was Gollancz himself. There he also told of Putnam's dismissal, for only a week or two after our meeting the blow fell on him.

The unpleasant task of informing Putnam of this decision was assigned to Latham, the chief editor. It must have been almost unbearable to him, for he was a friend of Putnam of long standing and especially because he shared Putnam's enthusiasm for *Worlds in Collision.* I do not know the words in which he clad the message that had no precedent in American book publishing; people have been discharged, of course, but not after bringing to a publishing house a number one national best seller, a book that had aroused spontaneous interest in the entire world and become a subject of discussion everywhere.

For twenty-five years James Putnam had been with Macmillan, where, for a number of years, he had been assistant to the president. He served in World War II, carrying out assignments for the State

Department in North Africa and the Middle East. Upon his return to Macmillan he found his old position filled and settled into the job of associate editor. In his relations with authors Putnam showed a warmth and devotion that were unsurpassable. He advised the author and asked his advice; he took manuscripts home and worked on them late into the night. He often came to me on Sundays, thus denying himself a day of rest, and he waited at my home until two in the morning for my last corrections. In no way a scientist (as a young man he had taught French at Cornell for a few years), he conscientiously sought the advice of those whom he regarded as competent to judge a manuscript; he had not brought me a contract until he had had the favorable opinion of the curator of the Hayden Planetarium and the science editor of the *Herald Tribune* and a number of other people whose names I did not know but about whose criticism I was informed.

It was not enough that the book was dropped from the publisher's list and its editor thrown out of the job he had occupied for a quarter of a century; a demand was made of the publisher to recant. This demand I read in a letter from an astronomer at Ann Arbor when I was in Mr. Brett's office: Macmillan must publicly renounce its crime. As we shall see, this was done by one of its staff half a year later in unusual circumstances. Nothing was omitted of the procedure known to us from newspaper reports of cases overseas in which scientists guilty of deviation from the prescribed tenets used to be summoned with their editors before the public to beat their breasts and castigate themselves for their crimes and to promise not to do it ever again.

A group of three women executives from Macmillan secretly visited me in my studio to express their feelings and to tell me how horrified they were. Two other executives told Bradbury, my editor at Doubleday, of their disappointment that I was leaving Macmillan. And in the years that followed, at Christmas, I regularly received kind lines with expressions of regret that I was no longer at Macmillan.*

I heard of Putnam's dismissal from someone on the staff at Mac-

* In 1965 Harold Latham wrote me: "I remember well the commotion caused by *Worlds in Collision* and I do not remember with any pleasure the part that Macmillan played in the episode. I always felt that we made a mistake in taking so seriously the criticisms and demands of the scientists and textbook authors. I should have preferred to stand our ground and face our detractors and I think they might very soon have been put to the rout. But the decision was not mine to make."

millan; I called him and found that it was true. So I now had two men on my conscience. But I knew that they were also on the consciences of a little group of willful men.

I called a press conference in my studio to answer questions about my going over to Doubleday, and on that occasion I disclosed that Putnam had been discharged. Some of the newspapermen perceived the sensation in this new turn of events and went to Putnam. The next day (June 22) the news was given to the reading public by the *Herald Tribune* and some other papers. Putnam did not play the hero or the martyr, though he had reason to. That summer he was without a job. He was like a soldier left behind by his regiment in no-man's-land; he tried to show a good spirit, but I felt that his sense of human dignity had been injured.

The night before the press conference I called Atwater's house. His wife answered the phone. I told her that I intended to reveal that Atwater had lost his position even before Putnam on account of my book. Mrs. Atwater told me that her husband had gone to Bermuda to participate in the sailboat races, about which he was an enthusiast, and she asked me very insistently not to mention his dismissal at the press conference the next day. I could not do other than promise to follow her request. She called me back to ascertain once more that I would not break my promise.

A year or two later, when I asked Professor Horace Kallen why he had not taken upon himself the role of a Zola to defend Atwater, he replied: "Didn't Atwater go away to the boat races when the storm was about to break here?" By this he implied that had he been given the green light, he would have thrown down the gage to the suppressors of liberty.

I later found out that Atwater had left town not because of lack of concern, but because of the sadness that gripped him. He had thought that scientists were open-minded and found that he had been mistaken; he had believed that they struggled for truth and found that they would bend into the dust anyone from among their ranks who would question the fundamentals. Atwater needed a pause, like a man in the ring who has been hit low and who in his pain does not complain but stands mute, trying to orient himself. His offense was greater than that of the heretic; he was one of their own team who had given a helping hand to the enemy—that is, to me.

Once Atwater came to my studio with his wife. He was outwardly quiet and spoke very little, but one could sense depression in this brave man as he listened attentively to my words of encouragement and defiance. More than a year later he wrote to me that he had gone through a period of depression lasting all that time but had finally emerged with new energy. Still, at the very time when he felt most humiliated and depressed, six months after his dismissal, on October 1, 1950, the day his last (financial) tie with the museum was severed, Atwater wrote to me:

> I have followed your book and have been thrilled by the fine success it has made. Despite the unfavorable reaction which it caused in the Museum, and which . . . led to acceptance of my resignation, I do not regret that I was among those who gave you the encouragement to publish.*

* [In January 1980 Clark Whelton, a writer, invited Gordon Atwater to speak before a special course on Velikovsky which Whelton was teaching at the New School for Social Research in New York City. He later asked Atwater if he had any regrets about his experience with *Worlds in Collision.* Atwater replied: "Yes. I regret the way they treated Dr. Velikovsky. He was a wonderful man, and what they did to him was a disgrace. That's what hurt me the most."]

"AN IMMENSE COSMIC COLLISION"

AT THE VERY TIME when the fury against *Worlds in Collision* raged at its fiercest, just three weeks after Macmillan had relinquished its rights to that book, a scientific announcement of great importance was made by Dr. Walter Baade of the Mount Wilson and Palomar observatories and Dr. Lyman Spitzer, director of the Princeton University Observatory. They read a paper at the opening session of the convention of the American Astronomical Society at Indiana University, Bloomington, Indiana. A column-long telegram sent from there on June 19, 1950, by Charles Federer of the Harvard College Observatory to *The New York Times* carried the heading "Astronomers Give a Collision Theory." The universe that was supposed to be a peaceful structure in a nearly static state suddenly appeared in certain broad areas to have been involved "in an immense cosmic collision," in which not just a few satellites of one star but entire galaxies participated. Those at the convention heard the belief that the "thousands of millions of stars in each galaxy may go by each other relatively undisturbed because of the tremendous distances between the stars," but that the gases and dust that fill interstellar space must suffer "catastrophic collision," to use Spitzer's expression, and undergo "a temperature increase of many millions of degrees."

Against such reality, collisions in our own solar system a few thousand years ago were a minute thing, a pageant in miniature, though they meant terror and devastation for the inhabitants of our planet.

The principle of harmony or stability in the celestial sphere, the credo of modern astronomy, reeled under the impact of the newly understood phenomenon; the words "worlds in collision," so shrilly derided when referring to a few planets of the solar system in the historical past, were repeated, and meant events on a much larger scale, observable now. Other addresses at that convention, as if by some summons of history, spoke of catastrophes in the solar system. Clyde W. Tombaugh, the discoverer of Pluto, offered an explanation of the origin of the "oases" and canals of Mars. The oases or dark areas are the impact craters caused by collisions with asteroids, and the canals, which in most cases radiate from the oases, are fracture lines in the crust resulting from the impact of the asteroids. Dr. Dirk Brouwer of the Yale University Observatory spoke of the asteroids as fragments from the shattering of one or more planets. Dr. Fred Whipple theorized about two collisions between asteroids and a comet (Encke's) in the historical past.

"I AM ONE OF THOSE WHO PARTICIPATED"

George Sokolsky, whose column was syndicated to a great many newspapers in the United States, wrote early in July 1950 on the suppression of *Worlds in Collision.* He said clearly that he had not read the book, only a review of it. He then told of the boycott of Macmillan:

> Of course, what the learned and liberal professors wanted really was the total suppression of a book which opposed their dogma. Scientists tend to become dogmatic like theologians, whom they denounce as dogmatic . . . assuming that anyone who does not belong to their particular trade union ought to be silenced. . . . Neither Benjamin Franklin nor Thomas Edison would have qualified as members of the American Association of University Professors. . . . Macmillan owes the country an explanation which thus far has not been forthcoming. The public is entitled to know who precisely put the pressures on Macmillan; who wrote the letters; who called on the editors or publishers; who demanded action. It must have been a matter for consideration and discussion before they took the drastic step of giving up a best seller. A very powerful group, these buyers of textbooks have become.

Sokolsky's column was so widely syndicated that clippings came almost by the bushel.

Later in the month he devoted another column to the subject.

He had received a letter from Paul Herget, professor at the University of Cincinnati and director of its observatory. Herget took issue with Sokolsky for writing on the suppression and for admitting in his (first) article that he had not read the book. Herget's first paragraph, reprinted by Sokolsky, reads:

> This is not a reflection on columnists, but on frauds: you and Velikovsky. You are certainly a fraud, writing such a long column on something you have not read or investigated. He is certainly a fraud, writing a book which is so obviously prejudiced and untenable, and calling it scientific. I am one of those who participated in this campaign against Macmillan. . . .

Writing on something one has not read is a fraud, according to Professor Herget's definition. Sokolsky did not commit a fraud because he made it clear from the beginning that he had not read the book, was not appraising its content, but was defending freedom of thought and opposing the suppression of a book. But Herget's definition covered with mathematical precision the behavior of his colleagues and, if he followed their procedure, of himself.

Herget wrote, as quoted by Sokolsky, ". . . I do not believe he [Shapley] was in any sense the leader in this campaign. I was a very vigorous participant myself. . . . For your information I enclose copies of some of my correspondence." And he included copies of his letters to De Witt Wallace, founder and editor of the *Reader's Digest,* and B. T. Harris of the Macmillan Company. Sokolsky expressed his wonder: "Does the professor justify burning heretics at the stake? . . . Does he justify cutting the ears off Quakers in New England. . . ?

"The professor may know his astronomy. Of that I am no judge. But his logic pursues the non sequitur to a bitter end."

"A VERY GENUINE RESPONSIBILITY"

DEAN B. MCLAUGHLIN, astronomer at the University of Michigan at Ann Arbor, the very man who on May 20 had written to Macmillan that in his considered opinion *Worlds in Collision* was only lies and that he would never read that book, less than three weeks later, on June 16, wrote a long letter to Fulton Oursler.

> Several days ago I read your article "The Twilight of Honor" in the June issue of Reader's Digest. For that article, taken by itself, I commend you. I regret the necessity of qualifying this by admitting that my view of it was strongly discolored by your review of "Worlds in Collision" in the March issue.

After asserting that he was "not in the habit" of writing such letters, he explained:

> My reason for writing to you at this time is that you had a part in advancing to the best-seller category a book that scientists confidently appraise as mere rubbish and the most flagrant intellectual fraud ever foisted upon the public. To put it bluntly, for which I apologize, your one article earnestly attacks dishonesty, and your review applauds it! . . .

McLaughlin went on: "We are aware *which* sections [of science] are certain, which are only probable, and which extremely uncertain. The Velikovsky book is not concerned with questions that lie at the very frontier of knowledge" but conflicts with the most secured portions of it.

> One could write a voluminous book presenting all the facts and completely demolishing Velikovsky's thesis. I doubt that any scientist or group of them will waste their time that way. . . .
>
> One thing that is most astonishing is your uncritical approach. Probably that is to be charged to the cleverly designed bait that the author uses: agreement between "science" and the Bible. However it surprises me that you did not notice that his arguments are often completely circular. . . .
>
> Most of all it is hard to see why you were not suspicious of his claims to such extensive knowledge. . . . Here I am talking to you like the proverbial "Dutch uncle"! I hate to adopt an attitude of "I know and you don't." Please understand that I am speaking for a great number of experts collectively. . . . If this were merely a crackpot book about astronomy I would just laugh it off. But it is worse than that; worse than an attack on science; it is an attack on reason, especially it is a boomerang attack on religion! . . .
>
> Many religious people are "falling for" this crazy "theory." I can appreciate their confusion about the modern world, with science and religion *apparently* in conflict. But what they do not see is this: if the Biblical miracles are explained as mere natural phenomena or explained by Velikovsky's "science," then they are no longer miracles; we then have merely science—and no religion at all! This is no solution.

The solution is apparently a permanent conflict between science and religion, with miracles or events that took place against natural laws assigned to the domain of religion, and natural phenomena to the domain of science.

McLaughlin continued: "All of us who write have a very genuine responsibility to the public: we must be honest and responsible, and here we are back to 'The Twilight of Honor.' To be honest and responsible, we must be self-critical." By being uncritical, Oursler abetted dishonesty.

"Experts of course can be wrong. We have to take that risk." Nevertheless, failure to agree with experts "practically suggests a 'Twilight of Intelligence.' "

McLaughlin went on to say:

"Worlds in Collision" has just changed hands, from Macmillan to Doubleday. I am frank to state that this change was the result of pressure that scientists and scholars brought to bear on the Macmillan Company. It is our duty to the public to prevent such frauds insofar as we can. But the transfer merely means that the first publisher has "saved face" and the fraud can still go on. It is our belief that freedom of the press is abused when the public can be widely misinformed by the elevation of such a book to the best-seller class. The payment of royalties and the reaping of profit from a book like "Worlds in Collision" do indeed mark "The Twilight of Honor."

The Reader's Digest
Pleasantville, N.Y.

June 27th, 1950

Hotel Navarro
112 Central Park South
New York 19, N.Y.

Dear Professor McLaughlin:

I appreciate the long and thoughtful letter that you wrote me although I find some parts of it difficult to understand.

One part has to do with the pride you express in the pressure of scientists against the house of Macmillan to discontinue publishing the Velikovsky book. This procedure horrifies me; some of the details of which I have been told are witchhunting tactics. Is not this book burning by intellectuals? And isn't that a matter for shame rather than pride? This, above all in your letter, I cannot understand. . . .

Again you state that my review applauds dishonesty. Do you consider that remark an example of objective scientific observation? To use your own words, that comment of yours is "mere rubbish and a flagrant intellectual fraud." Because you know perfectly well that my review does not applaud dishonesty. . . . I mention it here only to point out that a serious discussion should be conducted in less extravagant and emotional terms.

You go on to say that scientists admit the limitations of their knowledge but are aware of *which* sections are certain, *which* are only probable and *which* extremely uncertain. That, I take it, is a statement much more sweeping and infallible than you can possibly have intended. All the tragic history of the self-sufficiency of experts in every field contradicts it. . . .

Another unscientific attitude on your part is indicated when you discuss the "probability" that I rose to the "bait" of scientific proof of the Bible. Here, my dear Professor, you indulge in mind reading. . . .

You are quite right in saying that you talk to me like a Dutch uncle and I am sure you will not deny me the privilege of talking back to you like an American uncle. Therefore I must point out to you that when you ask me to believe that Velikovsky's "science" vitiates the Biblical miracles, you are very far from the truth. Let me remind you of your own remarks to beware of a man who claims to know everything. Aren't you dangerously near to doing that at this point? There is nothing in Velikovsky's theory that removes the miraculous intervention of God at just the right time, in full accord with the Biblical position; at least that is the point of view of some of the theologians with whom I discussed the matter.

I am sufficiently interested in what you say to take your letter to Dr. Velikovsky and hear what he has to say about it. It is well worth exploring but only so long as it can be done in a dignified atmosphere without the shrill note that I detect in the voices of some of his critics.

Sincerely yours,
Fulton Oursler
Senior Editor

P.S. Is it true that this agitation among scientists originated with Professor Harlow Shapley? If so, I am bound to regard these hysterical attitudes and attempts at book-burnings in a light even more dubious.

"PROFESSORS AS SUPPRESSORS"

On July 3, 1950, *Newsweek*, in its "National Affairs" pages—the leading section of the magazine—published one column on the outbreak of war in Korea and two columns entitled "Academic Freedom: Professors as Suppressors." It was, as usual, on the stands a few days before its date.

> One of the most cherished rights of the nation's teaching profession is academic freedom, and college professors customarily will fight fiercely to defend it. . . . Yet last week a small group of professors themselves stood accused of a major assault on academic freedom. New York publishing circles charged them with attempted suppression of a book, Dr. Immanuel Velikovsky's intensely controversial "Worlds in Collision," which has led the best-seller lists since April, when Macmillan brought it out.
>
> Many of the facts were in dispute, and Macmillan was maintaining a grim silence, refusing to confirm or deny them. Company officials would say nothing beyond a terse admission that, after selling 55,000 copies of the book at $4.50, they had suddenly transferred all rights to the most valuable literary property of the year to a rival, Doubleday. . . . Off the record Macmillan's competitors reported that a boycott had actually been started against the company. Macmillan salesmen were finding that at several universities, including one with an international reputation, the professors wouldn't even talk.

Although some of the critics who reviewed Velikovsky's book considered it a major scientific contribution, there could be little question but that it had driven the vast majority of the nation's scientists into a highly unacademic fury. For Velikovsky challenges all the present concepts and laws of history, astronomy, biology, and geology. . . . Whether the attack on the Velikovsky book and the Macmillan company was merely an outburst of their resentment against an attack on themselves or whether it was an organized campaign last week remained a matter of controversy. In the "New York Post," columnist Leonard Lyons declared that it was an organized campaign and the leader, he said, was Dr. Harlow Shapley, director of the Harvard Observatory and member of the fellow-traveling National Council of the Arts, Sciences, and Professions. Shapley bitterly denied the charge.

One thing seemed indisputable: Most of the attacks on Dr. Velikovsky sent to Macmillan had been from astronomers, and the bitterest had been from members of the Harvard Observatory, including Shapley. It was true, also, that a great deal of furor over the book in academic circles had been stirred up primarily by two articles, one entitled "Nonsense, Dr. Velikovsky!" which appeared in the March 14 issue of "The Reporter," and the other a piece in the "Science News Letter." The author of the "Reporter" article was Dr. Cecilia Payne-Gaposchkin, a member of the Harvard Observatory, and it was charged that Dr. Shapley had encouraged her to write it. Shapley, moreover, is president of Science Service, which publishes "Science News Letter," and its story quoted him at length.

This evidence was, of course, wholly circumstantial, and Dr. Shapley last week denied heatedly that he conducted "any kind of campaign against the book." Nor had the Harvard Observatory, he added. He did write Macmillan about the book and so did other members of the Observatory, but "I didn't make any threats and I don't know anyone who did."

THE THREAT

THE EFFORT TO SUPPRESS my book and the boycott of Macmillan's textbook department were an organized affair.* This can be seen from two letters addressed to Doubleday on June 30, 1950, when the July 3 issue of *Newsweek* was on its way to subscribers. David Grahame, associate professor of chemistry at Amherst College, wrote:

> Macmillan Company abandoned it [*Worlds in Collision*] because of the storm of protest it aroused among informed persons, and you, too, may find yourself kept busy answering letters of indignation from scientists the country over. Scientists are now engaged in an active boycott of the Macmillan books, and though scientists are not important buyers of your books, their opinion should be heeded by any publisher who intends to publish a book which purports to be science. I trust that you can be dissuaded.

On the same June 30, 1950, Professor Fred L. Whipple, who until shortly before had served as chief assistant to Shapley and

* Several years later Professor Livio Stecchini told of his experience in the campaign of collective letter writing. In 1950 he was on the staff of the University of Chicago. The head of his department appealed to a group of faculty members in his department to write protest letters to Macmillan against the publication of *Worlds in Collision*. When Stecchini objected that he had not read the book (it happened to be the first time he had heard of it), he was told, according to Stecchini's account: "Never mind. You go to my secretary and she will compose a letter for you. All that you will need to do is to sign it."

later took over Shapley's post as director of the Harvard College Observatory, wrote to the Blakiston Company in Philadelphia, the publisher of his *Earth, Moon, and Planets.* He said he had heard that Doubleday and Company "had taken over the 'golden chestnut' called Worlds in Collision." He explained the rage of the scientists against Macmillan for not having labeled the book as fiction: "Velikovsky differs from other crank scientific writers in that he has the art of making the impossible seem plausible. . . . I must say that in areas of the book where I am not fully informed the writing seems almost convincing. . . ."

It is not excluded, he wrote, that the Macmillan Company was "led astray by this high degree of plausibility" or by my ability to make the impossible seem plausible. "Hence, the position of the Doubleday Company in buying the rights to Worlds in Collision represents a considerably lower ethical level than that of Macmillan Company, since the Doubleday Company cannot have avoided obtaining the opinion of many competent scientists." At the time he composed his letter he came upon the article in *Newsweek.* "Oddly enough," he says, "Newsweek has unwittingly done the Doubleday Company a considerable amount of harm. They have made public the high success of the spontaneous boycott of the Macmillan Company by scientifically minded people. This in turn amounts to organizing a boycott of the Doubleday Company by the thinking people who buy books. My guess is that Doubleday Co. will never publish Volumes 3 and 4."*

He went on:

> In any case, since I believe that the Blakiston Company is owned by the Doubleday Company, which controls its policies as well as the distribution of its books, I am now then a fellow author of the Doubleday Company along with Velikovsky. My natural inclination, were it possible, is to take *Earth, Moon, and Planets* off the market and find a publisher who is not associated with one who has such a lacuna in its publication ethics. This is not possible, however, so the next best that I can do is to turn over the future royalty checks to the Boston Community Fund and to let *Earth, Moon, and Planets* die of senescence. In other words, there will be no revision of *Earth, Moon*

* Up to now Doubleday & Company have published *Worlds in Collision, Ages in Chaos,* I, *Earth in Upheaval, Oedipus and Akhnaton, Peoples of the Sea, Ramses II and His Time,* and *Mankind in Amnesia.*

and Planets forthcoming so long as Doubleday owns Blakiston, controls its policies and publishes *Worlds in Collision.*

Ken McCormick, editor in chief of Doubleday, wrote to Whipple that his letter to the Blakiston Company had been sent to him from Philadelphia, that he was distressed that Doubleday's editorial policy had disturbed Whipple, that the company exercised no control over or influence on Blakiston's editorial policy—and Blakiston exercised no control over Doubleday. They took over *Worlds in Collision*

> ... because there was a great demand for it and we believe that the book business cannot let itself be pressured into censorship. You know, better than I, how much important work would have been lost to the world if such were the custom. When Doubleday took the book, *Worlds in Collision* had already had a public trial. It had been widely reviewed and discussed in the public press, receiving both condemnation and commendation. We have not forced the book on anyone nor do we offer it as a textbook, [but] as one man's personal theory.

In the advertisements "the various opinions of prominent writers, scientists, statesmen, and reviewers" are quoted with pros and cons, and "the public cannot miss knowing" about the violent disagreement that greeted the book. Ken McCormick continued:

> We can understand that scientists feel bound to challenge Prof. [read Dr.] Velikovsky; but we contend that the way to disprove his theory is not to ban his book or boycott his publishers, but to answer him. If any of the scientists aroused by this book will present a counterargument in a manuscript as interesting, Doubleday will be very glad to consider it for publication.

He ended his letter by saying that he hoped Professor Whipple would revise his opinion of the editorial ethics of Doubleday & Company and endeavor to see that "from our point of view, there are ethics involved in protecting the right of a man to have a hearing and keeping the publishing business free for the expression of ideas." Since this and other letters received by Doubleday, good and bad, dealt with my book, they were shown to me, and I wrote to Ken McCormick.

> Thankful as I am to you for letting me see this correspondence, I do not think that these gentlemen received the answers that they deserved.
>
> Dr. Whipple says that "the position of the Doubleday Company in buying the rights to *Worlds in Collision* represents a considerably lower ethical level than that of the Macmillan Company" because you were aware of what you were doing. He writes his letter after he read an article in *Newsweek*, "Professors as Suppressors." I believe that, acting now as he does, he stoops to a lower ethical level than when he and his colleagues at [the] Harvard College observatory tried to suppress the book at Macmillan because, from this article of *Newsweek* and from editorials in various publications, he must know by now the definition of what he is doing. . . .
>
> In the brief of Dr. Whipple to the Blakiston Company, he makes the threat that "there will be no revision of *Earth, Moon, and Planets* forthcoming so long as Doubleday owns Blakiston, controls its policies and publishes *Worlds in Collision.*" He finished by accusing Doubleday of lack of ethics.

I drew McCormick's attention to the fact that although Whipple referred to the book as "rot," albeit "almost convincing," neither he nor anybody else had been able to cite one instance of an incorrect statement in my book in the field of astronomy or elsewhere. Doubleday had accepted the book not only because "there is a public demand for it" but also because

> . . . in your own judgement it is a book worth publication which you intended to do with pride. . . .
>
> I regard my publisher not as a place of refuge and shelter from the fury of attacking scientists but as a bastion for the propagation of my literary or scientific efforts.

As for a new edition of *Earth, Moon, and Planets,* I expressed my doubt whether in a few years from then it would be possible to do it without incorporating some facts documented in *Worlds in Collision.*

> This Dr. Whipple, however, may keep his name for posterity, not by his scientific discoveries . . . but by his letters that, as the earlier letters from Shapley and his associates, in the opinion of my lawyer, have all the signs of conspiracy.

> I had to let this off my chest since I know that Ken McCormick is an editor of high principles, without compare.

The point stressed by all the defenders of the boycott against Macmillan was the high repute of that firm in the field of textbooks. Because of this reputation, a new theory published by Macmillan might be regarded as having the approval of the scientific world. This was a spurious motive. When the book was taken by Doubleday, the threats did not subside, and the scientists only regretted that Doubleday had no "soft underbelly" in the way of a textbook department. They thought to find it in the Blakiston Company, but obviously the books published by Doubleday could not reflect on the standard of the Blakiston books.

My prediction that a new edition of *Earth, Moon, and Planets,* should there be one, would require the incorporation of some facts in astronomy that found their reflection in folklore as described in my book was fulfilled with a speed I had not expected. Only four months later, in the October 1950 issue of the *Astronomical Journal,* appeared a paper by Dr. Whipple in which he, on the basis of computations, postulated worlds in collision only 1,500 and 4,700 years ago, when a comet collided with and disrupted the planetoids that revolve by the thousands between the orbits of Mars and Jupiter. Cosmic catastrophes in the neighborhood of the earth disrupting the cosmic order in historical times were solemnly characterized as rubbish; recent changes in the constitution of the solar system, as nonsense. But Whipple calculated from the orbits of the planetoids and the disruption of the comet Encke that the last "encounters" took place only 1,500 years ago, or the year 450 of the present era, though no eyewitness account of this great catastrophe has been preserved from that time. Would it not have been the proper approach from the beginning for astronomers who did not believe in the interpretation that I evolved from the literary memory of many nations all over the globe to have offered a different interpretation? Such a constructive procedure would have borne fruit in time, and either I would have been vindicated or at least the material assembled in my book would have served a constructive purpose.

There was no new edition of Whipple's book by Blakiston. The entire series of popularly written Harvard books on astronomy was withdrawn from Blakiston and transferred to the Harvard University Press. The threat was not made only to scare.

THE HARVARD CRIMSON BLUSHES

THE FALL REGISTRATION number of the *Harvard Crimson* (September 25, 1950), the well-known Harvard College student paper, carried on two folio pages an article by Humphrey Doermann of the editorial board, with pictures of Shapley, Velikovsky, and Pfeiffer. The title of the article running across the page read: "Shapley Brands 'Worlds in Collision' a Hoax," and the subtitle: "Scientists' Attacks, Pressure Make Macmillan Call Off Publication."

The title in large characters augured a devastating criticism of the book, yet the real intent of the writer was to present the issue fairly. The article began with this observation:

> A surprising number of the country's reputable astronomers have descended from their telescopes during the past nine months to denounce Dr. Immanuel Velikovsky's new book, "Worlds in Collision," in what has been described as the "biggest uproar in scientific circles since Newton and Darwin."

The article described what happened:

> It is known that certain college astronomers threatened Macmillan with a textbook boycott. Two prominent men early associated with "Worlds in Collision" lost their jobs. In a world where crackpot scientific theories appear and pass unnoticed

> every day, some began to wonder: If there is nothing to Dr. Velikovsky's thesis, why were so many people trying to discredit and silence him?

After giving a correct presentation of the content of the book, the *Harvard Crimson* went on:

> Dr. Velikovsky draws his proofs from a wide range of fields and sciences: from cross-checking the world's folk legends and classical literature, and re-examining ancient astronomical observations—to bringing forth geological, archaeological, biological and psychological data.
>
> Hence, if his theories, or any large part of them, are found to be valid, scientists in a great many fields will have to change the underpinnings of their life's work.
>
> If the force which caused the earth to stop rotating briefly was magnetic, then the whole Newtonian theory of gravitation (which for quite a while was thought to have been governing the neutral bodies of the universe) comes into severe question. Hitherto secure ideas on how mountain ranges are formed, how continents gradually rise from or sink into the sea, why certain thriving civilizations suddenly died out, and how the solar system has reacted throughout time, may have to be revised.
>
> Possibly reluctance to make this sweeping re-examination of fundamentals caused the group of astronomers to react so violently, so early.
>
> First notice of the book, then unpublished, came in January as *Harper's*, *Collier's*, and (with a strong fundamentalist slant) the *Reader's Digest* came out with condensed versions.
>
> Although most scientists had not yet had an opportunity to read the book itself, response was heated.

The article gave as examples of writers who expressed opinions without having read the book: Harlow Shapley, who announced that the book was nonsense and rubbish, and Cecilia Payne-Gaposchkin, who elaborated on the unread book.

Then followed quotations from Robert Pfeiffer of Harvard University ("I was amazed at the depth and vastness of your erudition") and the *Daily Worker* ("It is a sign of the bankruptcy of capitalism that it pays serious attention to such a denial of all that science has learned").

The article told the story of the suppression of the book by scientists when it was at Macmillan and of its transfer to Doubleday. It stated that "Abroad, *Paris-Match* pointed out 'Le foyer de l'antivelikovskysme est Harvard' " and it quoted the New York columnist Leonard Lyons to the effect that the leader of the group was Shapley.

"That pressure had been exerted seemed evident. Two of the men early associated with Dr. Velikovsky's book found their 'resignation accepted' suddenly and without apparent explanation."

After relating the story of Putnam and Atwater, the article proceeded:

> Questioned on the events of the past few months, Velikovsky indicated that pressure had been brought to bear, but he refused to give names. Summarizing the activities of his adversaries, he said, "Without specific personal references, it is wrong to try to suppress a book. Secondly, it is wrong to do so in a clandestine manner. Thirdly, and worse yet, it is wrong to do so without even reading the book. Fourth, it is wrong to try to influence its reviewers. And lastly, having done all this, it is wrong not to admit it."

The article continued: "Last week new light appeared on the alleged suppression attempt when a letter from the publisher of a New York City daily newspaper to Shapley dated March 7 was released to *Crimson.*" Thackrey's letter to Shapley, reproduced on pages 98–101, was quoted in part.

The *Crimson* went on: "The evidence tying Shapley to any organized boycott attempt of the Macmillan Company, however, remains circumstantial. Shapley's statement denying any organized boycott attempt appears on the preceding page."

And on that page, in fat characters, in quotation marks signifying an authentic statement, over the signature of Harlow Shapley, were eight lines:

> "The claim that Dr. Velikovsky's book is being suppressed is nothing but a publicity stunt. Like having a book banned in Boston, it improves the sales. Several attempts have been made to link such a move to stop the book's publication to

some organization or to the Harvard Observatory. This idea is absolutely false."

Harlow Shapley

My picture on the page looks at his picture. In it I look older, though I am ten years younger. He looks away. The reader will remember the *Crimson*'s statement that I refused to name names.

QUARTERED AT YALE

FOUR YALE PROFESSORS united their forces to disprove *Worlds in Collision.* Together they prepared an article for the *American Journal of Science* published at Yale. The editor, Professor Chester R. Longwell, himself a geologist and one of the four authors, arranged to have this article printed in the daily press, too, in advance of its appearance in the *Journal.* In the New Haven *Register* of June 25, 1950, the large blue letters of a six-column headline announced: "4 Yale Scholars 'Expose' Non-Fiction Best-Seller."

The three other authors were Kenneth Latourette, Sinologist; George Kubler, Mexicologist; and Rupert Wildt, astronomer.

Professor Latourette, who as a missionary spent many years in China, put forth this argument against my book: Velikovsky has generally preferred older sources, and according to modern views, Emperor Yao (Yahou) belongs to the legendary period of Chinese history (which is usually divided into three periods: mythical or fabulous, legendary, and historical).

It can hardly be called an argument, still less an "exposure," since in my treatment I deliberately used legendary material of ancient origin. King Yao was not my invention. "Every Chinese schoolboy is familiar with the names of Yao, Shun, and Yu," said the same Latourette in his *The Development of China* (1917, page 16). There he also said that "native historians" regarded this period in the Chinese past as completely historical. And the modern view of Western scholars was this: "Even the historicity of the three [kings] is to be viewed with some doubt, but they are usually regarded as authentic." This sentence is from the article "China" in the *Encyclopedia Britannica* (14th edition), and the author of the article was Latourette. An earlier authority, Jean-Baptiste du Halde, in the second volume of his *History of China* (1736), said that "should anybody question the historicity of Yao, he would not only be ridiculed, but severely chastized." (He would probably be handled like a traditional Jew who questioned the existence of Moses.)

"The history of China preceding his [Yao's] reign is ascribed to the mythical period of the Chinese past," I wrote in *Worlds in Collision* (pages 100–01). "In the days of Yahou [Yao] the event occurred which separates the almost obliterated and very dim past of China from the period that is considered historical: China was overwhelmed by an immense catastrophe." Then I quoted the numerous sources ("an amazing range of historical records," in Latourette's estimate). In the reign of Yao for ten days the sun remained above the horizon; all the forests burned; a multitude of "abominable vermin" was brought forth; an immense wave that "reached the sky" fell on China and swept over high mountains, and thereafter the lower regions of the country remained inundated for more than two generations; the calendar was disordered, and it was also necessary to find anew the cardinal points—east, west, north, and south—which were difficult to locate because the land was covered with gloom for many years. It is said also that a new bright star was born in the days of Yao.

All this, I demonstrated in my book, has exact counterparts in Hebrew traditions and legends, as narrated in the Scriptures, Midrash, and Talmud, relative to the time of the Exodus, and in Egyptian traditions as well. The sole difference is that according to the Egyptian source, the sun remained *below* the horizon causing "Egyptian darkness" for nine days—or for seven days according to midrashic tradition. This shows there was no borrowing by the Chinese from Egypt or Judea, or the other way around, by Egypt or Judea from China, where tradition has the sun remaining *above* the horizon.

Nothing of this was questioned by Latourette. What did he disprove or expose?

George Kubler, professor of the history of art at Yale and a student of Mesoamerican civilization, brought the following issues to the discussion. First, he wondered that I interpreted the fifty-two-year cycle of the Mayan and the Mexican Indians "as an historical survival of the terrors experienced between the two 'contacts' of the Venus-comet with the earth."

I have not concealed my sources. Fernando de Alva Ixtlilxochitl, the early Mexican scholar (c. 1568–1648) who was able to read old Mexican texts, preserved the ancient tradition according to which multiples of the fifty-two-year period played a prominent role in the recurrence of world catastrophes. Also, the Codex Vaticanus, one of the few manuscripts surviving from pre-Columbian times, reckons world ages in multiples of fifty-two years. At the expiration of every fifty-two year period the natives of Mexico congregated to await a new catastrophe. "When the night of this ceremony arrived, all the people were seized with fear and waited in anxiety for what might take place," wrote Bernardino de Sahagun, the sixteenth-century Spanish authority, regarded as the best of all sources pertaining to Latin America. The Mexicans were afraid that "it will be the end of the human race and that the darkness of the night may become permanent: the sun may not rise anymore." They watched for the appearance of the planet Venus, and when on the dreaded night no catastrophe befell them, the Mayan people rejoiced. Great bonfires announced that a new period of grace was granted, and a new Venus cycle of fifty-two years started. The period is called the Venus cycle, as is known to every student of Mexican lore.* Sahagun also narrated that the Mexicans called Venus a comet, or a star that fumes. And George A. Dorsey, of the Field Museum of Natural History, described the ceremony of sacrifice to the Morning Star (Venus) as a "dramatization of the acts performed by the Morning Star." A human offering was made by the Pawnee Indians only a few generations ago, when Venus "appeared especially bright or in years when there was a comet in the sky."†

The other issue for which Professor Kubler took me to task concerned my dating of certain events in Mesoamerican history (*Worlds in Collision*, p. 254): "The Mesoamerican cosmology to which Velikovsky repeatedly appeals for proof did not originate and could not originate until about the beginning of our era."

Professor Kubler stressed a full 1,000 years of discrepancy between the datings of *Worlds in Collision* and the proved archaeology. Neither in the fifteenth century nor in the eighth century before our era was there any script, regulated calendar, or mythology as we

* Seler, *Gesammelte Abhandlungen* (1903), vol. I, p. 618.

† *Worlds in Collision*, p. 154, see references there; see also pp. 163, 192.

know it, and the rise of Mesoamerican civilizations was of an incomparably later date.

A few years later measurements using the radiocarbon method of dating decided the issue. On December 30, 1956, the National Geographic Society issued the following press release:

> Atomic science has proved the ancient civilizations of Mexico to be some 1,000 years older than had been believed, the National Geographic Society says.
>
> In findings basic to Middle American archaeology, artifacts dug up in La Venta, Mexico, have been proved to come from a period 800 to 400 years before the Christian era. Previously, they had been assigned to 400 or 500 A.D., more than 1,000 years later.
>
> Cultural parallels between La Venta and other Mexican archaeological excavations enable scientists to date one in terms of the others. Thus the new knowledge affects the datings of many finds. (See also *Science,* July 12, 1957.)

Professor Rupert Wildt of the Yale Observatory directed his attack against what he considered my convictions or my case of amnesia:

> No useful purpose would be served by summarizing here Velikovsky's "evidence" for the series of cosmic catastrophes that he supposes to have occurred between 1500 and 700 B.C. The crucial point is that Velikovsky, in effect, repudiates his earlier rejection of Newton: "The theory of cosmic catastrophe can, if required to do so, conform with the celestial mechanics of Newton" (*Worlds in Collision,* p. 384). But the readers of the book are spared the realization that its author ever professed belief in what he called "the empiric evidences of the fallacy of the law of gravitation" (*Cosmos Without Gravitation,* p. 11).*

* *Cosmos Without Gravitation: Attraction, Repulsion, and Electromagnetic Circumduction in the Solar System, Synopsis, 1946,* was printed by me as a short monograph in the series *Scripta Academica Hierosolymitana;* it was not offered for sale and was distributed only to a number of physicists for scientific appraisal and was placed in some selected libraries. The opening sentence is: "The fundamental theory of this paper is: Gravitation is an electromagnetic phenomenon"—a view heretical in 1946 but much considered in the 1970's. Various tests were offered in the synopsis for performance in laboratory or in space.

> We look in vain for an explanation of what possessed the man between 1946 and 1950 and cannot help wondering—is this a case of individual amnesia overtaking the author, or does he have so little respect for scientific critics as to rely on their collective amnesia?

Wildt looked in vain, yet it was easy to find. Three pages after the sentence he quoted from *Worlds in Collision,* and still in the same context, I said (p. 387):

> Thus celestial mechanics does not conflict with cosmic catastrophism. I must admit, however, that in searching for the causes of the great upheavals of the past and in considering their effects, I became skeptical of the great theories concerning the celestial motions that were formulated when the historical facts described here were not known to science. . . . Fundamental principles in celestial mechanics, including the law of gravitation, must come into question if the sun possesses a charge sufficient to influence the planets in their orbits or the comets in theirs. In the Newtonian celestial mechanics, based on the theory of gravitation, electricity and magnetism play no role.

Anyone who reads only the first page of *Worlds in Collision* is informed that if Newton is "sacrosanct, this book is a heresy."

Here I feel induced to quote Freud, from the Preface to the second edition of his *The Interpretation of Dreams:* "The few reviews which have appeared in the scientific journals are so full of misconceptions and lack of comprehension that my only possible answer to my critics would be a request that they should read this book again—or perhaps merely—that they should read it!"

Last comes Chester R. Longwell, who says that

> the geologist is both amused and appalled by the ideas and the methods of Dr. Velikovsky. . . .
>
> In discussing the origin of petroleum he lists two theories—the inorganic and the organic—but does not go on to inform the reader that to modern students of the subject the inorganic theory has historical interest only.

Once more I am accused of hiding something from my readers. Yet page 369 of *Worlds in Collision* states: "The modern theory of the origin of petroleum, based upon its polarizing quality, regards petroleum as originating from organic, not inorganic, matter."

I could not make it clearer. So much for my appalling method.

As for the geological aspect of the theory of *Worlds in Collision*, Longwell says:

> Velikovsky raises anew the matter of "erratic blocks"—masses of rock that clearly have been displaced through distances of tens or even hundreds of miles from the localities of their origin. No problem that has confronted geologists seems to be more convincingly solved than this one. The "erratics" occur only in areas that are known, on independent evidence, to have been covered with glacier ice in the geologic past.... Every essential link from effect to cause has been adequately supplied, in the judgment of informed students.

But the author of *Worlds in Collision* disregarded all the evidence accumulated in the course of 100 years and "wants the 'erratics' as witnesses to a gigantic tide that swept the lands during his cosmic catastrophe," and "unhampered by embarrassing facts, he rushes in with his own grandiose speculation."

Actually I wrote on page 76 that "the problem of the migration of the stones must be regarded as only partially connected with the progress and retreat of the ice sheet. . . ." (In *Earth in Upheaval* I give a more detailed treatment of the subject.) But already in *Worlds in Collision* I pointed to the embarrassing fact of stones transferred from plains up mountain glaciers, though at present no such phenomenon was observable in the mountain glaciers. Erratics were carried from India up the Himalayas. They were also carried from equatorial Africa toward the higher latitudes, "across the prairies and deserts and forests of the black continent." That not "every link" was supplied can be judged from the words of Professor Reginald Daly of Harvard, who wrote* that the ice age history of North America "holds ten major mysteries for every one that has already been solved" and that "the very cause of excessive ice-making on the lands remains a baffling mystery, a major question for the future reader of earth's riddles."†

The statement that scientific study in the last 100 years has proved that erratics are found only where other vestiges of ice

* Reginald Daly, *The Changing World of the Ice Age* (1934), p. 111.
† Ibid., p. 16.

movement are also present is embarrassingly wrong. Darwin inquired and received the answer that in the Azores—where there was no ice cover—erratics are found in abundance. J. G. Cumming described erratics carried high up on the Isle of Man, in the Irish Sea, and admitted that ice could not have transported them there. J. S. Lee described erratic blocks and at the same time the "general absence of ice-sculptured features" in northern China, or "two sets of facts pointing in opposite directions."*

It happened that at about the time the *American Journal of Science* published the article by the four scholars, I received a letter from one of my readers who referred to the problem of erratic boulders.

> What you have to say about glaciation may help to explain some of the difficulties in the glacial theory. On Macquarie Island, south of New Zealand, for instance, erratic boulders from the western coast were carried to the eastern coast to a 750-foot-higher elevation. By the glacial theory, it is hard to explain why the glacier should have come from one side, instead of radiating from the center, and why the erratics were lifted.

My work was torn apart at Yale. It was quartered by four famous professors. Yet, after being executed, the book left the place unharmed.

To quote Victor Hugo: "And then, while critics fall foul of the preface and the scholars of the notes, it may happen that the work itself will escape them, passing uninjured between their crossfires."†

* J. S. Lee, *Geology of China* (1939), pp. 357, 373.
† Preface to *Cromwell* (1827).

THE THIRD DEGREE

IN THE FALL OF 1950 a psychoanalytic patient of mine—at the time I was seeing a few patients—brought me a leaflet that had been given him by his neighbor. It was a reprint of a review of my book by Professor Otto Neugebauer of Brown University and the Institute for Advanced Study in Princeton; the reprint was from *Isis,* a journal of the history of science, then edited by Professor George Sarton of Harvard.

In the very first sentence of his review Neugebauer said that I invoked "collective amnesia to explain the lack of documents"—this despite the fact that I presented evidence based on documents numbering in the hundreds, if not the thousands, and in disregard of what I wrote on page 300 of *Worlds in Collision:*

> The memory of the cataclysms was erased, not because of lack of written traditions, but because of some characteristic process that later caused entire nations, together with their literate men, to read into these traditions allegories or metaphors where actually cosmic disturbances were clearly described.

Neugebauer, after characterizing my book in the opening paragraph as a "389-pages-long list of absurdities" and stating that "in its attempt to explain Biblical narratives rationally, it shares all the characteristics of a widespread type of crackpot publication," ended the paragraph with this accusation: "It attains, however, an exceptionally high degree of distortion of scientific literature. It is this latter aspect which may justify the waste of space in a scientific journal."

As evidence to support this grave and generalized statement, Neugebauer immediately gave an example. He quoted from page 349 of my book and confronted me with my source, Franz Xaver Kugler, a Jesuit priest.

Kugler wrote in German a series of books on Babylonian astronomy, from each of which I quote in several places in *Worlds in Collision.* One of Kugler's books is *The Babylonian Moon Computation: Two Chaldean Systems Concerning the Movement of the Moon and the Sun.** As the title indicates, a certain collection of Babylonian astronomical tablets contains two (and in part even three) systems of planetary motions. Each system is complete in itself; the periods of revolution and the positions of the luminaries—Sun, Moon, and planets—are worked out in detail and are consistent within each system, but the two systems differ from each other in many respects. Kugler, not conceiving of any change in the order of the solar system in the historical past, tried to give some explanation for this very enigmatic situation; he thought there might have been two, or even three, schools of astronomy, each of which devised its own system of recording, but he found that these systems did not represent reality. For instance, according to the length of the day at the spring solstice in one system, the geographical position of Babylon would have to be two and a half degrees farther to the north. Could the Babylonian astronomers have made such a mistake? he asked, and he answered that "it is hardly believable." Therefore, he concluded: "With this we stand before a strange enigma" ("*Wir stehen damit vor einem merkwürdigen Rätsel*"). Kugler considered the possibility that in accordance with System II, Babylon was actually situated farther to the north, almost 300 kilometers from its identified ruins.

Kugler also found that the position of the sun in relation to the fixed stars at the solstices and equinoxes differed from what is known from modern observations and computations: These points in the tablets of one system lie six degrees too far to the east ("*zu weit nach Osten*"). The sun's position in relation to the stars at perihelion and aphelion is designated in various systems at points which are displaced by many degrees. Equally displaced are the positions (stations) of the new moon and the distances our satellite covers from one new moon to another.

My explanation of these various systems of celestial motions and

* F. X. Kugler, *Die Babylonische Mondrechnung. Zwei Systeme der Chaldäer über den Lauf des Mondes und der Sonne* (1900).

positions was in harmony with what is found in the lore of other peoples of antiquity and was reflected in the calendar reforms of the Chinese, Hindus, Persians, Israelites, Egyptians, Mayans, and others—namely, that these systems represent true observations at various epochs, before and after the repeated disturbances of the seventh to eighth century B.C. I consider the parts of *Worlds in Collision*, pages 120–25, 313–59, dealing with the calendar observances and reforms the most valuable from the point of view of science.

Now I return to Neugebauer. To illustrate my "exceptionally high degree of distortion of scientific literature," he gave as the first example:

> On p. 349 the author [Velikovsky] writes in quotes under reference to Kugler, *Mondrechnung*, p. 90, "The distances traveled by the moon on the Chaldean ecliptic from one new moon to the next are according to Tablet No. 272, on the average **33° 14′** too great." The actual statement of Kugler, however, is the following: [Neugebauer translates from the German]* "In order to demonstrate this we must anticipate our discussion of the relation of the Chaldean ecliptic of No. 272 and of the movable ecliptic and mention that the longitudes of the new moons with reference to the first are in the mean **3° 14′** greater than with reference to the second" [emphasis added].

Neugebauer commented: "No word of from 'one new moon to the next' but a totally different statement concerning the counting of longitudes in two different coordinate systems."

I cited only the relevant, last part of the passage and rendered it so that its meaning could be understood. I took care to preserve the meaning of the passage in the original. Kugler's comparison of "the longitudes of the new moons" in the two different systems is exactly the same—only in technical language—as "the distances traveled by the moon . . . from one new moon to the next." As a matter of fact, on another page in the same book Kugler explains it as I do: "the longitudinal shifting of successive new moons."† Yet it is true that in paraphrasing Kugler, I should not have used quotation marks.

* *"Um dies zeigen zu können, müssen wir, der spätern Erörterung des Verhältnisses der chaldäischen Ekliptik von No. 272 vorgreifend, schon jetzt erwähnen, dass die Neumondlängen auf der erstern gezählt durchschnittlich um 3°14′ grösser ausfallen als nach Zählung auf der letztern."*

† *"Längeverschiebung der aufeinander folgenden Neumonde."*

But of primary concern for me is the fact that the reader must be painfully impressed by my substitution of 33° 14′ for 3° 14′ in my quotation from Kugler. He must conclude that I am very negligent with figures, that I actually falsify them in order to suit my own purposes, and that here I am finally pinned down. The reader must say: "Velikovsky magnified the difference between the two systems tenfold." And since Neugebauer twice quoted Kugler, in German and in English, confronting his text and figures with my text and figures, the impression must be very damaging.

Can I say anything in my defense? *In my book (in every printing, from the first on) the figure is 3° 14′ and not 33° 14′ as Neugebauer put it in his quotation from my book.* Whose, then, is "the high degree of distortion"?

I can close Neugebauer's case here. If my book, for this "error," should be regarded as discredited, the same rule should apply to his review.*

When I asked for redress, Neugebauer wrote to George Sarton, the editor of *Isis,* that the wrongly inserted figure was "a simple misprint of no concern."

Neugebauer did not correct the wrong figure on the reprints he sent out, nor did he or Sarton ever make a correction on the pages of *Isis,* where his review had been printed. He left such a glaring error in a statement by him, a professor of astronomy and philology—two disciplines that require great precision—accusing me of "a high degree of distortion."

* In another place the rest of Neugebauer's statements will be analyzed and tested against texts.

AN AUTHORITY CALLED TO WITNESS

THE LEARNED PRIEST Franz Xaver Kugler believed for most of his life that the Babylonian astronomical texts from before c. −750 are void of scientific value because their figures and dates are at great variance with the true movements of planetary bodies; thus he assumed that they must have been of legendary character. In this he differed from several other authors, like J. K. Fotheringham, who regarded these texts as historical.

Kugler was therefore called upon, as the highest authority in his field, by Otto Neugebauer to disprove my discourse on world catastrophes caused by extraterrestrial agents and generally my interpretation of ancient legends and traditions as reflecting true natural events.

However, before Kugler completed the last volume of his monumental work on Babylonian astronomy, he had published a short essay, "The Sibylline Star War and Phaëthon in the Light of Natural History."* I came across it when I restudied Kugler, following the attack by Neugebauer. In this essay Kugler wrote:

> Many long years of occupation with the decipherment of cuneiform texts that concern astrological and astromythological conceptions of the Babylonians have in the meantime taught me that very much of what appears to us modern Westerners nonsensical about the world views of the Easterners, and of the ancient Orientals in particular, in reality lacks neither factual foundations nor sound logic.

* *"Sibyllinischer Sternkampf und Phaëthon in naturgeschichtlicher Beleuchtung"* (1927).

Why are the stars called "heavenly host" in Genesis, in Deuteronomy, in Judges, and in Kings? What does the battle of stars signify in the Sibylline Books? What is the meaning of the Phaëthon legend, describing disorder among the luminaries in the sky and continents burned and flooded?

Kugler asked these questions and expressed his conviction that the battle of the stars in the fifth of the Sibylline Books and the Phaëthon legend have a factual, natural-historical basis (*tatsächliche, naturgeschichtliche Grundlage*).

He quoted opinions of other scholars and noted that "until now nobody recognized in the battle of the stars a sense-making allegory, and still less, factual cosmic happenings."

He came to the conclusion that the battle of the stars in the fifth book of the sibyl, regarded by some authors as an "insane finale," is a reflection of real events in nature. He wondered only why it was so definitely said that the Morning Star—Venus—had started the battle which caused a complete upheaval on earth and in the sky and which ended with a new order in the heavens. Kugler did not know the answer to the question he asked: "Why is the Morning Star the leader of the battle?" He did not elaborate on the idea of stars in battle, aside from recognizing that at some time in the memory of the human race the solar system went through convulsions; on that occasion, according to the sibyl, the eastern stars changed their paths and returned to the ocean, and the earth burned.

In the other legend, that of Phaëthon, who drove the solar chariot off its path and burned the world, eminent classicists like Ulrich Wilamowitz-Moellendorff and others identified Phaëthon as the Morning Star. Kugler, however, felt compelled to reject this accepted explanation because "the appearance of Venus as the Morning Star could not evoke, even in the boldest fantasy, the idea of a world catastrophe."

Kugler thought that a world catastrophe took place when a huge meteoric train caused simultaneously a flood in Attica and a fire in Africa, because numerous ancient authors connected these two events with the disturbances caused by Phaëthon's unlucky ride in the sky. The literary tradition of the early centuries of the present era dated Phaëthon's conflagration and the coincident Deucalion's flood in the lifetime of Moses. Kugler would not regard these dates as necessarily correct; nevertheless, "we have no right to deny these traditions their historical substratum."

Even if Kugler did not discern the full expanse of the cataclysms and did not dare recognize the role of Venus, he still wondered at the insistence with which the Morning Star was mentioned in the traditions of the catastrophe, and he drew conclusions which qualify him as the least appropriate witness to testify against *Worlds in Collision.* He wrote:

> Above all, our essay brings forth the very urgent lesson that the traditions of antiquity, even when clad as myths and legends, are not to be dismissed lightly as fantasy or even as senseless fabrications. And this careful attitude is particularly called for in the case of serious reports of a religious nature, as they are found especially in the Old Testament in great abundance.*

* Cf. Livio C. Stecchini, "Cuneiform Astronomical Records and Celestial Instability," in *The Velikovsky Affair,* 2nd ed. (1978), p. 120 ff.

"I AM PASSIONATELY DEVOTED TO THE PRINCIPLE OF FREEDOM OF THOUGHT"

In November 1950, shortly after I had signed my contract with Doubleday for *Ages in Chaos,* and long before the publication date, Dr. Ferris J. Stephens, secretary-treasurer of the American Oriental Society, wrote a letter to John J. O'Neill. At the time I did not see the letter, but I saw O'Neill's reply, which was very long. I shall quote some excerpts from a copy that O'Neill mailed to me. From the answer I judged that Stephens had sent O'Neill a copy of the review of *Worlds in Collision* by Neugebauer in *Isis* and that he had previously asked O'Neill's help in having Neugebauer appointed one of the publisher's censors of that book—on the eve of its publication. Now he reminded O'Neill of the disastrous results of his not having followed this advice and proposed that O'Neill, too, write to Macmillan, my original publisher, a chiding letter. O'Neill answered:

> I am unable to see eye to eye with you on the statement that Velikovsky's work is a hindrance to the cause of learning rather than a help. I, perhaps, am the only one who has had opportunity to become acquainted with Velikovsky's complete work. It seems to me that it is the wise, and the usual, procedure in scholarly circles to await publication of a man's full report before passing final judgement on his work. Only 20% of his report has been published and that is but a nexus to his thesis which has not yet been mentioned. . . .
>
> Velikovsky has made an extremely interesting experiment

in seeking to exhaust all the realms of scholarship [for his thesis, and] such an experiment is worthy of the most sincere consideration of all scholars.

This does not mean that I am in agreement with Velikovsky. I am very much in disagreement with him concerning many of his general concepts. . . . Such an attitude on the part of myself, or anyone else, furnishes no adequate grounds for failing to give Velikovsky's work a consideration equal in sincerity and commensurate with the effort he has put forth.

I am passionately devoted to the principle of freedom of thought, freedom of speech, freedom to publish, not only as it applies to ideas with which I am in agreement but even to those with which I am in most complete disagreement. To meet sincere effort with ridicule, or to condemn an idea without a complete hearing is the full equivalent of suppression of freedom of speech. . . .

Ordinarily I do not give consent for the use of quotations from my articles for commercial exploitation and in this case I might not have done so* but for the fact that Mr. Shapley started a campaign of ridicule and suppression against the book as nasty as anything that has ever befouled American science and scholarship. The attack started before he read even the first volume and had available to him only a very unrepresentative magazine article in which the "sun stood still" episode was played up in spectacular fashion.

Mr. Shapley caused members of the Observatory staff to write letters to me urging withdrawal of support for the book and uniting in an effort to bring about its suppression. Many others received such letters. He urged astronomers in other observatories to write such letters. . . .

I offered to write a review of the book for my paper and would have written a well balanced article giving the pros and cons. The offer was declined on the grounds that it was desired to avoid the slightest taint of bias on the part of the reviewers. . . . The book was given for review to Dr. Otto Struve, of Yerkes Observatory, and his review was published. Dr. Struve, at the behest of Dr. Shapley, had previously written a letter to me asking to withdraw support and aid in suppressing the

* A sentence from O'Neill's article in the New York *Herald Tribune* of August 11, 1946, was among those quoted by the publisher on the back of the dust jacket.

> book! His review was not worthy of a man of his high intellectual status, but was a piece of ridicule in harmony with other such scripts emanating from the Shapley group. . . .
>
> This campaign by Dr. Shapley does violence to my concept of freedom of speech and of the fundamentals of our American democracy and of ethical behavior.
>
> I can assure you that a diametrically opposed course of action will be productive of beneficial results for the advancement of science. . . .
>
> Courageous thinking is a rare gem. . . .
>
> Instead of accepting your suggestion that I chide some folks at the Macmillan Co. for publishing *Worlds in Collision* you find me sponsoring its publication and defending its author to the greatest extent possible. In the light of the additional information I have given you herein you may, perhaps, find some justification for my viewpoint. On the other hand, it may be possible that my attitude may strike an inharmonious note with members of the society and for that, of course, I would provide a quick remedy. You are aware, I am sure, that I hold you in the highest esteem.

The "quick remedy" implied O'Neill's resignation from membership in the American Oriental Society, which, I know, he valued very much. I wonder if in textbooks on the history of science to be written in the future, excerpts from this letter will be given. Will O'Neill be quoted for praise or for ridicule?

"WITH HATBRIMS PULLED DOWN"

IN MANY QUARTERS the reading of *Worlds in Collision* became a clandestine affair. Inquisitive minds among members of the teaching profession would read the book enclosed in four walls but would hardly show themselves in public with it under their arms. No student of the sciences who cared about the opinion of his examiners would openly read my book. I can hardly imagine anybody crossing the Harvard or Yale campus with the heretical book in the red dust jacket in his hand. The astronomers at the Harvard College Observatory borrowed from Professor Pfeiffer the copy I had inscribed for him and never returned it to him, probably believing that one book taken out of circulation is like one more weed pulled from a garden sown with seeds of evil.

A resident of New York City who, as was evident from his letter, had done some research and thinking in the field of ancient astronomy, especially the history of the astrolabe, the instrument used for measuring the positions of the stars before the telescope was invented, wrote in July 1951:

> The vituperation and hurling of epithets precipitated by your book *Worlds in Collision* moves me . . . to advise you to prepare for at least a ten-year siege by entrenched bigots. During that time you will come to understand why Copernicus and others have waited until the last moment before breaking into public proclamation of their findings. The siege, you will find, will not be limited to yourself but will also menace your family.

But if my personal security and that of my family were not menaced, the position of anybody occupying an academic post who gave me professional help could become precarious.

A veil of intimidation hung over my book. A man wrote from Exeter, New Hampshire:

> I need only turn off the porch light and pull down the shades, step outside, and shoot out the streetlight when, lo and behold, furtive figures muffled in coat collars with hatbrims pulled down would come marching in to read my copy and discuss *Worlds in Collision* and cram your book down their necks. . . . An enormous amount of midnight oil is being burned; a lot of faces are very, very red.

"A SILLY SEASON"

Ben Hibbs, editor in chief of the *Saturday Evening Post,* sent me one of his associate editors, Frederic Nelson, to obtain unpublished material on the attempted suppression of *Worlds in Collision.* After spending some time with me, Mr. Nelson went away without the material and with only half a promise from me to write an article on the subject for the *Post.* I had all the pertinent material and could have very effectively defended my book and myself, but I was reluctant to give the facts and to name names.

I never fulfilled my promise to Mr. Nelson. Two considerations guided me in keeping silent, though I became increasingly apprehensive of the great damage my book and I personally suffered. I wished to debate my book on scientific grounds; I wished to forgive my detractors without naming them, in the hope that, their emotions spent, they would turn to a constructive analysis of the book. I also wished to spare the good name of science in the mind of the general public, even though I took an undeserved beating; I was prepared to part with my status as the author of a best seller in order to go ahead unperturbedly working on the volumes that were to follow, dealing with the astronomical and geological and historical aspects of my theory. I felt myself one of the group that serves humanity by devotion to science. I wanted the great fury to subside so that my book and my theory might find dispassionate treatment and a test in those areas where tests were suggested by me.

Though I did not decline to write a piece or to disclose the material in my files, I postponed and procrastinated doing so until the *Saturday Evening Post,* no longer waiting for my material, published in the issue of November 18, 1950, an editorial on the subject carrying the title "The 1950 Silly Season Looks Unusually Silly." It said in part:

> One of the most astonishing episodes of the summer idiot's delight was the effort of American scientists to suppress a book, *Worlds in Collision,* by Dr. Immanuel Velikovsky. The scientists did succeed in forcing the Macmillan Company to withdraw the book ... by threatening to boycott Macmillan textbooks. Fortunately, another publisher, Doubleday and Company, took over the publication of the book, which is still going great guns. Doctor Velikovsky's offense seems to be that he writes better than most scientists and in his book expounds a theory of astronomical activity which differs widely from orthodox theories.

Then, after giving my theory in a nutshell, the editorial proceeded:

> So the orthodox scientists, forgetting about Galileo, and the long, woeful struggle of scientists, or even pseudo-scientists, to be free of dogma, acted like the authoritarians with whom they are continually in conflict.... Not even a silly season ought to excuse scientists for book burning. After all, they are always the chief victims of this kind of intolerance.

The exercise of the art of book reviewing is a public trust. A reviewer is human, and his subjectivity of necessity must color his judgment. But basically his is the purpose of describing and evaluating objectively the work of an author. Indignant the reviewer may become, but to falsify in order to make his indignation appear righteous is not allowed by any code of journalistic ethics.

A certain Martin Gardner, writing in the *Antioch Review* about "the hermit scientist" and the "preposterous theory" of a comet that became Venus, said this about the content of *Worlds in Collision:* "The first visit to the earth of this erratic comet was 1500 B.C., precisely at the time Moses stretched out his hand and caused the Red Sea to divide." This would be an unbelievable coincidence. "Fifty-two years later the comet's return coincided with Joshua's successful attempt to make the sun and moon stand still." Another unbelievable coincidence. With these few lines the reviewer circumscribed the story of the book.

In *Worlds in Collision* I describe the flight of the Israelites as the result of a natural catastrophe, and in the description of the debacle at the sea, where many Israelites also found their death, I do not even mention Moses, who plays practically no role in my book. On page 306 in the chapter on the origin of folkloristic ideas, the section "The Subjective Interpretation of the Events and Their Authenticity," I wrote:

> What helped to discredit the traditions of the peoples about the catastrophes was their subjective and magical interpretation of the events. The sea was torn apart. The people attributed this act to the intervention of their leader; he lifted his staff over the waters and they divided. Of course, there is no person who can do this, and no staff with which it can be done. Likewise in the case of Joshua who commanded the sun and the moon to halt in their movements.

The miracle of comets arriving at the request of holy persons for the performance of some act is not to be found in my book.

It is an ugly thing to impose guilt by association. Gardner began his article with a quotation from L. Ron Hubbard's *Dianetics*—"The creation of Dianetics is a milestone for man comparable to his discovery of fire and superior to his invention of the wheel and the arch"—and ended it by telling derisively of Wilhelm Reich's organon and orgone accumulators—"large, black-painted boxes of wood on the outside and metal on the inside"—in which Reich placed his patients to collect orgone, "a non-electro-magnetic radiant energy coming from outer space." Having thus made out a perfect case of guilt by associating me with Dianetics and organon, Voliva with his flat earth also being made my partner, the reviewer thundered: Is the author of *Worlds in Collision* a deliberate hoaxer, "out to make a dishonest dollar," or is he sincere in believing his own theory?

The reviewer who fails in a public trust is guilty of one or more of three things: He is dishonest; he is illiterate; he sees visions and things that are not in the book. He receives a reviewer's fee for a misleading job. Being after a dollar, Martin Gardner remade his article into a book (*In the Name of Science,* 1952)* and repeated in my name the same things about Moses and Joshua and the unbe-

* [Gardner's book was revived under a new title in 1957; the essay on Velikovsky again reappeared in 1982 in another book by Gardner.]

lievable coincidences ("According to Velikovsky, it was the stopping [or slowing] of the earth's spin which caused the Red Sea to divide precisely at the time Moses stretched out his hand"; "The earth stopped rotating precisely at the moment Joshua commanded the sun to stand still"). In the opening chapter he asserted that "the scientists who threatened to boycott the firm's textbooks unless it dropped Velikovsky from its list, were exercising their democratic privilege of organized protest."

Although the Velikovsky section was only six pages long, the publisher of the Gardner book advertised it as a disproval of my theories.

One of Gardner's main arguments had to do with the role of electromagnetic forces in the solar system:

> Velikovsky . . . invents electro-magnetic forces capable of doing precisely what he wants them to do. There is no scientific evidence whatever for the power of these forces. They serve the same function for Velikovsky that curious optical laws served for Cyrus Teed [who claimed that we live inside the terrestrial globe and the sun hangs as a lantern in the middle]. They explain the unexplainable. But so convinced is the hermit scientist that everyone is prejudiced except himself, that he can—with a straight face—belabor the "orthodox" for refusing to recognize these imaginary energies!

I did not answer Gardner. But there will come the day when the electromagnetic forces and interrelations in the solar system will be discovered;* then I shall be thankful to have these phrases on record because invariably there will be voices heard that "we always knew it."

* [See the Epilogue. In 1978 Bernard Lovell wrote (*In the Center of Immensities,* page 21) about "the recognition during the last ten or twenty years that magnetic fields must have a significant role in the Universe."]

"THE GREAT PERIL OF OUR AGE"

IN APRIL 1952—at the time my *Ages in Chaos* came out—the *Journal of Near Eastern Studies* published a review of my first book, *Worlds in Collision,* two years after its publication. The reviewer, William A. Irwin, of Southern Methodist University in Dallas, Texas, saw in that book a work of superstition. What served him as a basis for this conclusion he did not disclose. Possibly he thought so because the book discusses the Bible, miracles, and planets. It sounds like astrology, which is superstition. However, nobody protests against the publishers of astrological books. The emotion that carried the reviewer away impelled him to assert by implication that *Worlds in Collision,* the subject of his review, was a sin worse than prostitution, worse even than communism, and announced it to be "the great peril of our age." And he spoke in the name of "a free and enlightened society."

> . . . To live at all they [publishers] must make profits, but such a mediate end must never obscure their ultimate responsibility to serve the spread of truth and raising of the public's level of thought. To do other is prostitution, far more damnable than the nasty personal sins that commonly go under that word. Further, it is self-defeating. Publishing houses can thrive only in a free and enlightened society. Rampant superstition is intolerant; when it gains the power, it decides by its own distorted principles what may and may not be said or published. The great peril of our age is not imperialist communism—that

> is an acute but transient aberration; our real danger is medievalism. Its assault is peculiarly pernicious because its roots are deep in every one of us; man is a superstitious animal. When organized and triumphant, it seeks to deny our glorious gains of recent centuries and enthrall us once more beneath a despotism worse than that of the Kremlin. . . . To judge by the early success of Velikovsky's book, the Macmillans found their venture incredibly profitable. But also they served their own undoing.

Irwin expressed his "devout hope" that Velikovsky "will be deterred from his announced intention of publishing a work on ancient chronology." It was already in the bookstores.

Should not the words of the castigator be applied to himself and the views he represents: "Rampant superstition is intolerant; when it gains the power, it decides by its own distorted principles what may and may not be said or published."

CENSORS, PEERS, AND GHOSTWRITERS

THE AMERICAN ASSOCIATION for the Advancement of Science was an organization open to everyone. In 1950 it had a membership of about 50,000. It published two magazines, *Science* for scientists, with a strong bent for biochemistry, and *Scientific Monthly* for the general reader or the scientist who wanted to be informed on a variety of subjects. Members had their choice of one of the magazines, or they could receive both, depending on the dues they paid. The association held its annual meeting in December of each year, and a large number of papers were read.

In December 1950 the annual meeting convened in Cleveland. Several hundred papers were read. Since this was the first occasion to debate in this forum the book that was causing such a furor, a panel discussion took place. Its chairman, or moderator, Warren Guthrie, of the Department of Speech, Western Reserve University, Cleveland, reported on it in an article, "Books, Civilization, and Science," in the April 20, 1951, issue of *Science.* Guthrie began with an expression of great awe in the presence of science: "It is with a great deal of uncertainty and hesitation that one whose field is rhetoric and public speaking—that knack little better than cookery in Plato's eyes—even ventures near the habitat of men of science. To us science *is* a sacred cow." But he moderated the meeting, and this was his reason for writing his piece.

He named the great luminaries from the field of science who had participated in the discussion, Kirtley Mather, geologist of Harvard, heading the list, and the representatives of the publishers of scientific literature. *Worlds in Collision* was high on the agenda; actually it was the theme of the panel. "More sound, more responsible, though less sensational works, even when written with an eye to the general public, are seldom as widely read. It was with this problem that our group became largely concerned."

Publishers were questioned as to their responsibility and honesty. Charles Skelley of the Macmillan Company (I did not know his position there), in his defense against outraged scientists, pointed out that "in at least one case in which a book that the panel regarded as unsound enjoyed a wide sale, the publisher voluntarily transferred his right to another company at heavy financial loss." At last a representative of my former publisher made the gesture that was required of him, confessing its guilt in public and paying the penalty. However, as to "voluntarily," I would not agree after having seen all the pressure exerted and heard President Brett's version, and as to the "heavy financial loss," it was a loss only insofar as Macmillan had to stop the sale after having made a profit on 54,000 copies. According to Guthrie, "other representatives of the publishing group made clear their interest in seeing that books presented on their scientific lists are acceptable to the scientific fraternity." They were witnessing the public castigation of a publisher, and they made their bows to the cow.

In order that there be a reliable or regimented list of books published for the elucidation of the general reader, "it was suggested that some board of review be created from the ranks of the scientists themselves." To the criticism that such a review might involve a kind of censorship that would deny the right of publication to any truly revolutionary work—sound or unsound—there was, however, no final answer. Consequently, the panel began to explore other means by which the same problem might be met. The answers seemed to lie in the development of a set of principles by which publishers might be guided, rather than in the support of a board of review.

"Those principles followed, in general, a proposal presented by Dr. Mather."

In order to make the uneasy choice between "plausible but false" and "astonishing but true," and thus to avoid "a positive danger" to civilization, a new system must be introduced. The publisher must be reawakened to a cardinal principle of scientific methodology in a free society. Guthrie continued, paraphrasing Mather:

> In this sort of society the scientist is encouraged to be revolutionary, to conceive and proclaim new ideas. No truth is regarded as absolute, no answer ultimate. Only from new and frequently daring hypotheses can progress come. But this does not mean that every proponent of a new idea or theory deserves an immediate public hearing. . . . Before the new theory is presented to the frequently gullible public, it should be submitted to a jury of the writer's peers—to those who by training and experience are most competent to examine and to criticize it. Such juries are legion—they are the professional societies of scientists, the technical journals of each of our fields of learning. . . . Here a new theory may survive its ordeal by fire.

And no publisher should print anything about a new theory before he has learned "of the previous presentation of those ideas to the scrutiny of the author's scientific peers in technical journals or at professional meetings. Wide acceptance by those judges was not felt necessary—scientists are sometimes as guilty of reactionary conservatism as the rest of us. Louis Agassiz' theory of a 'great ice age' seemed just as preposterous to many people when first announced, as Velikovsky's theory of 'worlds in collision' seems today. Agassiz' theory, in fact, was ridiculed as the 'glacial nightmare.' But Agassiz adhered to the routine described above; Velikovsky bypassed astronomers and geologists and went straight to the general public."

Thus spoke Professor Mather. His "jury of peers" is another "board of review," or censorship, only differently named. To this I would only remark: It is well known from the history of science that many great revolutionary works in science would never have been published if the writer's peers had been asked. During his lifetime Copernicus had only one follower, Rheticus, and was rejected by all others. Kepler's discoveries were rejected by Galileo, his peer; Newton's gravitational theory was rejected by Leibnitz, his peer; and Agassiz, who was ridiculed, himself rejected Darwin. Virchow did not support Pasteur; Edison rejected and fought against Tesla and the use of alternating current. The list can be multiplied a hundred times. It goes back to Archimedes' rejection of Aristarchus, who taught that the earth revolves around the sun. It would make a fascinating story to tell, not of foolish professors rejecting Galileo, but of Galileo rejecting Kepler and other similar cases.

According to Mather, I had failed to submit my theory to the scrutiny of my "peers." As the reader knows by now, I was eager to have the criticism of astronomers and physicists, although my work was built mainly on literary and folkloristic material. Curiously, the charge of evading the scientists came from the same Harvard group that had refused to read the manuscript from the spring of 1946 on, when I asked Shapley, orally and in writing, to read it. The truth is that every statement in the book relating to matters of science was checked and rechecked with scientists in various fields. And the publisher submitted the manuscript to a board of review and to a "jury" and to "censors," including the head of the Department of Physics at New York University, and it passed all these reviews only to be attacked by scientists who neglected the first rule of inquiry: Read what you discuss; know what you reject.

I would like to propose that a jury be established for critics. A reviewer should be required to pass a test in which he would prove that he has read the book he reviews. Somebody read the blurb on the dust jacket or a review and wrote an article about the book. Another quoted this article as an authoritative statement by an expert. A third quoted the second as the authoritative opinion of the entire world of science.

The AAAS meeting went on. The members of the panel agreed that the publishers must live. Guthrie reports: "It was felt that even the most arrant nonsense might occasionally justify publication—even as does a *Forever Amber* or an *Anthony Adverse.*" Only *Worlds in Collision* is a "danger to civilization." Guthrie went on:

> To the other half of the problem posed—the fact that responsible works, even when written for the general public, seldom secure a wide audience—the answers were far less clear. It's the familiar problem common to all of us in education—thoroughly adjusted to the captive audiences we so often face, we are frequently less than satisfactorily effective when confronted by the free world outside.

The captive audience is a class of students who must listen or pretend to listen in order to get credits, and where no credits are given, "we" are ineffective. What is the reason? The answer, according to this meeting of scientists and publishers, is:

> Competent and successful research scientists are generally too busy to undertake the job of clear and simple writing. Even

> when they assume that responsibility, they are frequently incompetent in the sense that they do not possess the flair essential to the dramatization of their ideas. After all ... it is inherently an extremely difficult and time-consuming task to translate the language of modern science into the vocabulary of the general reader.

I always thought that clear and simple writing was a sign of clear and simple thinking. Confused thought, full of excuses and assumptions, produces involved sentences and improper use of words. To what conclusion, then, did the wise men of the panel come? Special science writers should be employed on a regular basis; scientists themselves should make an effort at journalistic writing; and "even the 'ghost writer' of Washington and Hollywood fame may one day find his niche in science also."

And what was the final impression from this august gathering? In the words of the speech professor who presided over the panel:

> It was a heartening experience to see this concern on the part of the scientist. . . . Only when we seek mutual understanding and progress on the highest popular level available, can that effect be the forward movement of all things—books, civilization, and science included.

What a pity that Jonathan Swift died so long ago.

THE OCEAN ENTERS THE DEBATE

REMARKABLE WAS THE circumstance that as soon as *Worlds in Collision* was published, even only previewed, a multitude of finds and observations were revealed in the scientific press and in the daily papers. The story of some of these observations has been told on previous pages. It was as if sky and sea competed to reveal facts pointing to the catastrophic nature of their past.

In the August 1950 issue of *Scientific American*, Professor Hans Pettersson published a preliminary report of the expedition of the Oceanographic Institute at Göteborg in Sweden which under his leadership covered large tracts of the Atlantic, Pacific, and Indian oceans and found "evidences of great catastrophes that have altered the face of the earth." He spoke of "climatic catastrophes" and "volcanic catastrophes" and "tectonic catastrophes [that] raised or lowered the ocean bottom hundreds and even thousands of feet, spreading huge tidal waves which destroyed plant and animal life on the coastal plains," meaning that the changes were catastrophic not only in the sense of their vastness but also in their suddenness of action. Pettersson discovered that the Pacific and Indian ocean beds consist "largely of volcanic ash that had settled on the bottom after great volcanic explosions." He also found a large nickel content in the clay of the ocean bottoms and decided that this abysmal nickel must have been of meteoric origin. Consequently, he concluded, there were "very heavy showers of meteors. . . . The principal difficulty of this explanation is that it requires a rate of accretion of meteoric dust several hundred times greater than that which astronomers . . . are presently prepared to admit."

Only nine months earlier—in November 1949—Professor Maurice Ewing of Columbia University had published a preliminary report of an expedition to the Atlantic Ocean.* In it he spoke of "new scientific puzzles. . . . One was the discovery of prehistoric beach sand . . . brought up in one case from the depth of two and the other nearly three and one half miles, far from any place where beaches exist today." One of these sand deposits was found 1,200 miles from land. Professor Ewing saw a dilemma: "Either the land must have sunk two to three miles, or the sea must have been two to three miles lower than now. Either conclusion is startling."

In the great flat basins on either side of the Mid-Atlantic Ridge, there was almost no sediment, certainly less than 100 feet in thickness, or the limit of the sensitivity of the method, "a fact so startling. . . . Always it had been thought the sediment must be extremely thick, since it had been accumulating for countless ages. . . . But on the level basins that flank the Mid-Atlantic Ridge our signals reflected from the bottom mud and from the bedrock came back too close together to measure the time between them." This indicates that the bottom of the Atlantic Ocean on both sides of the ridge was only very recently formed. Ewing saw in this a "scientific riddle"; "Granite and sedimentary rocks of the types which originally must have been a part of a continent" were found 3,600 feet under the surface of the ocean. What was a "riddle" for the discoverer was a familiar notion in the heretical theory.

In 1950 there was also published a book, *Marine Geology,* by a prominent Dutch scientist, Professor P. H. Kuenen of Leyden. He wrote that the drop of the ocean level found around the world first claimed by Reginald Daly thirty years earlier had been found verified and added:

> The time of the movement was estimated by Daly to be probably some 3000 to 4000 years ago. Detailed field work in the Netherlands and in eastern England has shown a recent eustatic depression of the same order of magnitude as deduced by Daly [ca. eighteen feet]. Here the time can be fixed as roughly 3000 to 3500 years ago.

* Maurice Ewing, "New Discoveries on the Mid-Atlantic Ridge," *National Geographic Magazine* (November 1949).

Thirty-five hundred years ago is the very time established in *Worlds in Collision* when a great catastrophe closed the Middle Kingdom in Egypt and caused the flight of the Israelites known from the Book of Exodus.*

* In the next decade the ocean revealed additional facts pointing to the catastrophic past of the earth.

In 1959 J. L. Worzel discovered a layer of ash of extraterrestrial origin underlying all oceans—the so-called Worzel Ash—leading him to exclaim in print: "It may be necessary to attribute the layer to a worldwide volcanism or perhaps to the fiery end of bodies of cosmic origin" (*Proceedings of the National Academy of Science,* Vol. 45, No. 3, March 15, 1959).

In 1960 B. Hezen reported the discovery of a gigantic submarine canyon that runs almost twice around the globe: "The discovery at this late date of the midocean ridge and rift has raised fundamental questions about basic geological processes and the history of the earth and has even had reverberations in cosmology" (*Scientific American,* October 1960).

THE ASTRONOMER ROYAL

WHEN IN SEPTEMBER 1950 *Worlds in Collision* was published in England, great guns went into action. The astronomer royal, Sir Harold Spencer Jones, headed the astronomers; J. B. S. Haldane, the evolutionists.

The astronomer royal published his piece, called "False Trail," in *The Spectator* (September 22, 1950). He started with a concise description of the catastrophes, so good that I should like to reproduce it here.

> The central theme of *Worlds in Collision* is that, according to Dr. Velikovsky, between the fifteenth and eighth centuries B.C. the earth experienced a series of violent catastrophes of global extent. Parts of its surface were heated to such a degree that they became molten and great streams of lava welled out; the sea boiled and evaporated; rivers ran with [the color of] blood; mountain ranges collapsed, while others were thrown up; continents were submerged; tremendous earthquakes occurred; enormous tides were raised causing great floods; showers of hot stones fell; electrical disturbances of great violence caused much havoc; hurricanes swept the earth; a pall of darkness shrouded it, to be followed by a deluge of fire. This picture of a period of intense turmoil within the period of recorded history is supported by a wealth of quotations from the Old Testament, from the Hindu Vedas, from Roman and Greek mythology, and from the myths, traditions and folklore of many races

> and peoples. The reader cannot but fail to be impressed by Dr. Velikovsky's extensive knowledge of such lore and by the wealth of references which he gives.

Then he told the story of single catastrophes, "awe-inspiring cosmic cataclysms." There occurred collisions between major planets, which brought about the birth of comets. "In the time of Moses, about the fifteenth century B.C., one of these comets nearly collided with the earth, which twice passed through its tail." Intense heating, enormous tides, incessant violent electrical discharges between the comet and the planet took place. Spencer Jones went on:

> This comet is supposed to have collided with Mars in the time of Joshua in the year 747 B.C. and, as the result of the collision, to have lost its tail and to have become transformed into the planet Venus. . . . Further catastrophes according to Dr. Velikovsky ensued. The new planet Venus collided with Mars; as a result the orbit of Venus became nearly circular but that of Mars was shifted nearer to the earth so that in the year 687 B.C. (March 23rd being the crucial date) Mars nearly collided with the earth.

Now Jones started the work of demolition since he was aware that:

> . . . the wide variety of the quotations which have been brought together as corroborative evidence may all too readily give the impression that these planetary collisions did actually occur and that Dr. Velikovsky has revealed some of the past history of the solar system, which could never otherwise have been known.
>
> If a collision between Mars and Venus had occurred in the past, as Dr. Velikovsky supposes, then, starting from the recent positions and motions and computing backwards, allowing for the perturbations of all the planets, we should find that, at a certain epoch in past time, the positions of Mars and Venus were identical [for one moment]. It is not difficult to compute back for the few thousand years which have elapsed since these events were supposed to have happened. It is found that no collision occurred.

This was the astronomer royal's argument.

I replied in a letter to the editor, which was published in the October 27, 1950, issue of *The Spectator:*

> The Astronomer Royal had done me the honor of writing me a review; . . . [he] finds that the story of catastrophic events of global character "is supported by a wealth of quotations" (thus leaving the theory of evolution to meet the challenge), but opposes the thesis that celestial bodies (planets or comets) could have been the cause.

I proceeded, with reference to the year −747: "To straighten things out, I should prefer to have in the quoted sentence, in conformity with my book, Isaiah instead of Joshua, and Earth instead of Venus ['This comet'] (pp. 205ff.)."

According to *Worlds in Collision,* the catastrophe of 747 B.C. was caused by a near contact between Mars and Earth and the time was that of the prophet Isaiah. How the astronomer royal, who appeared to have read the book, made this mistake, I do not know. Even if he had not read the book, he must have known that Joshua, the successor to Moses, did not live in the eighth century, in the days of the Assyrian kings who warred against the kingdoms of Israel and Judah.

Again, the astronomer royal correctly stated that the catastrophe between *Mars and Earth* occurred in 687 B.C., on March 23. I wrote in my reply:

> Thus it would be futile to try to show by calculations from present orbits of Venus and Mars the point of their encounter in the past. As to the vestiges of the close contacts between Mars and Earth in the past, which took place at fifteen-year intervals from 747 to 687, I pointed [in my book] to the fifteen-year period between the close approaches of Mars and Earth at present ("favourable oppositions"); also to the similarity in the inclination of the axes of Earth and Mars, which has a meaning if magnetic fields played a role in these contacts.

I could have added the similarity in the duration of one rotation of Earth and Mars (23 hours, 56 minutes, and 4 seconds for Earth; 24 hours, 37 minutes and 22.6 seconds for Mars).

I also took issue with the astronomer royal on his assertion that the tails of the comets are so thin that the pressure of light causes their repulsion:

> The pressure of light, ten thousand times weaker than the sun's attraction . . . cannot be made responsible for the velocities with which a cometary tail, as a rigid rod, makes its sweep in perihelion subject to some strong repulsive force which drives the matter composing the tail away from the sun with enormously high velocities, "in defiance of the law of gravitation, nay, even of the recorded laws of motion" (John F. Herschel).

To the astronomer royal's objection that comets are much too insubstantial bodies and, therefore, one of them could not have changed into Venus, I answered: "And were not Jupiter, Saturn, Venus or Earth in the category of comets when they moved on elongated ellipses after having erupted from the sun, as the tidal theory assumes they did?"

I could have added, though I did not, that Jones, in his textbook on astronomy described the enormous size of some comets—the head alone of the comet of 1811 was, according to him, 350 times the volume of Jupiter, which in its turn was 1,000 times the volume of the planet Venus—and that there he also referred to the theory of electrical repulsion between the Sun and the cometary tails elaborated by a Russian astronomer. More than this, Jones made it clear that "the presence of bright lines in the spectra [of comets] can only be due to a self-luminous body," not a body which merely reflects light, and that a comparison with "the electrical phenomena obtained by discharge through a Geissler's vacuum tube" makes it a matter of "a high degree of probability that a comet's self-luminosity is due not to an actual combustion but to an electrical phenomenon."*

* Harold Spencer Jones, *General Astronomy* (1922), pp. 273–74.

A REVIEWER AT THE STAKE

IN THE CELESTIAL judgment hall the reviewer was called before the throne and told: "All that the author hath is in thy power; only do not change his words." This is the only protection left to authors against their reviewers. Nails and teeth or hooves and horns the reviewer may use against the author, but he is not allowed to change the author's words.

The author usually does not claim infallibility, and by publishing a book, he ties himself to the stake, to receive as many blows as his judge-executioner may see fit to deliver according to his own temper. If the judge himself is an author, he may perchance desire to protect by these blows his own theories which are at variance with those of the author, or he may have an urge to repay somebody for the time when he himself was at the stake.

The particular case I am going to discuss was a page or two in *The New Statesman and Nation;* the reviewed author was I. As long as the reviewer thundered, "Are you a hoax or a crank?" I took it. I knew of some good companions, and I remembered reading how the members of my profession had accused Pasteur of charlatanry. Anyway, according to the prerogative given to the reviewer by the celestial court, I could not register a protest. When the reviewer whispered balefully, "Your book is blasphemy to science and religion," I did not raise my voice but thought to myself: My service to science and religion alike is in trying to reveal truth (in this case, historical truth). And I took it with good grace.

But then the reviewer told the throng of readers the content of

Worlds in Collision. And there he lost. According to the rule imposed on the reviewer, for the transgression of changing the content of a book he himself goes to the stake.

The reviewer wrote:

> I conclude that the book is fiction, and I think that its author has deliberately left several clues to this effect. On page 345 he states that "Among the planets it [Mars] exceeds even Jupiter in brightness." It can do so [the reviewer proceeded] as a cat can be larger than a dog; but it very seldom does. I conjecture that this . . . [was] inserted to warn the readers . . . not to take a very efficient hoax too seriously.

Now what is on page 345 of *Worlds in Collison*?*

> When Mars and the earth are on different sides of the sun, the distance between them rises to over 200,000,000 miles and may reach 248,600,000 miles. From this moment on, as the distance between these planets diminishes, Mars nightly grows more and more luminous, changing from an inconspicuous point of light to a most brilliant star. . . . During a period of little more than a year, it grows fifty-five times brighter. Among the planets it exceeds then even Jupiter in brilliance.

The reviewer left the word "then" out of the passage he put in quotation marks. Once every two years Mars *is* brighter than Jupiter, but the reviewer made it appear as though according to *Worlds in Collision,* Mars is permanently brighter than Jupiter, or that every cat is larger than every dog.

Not only was the sentence changed, but the public was assured that the author included it in his book in order to give a secret sign to the initiated that *Worlds in Collision* is a hoax. I certainly would have been a fool to have labored for ten years on a hoax, to have checked proofs for fourteen months in order to eliminate errors as far as possible, and then to have inscribed the hoax to my own wife as a sign of esteem.

The reviewer next made the accusation: "The index [of the author] does not refer to Schoch, Kugler or Fotheringham—the three greatest authorities on ancient chronology and astronomy." With

* Page 362 of the American edition.

indignation he told how these savants demonstrated that 2,000 years before the present era the Babylonians could calculate the sun's apparent motion more exactly than the scientists of Europe until about 1850 (more than 100 years after Newton). He concluded: "This was . . . quite impossible if the sun's apparent motion had recently altered." And he bluntly concluded that the author had not read Fotheringham.

It happens that the index in the author's book is not a bibliography; it is titled "Selective Name Index." In order to include all the sources mentioned in the text and in the footnotes, a much larger index would have been necessary. However, besides references to the works of Fotheringham in the footnotes, there are in *Worlds in Collision* two pages (198 and 199) of quotations from Langdon and Fotheringham on the Babylonian tablets of Venus (pages 195, 196, 197 of the British edition of *Worlds in Collision*). Kugler is quoted on pages 196, 254, 258, 264, 293, 302, 303, 304, 328, 329, 332, 333, 334.

What would you say if after you had placed in the collection plate two banknotes of one pound each, a gentleman rose in the congregation and loudly accused you of having failed to contribute your twopence, and to substantiate his accusation, he announced that he was a public accountant and always counted money by the sound of its jingle, and there was no jingle?

Should not the public accountant have looked into the plate before loudly accusing you, or a reviewer into the book instead of the index?

To invoke Kugler and Fotheringham is the same as to invoke the help of both Saint George and the Dragon. Fotheringham, Schoch, and their school argue that from very ancient times Babylonian astronomy was very exact and the observations of the eclipse as to place and date very precise. If this is so, the observations of the ancients (of which there are very many in *Worlds in Collision*) must have a very authenticated value, and there should be no jeers about the "legends" with which the author substantiates his theory. Kugler, on the other hand, found that no observation of the Babylonians before the seventh century B.C. has any value at all because the observations of the ancients, for some unexplained reason, differ widely from the real movements of the planets.

Now may I return the accusation and ask if the reviewer knows these names only from indexes?

* * *

In order to alienate everyone from the book, the reviewer said that *Worlds in Collision* "is equally a degradation of science and religion," that it is to the detriment of Israel, that it inspires even atomic warfare, and that those publications (apparently the New York *Herald Tribune* and *Harper's Magazine*) which supported the book "may urge the use of Britain as a base for atomic warfare." However, the book was accused by other reviewers of having been written for the glory of ancient Israel, and Harold L. Ickes in *The New Republic* wrote: "Dr. Velikovsky has conferred a great boon upon all of us. He has given us something to think about; something even to pray about. . . . Perhaps we shall have sense enough to put our heads between our hands and do some real thinking about universal and lasting peace."

I know of only one way to serve science and religion—by pursuing truth. I did not think to serve religion by concealing the historical events I believe I have discovered. And it is certainly not to the detriment of Israel that the Hebrew Bible is shown to be an essentially true book. My reviewer would prefer that we keep our belief in miracles rather than accept natural proofs of the veracity of the Bible. This reminds me of a cartoon I once saw. In an American church a tall seventeen-year-old young man sits on the knees of Santa Claus while small children wait from afar for their turn. In the foreground the parents of the young man explain emphatically to the pastor that they did "everything possible to keep his faith intact."

Now that justice has been done, and the reviewer has been proved guilty of commissions and omissions, he is sentenced to read J. B. S. Haldane's *Science and Ethics* (index and text) in order to improve his literary manners. An appeal on the ground that he himself wrote *Science and Ethics* and cannot profit from reading it will be rejected, and the sentence sustained.

"THE ORTHODOXIES ARE INTERESTS"

THE GENERAL PRESS in the British Isles showed itself as being uninfluenced by the negative criticisms of Harold Spencer Jones and J. B. S. Haldane. The Oxford *Mail* wrote of *Worlds in Collision* that it is "fascinating alike in its stupendous pictures of a world in the grip of cosmic forces, in its parallels drawn from the annals of the ancients in many lands, and its vast implications." The Aberdeen *Press* commented: "Probably no book in our generation has caused so much controversy. . . . In the scientific world it caused a veritable explosion of bad temper." A paper in Edinburgh wrote similarly:

> No book in recent years has been the subject of so much controversy. Some scientists let loose a flood of denunciatory criticism and hysterical protests against the publication. . . . What we have in this piece of scholarly research is the history of the earth as a planet, fascinatingly told and truthfully documented.

The Edinburgh papers also took pride in the fact that many years earlier I had studied for a term at the University of Edinburgh.

Thus wrote papers in the famous old university cities of England and Scotland. Some papers looked for hyperbole. The Glasgow *Daily Record* wrote: "Gigantic, sensational, staggering." I feel awkward repeating such "advertisement stuff," but I certainly have given prominence in this book to the derogatory criticisms. The *Times* ambiguously spoke of "dark stories of scientists allegedly applying pressure by boycotting the textbook department of the author's first publishing house in a frenzied effort to prevent the destruction of their own reputation and of orthodox physics."

Of the articles that were printed in Great Britain, the piece by W. J. Brown, Member of Parliament, in *Truth* magazine, October 20, 1950, attracted attention. He saw what George Brett of Macmillan called "circles" in their proper light, and he did not conceal his concern at the bad omens.

> Make a note of the name. It will make news for a long while to come. Possibly it will go ringing down the corridors of Time. Or possibly not, for the established orthodoxies are more than orthodoxies. They are interests; and the interests have at their command immense powers of suppression. How much, for example, does the average Christian know of Manichee, a name which once rang through and shook the Christian world? How much will the Russians of tomorrow know of Trotsky, when the textbooks and history books have been rewritten to eliminate him? But today, at any rate, Velikovsky's name is news.
>
> The man is a heretic, of course—and I see the Bell, the Book and the Candle advancing. Nor can I do very much for him. My own scientific orthodoxy, indeed my general orthodoxy, is itself suspect, and I must be careful of the company I keep. But my heresies are little ones. They have to do with minor matters, like the party system, or the true content of democracy, or the dangers of education, or "closed shop" . . . or individual liberty and the like. But Velikovsky's heresies are enormous. They reach to the stars. . . . The scope of his wickedness almost reestablishes me as virtuous!
>
> Already the orthodoxies have marked him down. Already the machines of repression are at work.

Brown described what happened in America with *Worlds in Collision,* and added:

> I have seen machines of repression at work in Britain, and I fancy I recognize the symptoms. . . .
>
> Now, a heretic may be defined as an orthodox who has got into the wrong tense. The orthodox is one who is in line with the thought of his day. The heretic is one who is in line with what will be thought tomorrow, or who is in line with the discarded thought of yesterday.

SCIENCE VERSUS COMMON SENSE

THE READER MAY REMEMBER that Professor Shapley, according to his own letter, spoke with Dr. James Conant, president of Harvard University, in order to have something done in the matter of *Worlds in Collision*, so important did this issue appear to him. I have been told that Dr. Conant, on seeing Frederick Allen, then editor in chief of *Harper's* and also a member of the Board of Overseers of Harvard University, said to him, with Larrabee's article in mind, just: "Really?"

A year later Dr. Conant came to New York and on February 16, 1951, according to the New York *Herald Tribune* of the following day, held a press conference "to advertise to the American public a book he has written entitled *Science and Common Sense*, written to clarify some ideas of science that are 'of life and death importance to the American people.' . . . He said," the *Herald Tribune* went on, "he hopes his book sales will give at least a small run of competition to Immanuel Velikovsky's *Worlds in Collision*, which he made clear he regards as pseudo-science of a kind that is befuddling the public."

Dr. Conant singled out my book with which he wanted to compete in sales. If the public had thought that Conant's book was a refutation of mine, *Science and Common Sense* might very well have given *Worlds in Collision* that "run." But all that he offered in this connection, on page 278, was: "The astonishing popularity of that fantastic book, *Worlds in Collision*, shows how eagerly the reading public welcomes a repudiation of the findings of modern science: the fact that such a volume has found wide distribution in the United States is a distressing phenomenon." However, he did not present any argument to disprove any portion of *Worlds in Collision.*

Since its publication, and even in advance of it, the public had been assured by the holders of academic chairs that the heretical *Worlds in Collision* damaged science and scientists and that Velikovsky's book would return science in all its branches to where it stood in 1600, when Giordano Bruno was burned at the stake, from where generations of men of science have brought it to where it is now.

If *Worlds in Collision* is a book of science fiction or pseudoscience, how could it possibly set science in all its branches back to the year 1600? Is science so insecurely grounded that a book can discredit it? Are the schools of learning so unsure about what they teach that they must unite to make a plea before the reading public against one book out of 10,000 published annually? So I thought, reading Dr. Conant.

His book was an endeavor to draw a line of demarcation between scientists and other people. He wrote: "Even a highly educated and intelligent citizen without research experience will almost always fail to grasp the essentials in a discussion which takes place among scientists" (page 3). "The remedy does not lie in a greater dissemination of scientific information among nonscientists" (page 4). The public's part in the enterprise is to provide funds: "The exposition that follows is addressed to the intelligent citizen who as a voter may, to an increasing extent, be interested in Congressional action on scientific matters" or who may have a stake in science when scientists urge "investment of money in this or that adventure."

In other words, there is nothing in common between "science" and "common sense." I, on the other hand, was confident that given the story in an intelligent presentation and supplied with sources, the general reader could be trusted to draw his own conclusions, provided the author did not conceal wherein he diverges from accepted views.

My great sin was to write a book about a new theory and offer it simultaneously to scientists and to the general public, instead of couching it in incomprehensible scientific jargon and submitting it to a closed circle in an inner chamber. In other words, I used the jury system, whereas only the closed trial is legitimate. With the jury system a person with "common sense" may make up his own mind.

Conant, in his effort to create an aura of sanctity around scientists, demanded their organization into bodies regulated by official science. He conceded that in the past the greatest discoveries were made by free-lance scholars who had no affiliation with universities, nor made their living from science, but he assured everyone that this is no longer so and only organized scientists can make discoveries.

In the campaign of suppression members of the Harvard College Observatory played a notable part. I like to believe that the former president of Harvard, himself for many years out of the scientific field and busy with administrative duties, was induced to act by his associates in the departments of Astronomy and Geology. Also, I cannot accuse the whole of Harvard University of being partial. The head of the Department of Semitic Languages and History, Robert H. Pfeiffer, wrote me at the same time concerning *Worlds in Collision:*

> Allow me first of all to congratulate you, not of course for the fact that your book has become "a run-away best seller," but for the magnificent qualities of content and form of your book. I read it with utter fascination and absorption, being carried away by the cosmic drama which you unfolded before me. I was amazed at the depth and vastness of your erudition, which I have not seen equalled except possibly in O. Spengler's *Decline of the West.*

My book is a collection of historical evidences, and therefore, the historians at Harvard, not the chemists or even the astronomers and geologists, are the proper judges.

Obviously Dr. Conant opposed my book, not because he found anything unscientific in it—he would have pointed it out—but because my theory was so much in conflict with conventionally held views. Just one year earlier Dr. Conant said (*The New York Times,* February 12, 1950):

> I have heard those in the United States bewail the fact that we have no unifying philosophy. . . . I suggest that they take another look at what is going on on the other side of the Iron Curtain and see whether their efforts toward uniformity in the

> United States are, in fact, well directed. I would say that the day that the educators in the United States can agree on one unifying philosophy is the day that freedom becomes seriously imperiled by our educational system.

This is the question of "life and death" in science, and not the non sequitur of *Science and Common Sense,* an appeal for regimentation in science made twelve months later.

A MAN OF STRIFE

When *Harper's* published Larrabee's article in its January 1950 issue, an editorial note announced an article by me to appear in one of the following issues. But soon plans had to be changed. In view of the criticism leveled against the book even before it was published, I decided to use the follow-up article as an answer to my critics, and since *Harper's* was also under attack, it decided to give the other side a word, too. That fall, in a telephone conversation, Frederick Allen informed me of the editorial staff's decision to publish an answer from me only when it had a rebuttal from a few specialists. To this I agreed but stipulated that in the debate I was to have the chance to answer my opponents. Allen assented to this since journalistic ethics requires that the accused have the last word. It turned out that this demand was the right move on my part.

Month after month passed, and *Harper's* could not find an opponent. Many an astronomer and geologist stated in the press that he could write an entire book to disprove Velikovsky; but when asked to write a rebuttal to me, nobody seemed willing to undertake the task, and *Harper's* efforts in approaching various scientists were futile. Shapley received *Harper's* invitation to take the stand, but he declined and suggested Neugebauer; the latter declined, too. After a few months of search it really seemed that nobody was willing to throw his hat into the ring; everyone preferred to stand outside and call names.

Early in 1951 I received an invitation to be present at the

monthly meeting of a local Presbyterian circle at which my book would be discussed. If I would be there, a debate could be arranged between me and Professor John Q. Stewart, astronomer of Princeton University. The circle was composed mainly of professors of the Princeton Theological Seminary in the town; for many years it has gathered once a month to discuss some current book. I agreed to be present.

When I arrived at the Princeton Tavern, a dignified-looking place, I met the group, scattered in a dimly lit hall. Stewart, a man of my own age, rose from his chair and measured me curiously from head to foot; it appeared as though he had not expected me to be superior in height, he being a tall man.

Seated at a U-shaped table, the group listened to the reviewer of the book, somebody from Rye, New York. In the debate after the lecture philologists engaged in some small skirmishes with me. Then Stewart announced that the bad thing about the book was its being well written and he could not stop reading it, though he had made up his mind many times to read only one section more, and thus he had read all of them. But of course, the theory was wrong. He presented his arguments, borrowed partly from Payne-Gaposchkin. Our debate was limited in time since the meeting had to break up before the last train left. Unable to develop my theme fully, I leaned over in back of the chairman toward Stewart and asked him: "The earth is a magnet and most probably charged electrically; the sun has a general magnetic field and solar spots are strong magnets. What do you do with these forces in your system?" Leaning over in back of the chairman, he whispered: "We do not need them. Our calculations are perfect without them."

Some time passed, and I heard that Professor Stewart had come to *Harper's* and offered to answer me in a debate; in another version I heard, Neugebauer had suggested Stewart who had probably consulted him. Stewart's offer was accepted, and he received the piece I had written, "Answer to My Critics." After a while I received his piece and wrote my answer to Stewart. Finally, in the June 1951 issue of *Harper's*, seventeen months after the article that unleashed the controversy and fourteen months after the publication of my book, I answered for the first and only time all my critics on every point that merited an answer.

Harper's editors prefaced the debate with an explanation, declaring: "Although the book and its author have been violently censured in reviews and comments, there has been a remarkable lack of explicit criticism of it based on careful reading. Believing that a theory so revolutionary ought to be met by careful appraisal rather than by denunciation and boycott," they invited me to reply to the "scattered points raised by his critics thus far" and asked Professor John Q. Stewart, Princeton University astronomical physicist, to answer me.

My piece bore a quotation from Jeremiah, which I wanted to omit when it seemed that the space at my disposal might better be employed for some additional point, but the editors insisted on keeping it. It reads: "Woe is me, my mother, that thou hast borne me a man of strife and a man of contention to the whole earth!"

I answered the arguments about the size of comets; about historical eclipses before 700 B.C. (the actual dates are not known; those we use have been fixed according to modern reckoning of time and represent time points when the eclipses *are supposed* to have occurred); about the Venus tablets (according to these tablets, Venus moved erratically); and about what would happen to the earth if it should stop rotating (water would move over the land from oceanic spaces, and it did so; the earth would not disintegrate if it did not stop suddenly). "As an alternative [in the book] I offered the explanation that a tilting of the axis in a magnetic field, even without the change in velocity of rotation, would produce the effect of disturbed solar motion." I showed how strong the magnetic field must be in order to retard or stop the earth in its rotation or to incline its axis. Here I went beyond my position in *Worlds in Collision:* I criticized the dogmatic reluctance to recognize the existence of the electrical and magnetic forces in the solar system and spoke of the form and behavior of the cometary tails, and the round shape of the sun, which should be flattened because of rotation, and of the motion of solar protuberances that return to the sun as if on a rubber band. "The behavior of cometary tails, the movement of solar protuberances, and the round shape of the sun are facts which astronomers have marked, 'High tension; do not touch.' "

I answered the criticism directed against carbohydrates (manna) coming from the same source as hydrocarbons (naphtha) by quoting a passage offered to me by Professor V. I. Komarewsky of the Illinois Institute of Technology, an authority on catalysis. I explained once more that "collective amnesia" does not mean that historical references to the catastrophes are lacking, but that though they are abundant, they were misunderstood, even when the statements are unequivocal. I quoted Sigmund Freud, from the Preface to his *The*

Interpretation of Dreams (second edition), on the "brilliant example of the aversion to learning anything new so characteristic of the scientists." I concluded: "Not so long ago science had to struggle to free itself from the shackles of religion. Now it is as dogmatic as religion once was. Ideas that were revolutionary, schismatic, and damned in the nineteenth century are beatified and pronounced infallible in the twentieth, by the same guardians of dogma."

A SKYSCRAPER AND A SPARROW

Professor Stewart criticized not so much my work as the methods applied in humanistic studies, contrasting them with the methods of the exact sciences. Consequently, he called his rebuttal "Disciplines in Collision." He wrote: "Science is not mere common sense. It is a severe and powerful way of thinking. Velikovsky inclines to appeal every judgment of scientists and engineers to ancient authorities and texts." But "Seneca knew little about torsion and moment of momentum, and extant Mayan manuscripts are notoriously weak when it comes to Young's modulus. . . ." (Young's modulus is a coefficient of deformation in elastic bodies, as in a stretched wire or a compressed pillar). There exists a "latent opposition between persons having a humane education and those with scientific training. *Worlds in Collision,* whatever its faults, has performed a service by focusing new attention on 'disciplines in collision.' ". . .

"Suppose a sparrow flutters past a tall building, which thereafter is condemned and dismantled. A person who lacked all experience in numerical reasoning but had intense sentiment for sparrows might argue that air currents from the bird's beating wings had dangerously strained the tower." As for an engineer, "no alleged eye-witness testimony collected from old diaries or tales told by grandmother long after the event would convince him that the close approach of a sparrow ever endangered a skyscraper." Proofs valid for him will not convince those "to whom logarithms are anathema and the flow of words enchanting." His opponent may duel "with footnotes, precedents, primary, secondary, and tertiary sources and commentators," but what really counts is "the masses of the skyscraper and sparrow . . . and the elastic restoring force of the building . . . as well as the area of the sparrow's wings and their frequency of beat. . . ."

Stewart took my book out of verbal sanctuary and put it within the range of mathematical artillery.

His first excursion into mathematics concerned a matter of scale, and he gave a long quotation from an article "by one of our leading woman scientists, Dr. Cecilia Payne-Gaposchkin," in *Popular Astronomy:*

> We are asked to believe that Venus was shot out from Jupiter and practically made a direct hit on the earth, and scored another bull's eye after fifty-two years. She then (we are asked to believe) encountered Mars . . . who propelled her into her present orbit, and proceeded to make two hits (or near hits) on the Earth on his own account, before returning to his present orbit. . . . We have here [in *Worlds in Collision*] an extraordinary achievement in a very difficult type of marksmanship—four hits [between the comet Venus and other planetary bodies] in a couple of thousand years. It is not only impossible. It is ridiculous.

Stewart agreed with Payne-Gaposchkin: "Her word 'marksmanship' is altogether appropriate because these planets are so very small in proportion to the distances which normally separate them." And he gave as a comparative scale a page of *Harper's* enlarged to a yard serving for space and a few dots on it for planets.

To this "heavy artillery" of mathematics, my answer was as follows:

> The image of "marksmanship" is not well derived. The planets revolve in the plane of the ecliptic; if one should move on a stretched orbit, it would contact its neighbor planets. And if a comet with a tail 100 million miles long should move in the ecliptic, no good fortune would keep the planets from passing through its fabric; at its every passage inside the terrestrial orbit, the Earth would have a better than 60 to 40 chance of going through its tail or head. A comet ejected from Jupiter (400 times heavier than Venus) would most probably move in the plane of the planetary orbits. Stewart's example discards

> the elementary fact that every planet is disturbed by all the others. Every passage of Mars once in two years causes a slight perturbation in the Earth's revolution. At orbits verging closer, stronger perturbations *must* have occurred, not only "may" have occurred.

I could also have illustrated what I said by citing the history of the comet Lexell. In 1767 this comet passed so close to Jupiter that the former's orbit was changed from a parabola to a path of six years' duration only. Then in 1770, three years later, it passed so close to Earth that the time of the cometary revolution was shortened by two and a half days. Again in the year 1779, on passing once more close to Jupiter, it was whisked by the planet from its orbit into a hyperbola and out of the solar system. Thus in twelve years it experienced three strong disturbances on near approaches to planets.

The "second objection" concerned the eclipses. Stewart said:

> Several modern scholars (notably Fotheringham) have examined Grecian, Babylonian, and Chinese records and listed passages which seem to describe solar eclipses. A brief survey of astronomical publications reveals at least three recorded total eclipses of the Sun before −687 (the supposed date of Velikovsky's last catastrophe) which have been considered by computers to fit the present motions. This evidence . . . strongly suggests that no unaccountable disturbance of the motion of the Earth or Moon occurred in that year.

Besides, Stewart argued, calculations have been made to establish the exact change in the velocity of terrestrial rotation, and it has been found that since ancient times the length of the day has increased by one-fortieth of a second. This has been done precisely with the help of ancient eclipses, futher proof that no changes, of the kind I described, in the position or motion of Earth and Moon could have taken place.

On this last point I wrote: "The retardation [of Earth's rotation] was computed by Fotheringham from eclipses reaching only [as far back as] to 585 B.C. Since the last catastrophe occurred 102 years earlier, Stewart's request that it show an effect on retardation is without justification."

It was particularly gratifying to be able to answer this argument of earlier eclipses. Although by then I had spent twelve years in libraries, it was only by chance that in a rare book by the Jesuit missionary Antoine Gaubil, an eighteenth-century authority on Chinese astronomy, I came upon the necessary information which now gave me the opportunity to dispose of this argument and turn it to my favor. I wrote:

> In referring to three solar eclipses before 687 B.C., Professor Stewart must have in mind Fotheringham's lecture, "Historical Eclipses" (1929). The dates in question are 1062 B.C. in Babylonia, 776 B.C. in China, 763 B.C. in Assyria. Hundreds of eclipses obviously occurred in those countries during early centuries, but only one for each country is thought to be fixed.
>
> (a) *Babylonia.* "On the 26th day of the month Siwan in the seventh year the day was turned to night. Heaven in flames." The century of occurrence is still a matter of debate. Fotheringham chose 1062 B.C. There can be no solar eclipse on the 26th day of a lunar calendar month. Kugler explains the phenomenon:
>
> "The Earth was going through an immense train of small, dust-like, and also large meteorites. The meteoric dust created darkness; the larger meteorites became incandescent through friction in the atmosphere and put the sky in flames. (*Sternkunde und Sterndienst in Babel,* II, 2, 373 n.)"
>
> (b) *China.* According to the Chinese book of songs, *Shiking,* the sun was obscured. The place where the observation was made is not known. The calculation 776 B.C. is made on the authority of the astronomer Y-hang [who lived in the eighth century A.D., *fourteen centuries later.* When] an expected eclipse did not take place[,] Y-hang informed the Emperor that "the sky changed the order of the motions which cause eclipses" (ibid.). He explained that already in earlier times, in the days of Tzin, "the sky changed the course of the planet Venus." (Compare Varro on change of course and form of Venus. *Worlds in Collision,* p. 158.)
>
> (c) *Assyria.* A chronicle relates, "insurrection in the city of Ashur. In the month Siwan the sun was obscured." The place of observation is not given. Nor the day of the month. The year is named in honor of a magistrate. By retrograde calculation an eclipse should have occurred on July [read June] 15, 763 B.C., if there were no changes. Placing the eclipse in 763 B.C.

> on July [read June] 15 and assigning the same year to the magistrate, an Assyrian chronology was built by reconstructing the lists of the magistrates. However, it required a change of 44 years in Biblical chronology.

Nevertheless, Stewart expressed pride in "such computations as these" concerning the ancient eclipses: They are "one of the most imposing demonstrations of the validity of celestial mechanics."

The smallest quantities were taken into account by astronomers, confirming the law and the method as well. The "degree of 'intricacy' may be conveyed by Dr. Payne-Gaposchkin's statement that lunar theory alone recognizes 155 major periodic terms and over 500 smaller ones. . . ." Stewart was proud that so many motions, all accounted for, had been observed in the Moon; such an achievement must convey to the layman an idea of the complexity of the problem and at the same time of the correctness of its solution.

To this I answered: "Stewart also finds the complexity of lunar motion 'one of the most imposing demonstrations of the validity of celestial mechanics.' S. Newcomb, however, on the basis of eclipses from Ptolemy to this century, found disturbing variations." I quoted Simon Newcomb, the great American mathematical astronomer, on this very problem of lunar motion as checked by ancient eclipses:

> I regard these fluctuations as the most enigmatical phenomenon presented by celestial motions, being so difficult to account for by the action of any known causes, that we cannot but suspect them to arise from some action in nature hitherto unknown. . . . It would be natural to associate them with the Sun's varying magnetic activity and the varying magnetism of the Earth.*

It also happened that between my oral debate with Stewart in February 1951 and our debate in *Harper's* in June of the same year, J. H. Nelson of RCA Laboratories reported a well-marked relationship between planetary positions and the quality of radio reception, a phenomenon not explainable by gravitational theory.† A press release stated:

* Simon Newcomb, Royal Astronomical Society, *Monthly Notices* (1909).
† *RCA Review* (March 1951).

> Evidence of a strange and unexplained correlation between the positions of Jupiter, Saturn, and Mars in their orbits around the sun and the presence of violent electrical disturbances in the earth's upper atmosphere . . . seems to indicate [that] the planets and the sun share in a cosmic electrical balance mechanism that extends a billion miles from the center of our solar system. Such an electrical balance is not accounted for in current astrophysical theories.*

The "third and crucial objection" of an astronomical nature Stewart found in the present positions of the planets: "If Venus were opportunely diverted by Mars from an earlier elongated ellipse, as asserted, then whatever new ellipse each of the two planets traced, from then on, they would continue for many thousands of years to pass near the original point where their encounter took place." This is one of the "fundamental principles of orbital motion, which are a consequence of Newton's laws."

Apparently Stewart borrowed this argument from the astronomer royal because he reproduced it together with the error that his source contained; therefore, my answer to both of them was identical. I wrote:

> If there was a planetary contact in the past, one should be able to find its traces in the orbits, *only, however, of the last contact.* Stewart cites my book to the effect that the last near-contacts were between Mars and Earth, and in a non-sequitur asks me to show the past meeting point of the earlier contacts of Mars and Venus. . . . The last close approaches between Mars and Earth at fifteen-year periods have their vestiges in the close oppositions of Mars that recur at fifteen-year periods. The similarity in the inclinations of the axes of Earth and Mars has meaning if magnetic fields played a role in these contacts.

These were the astronomical arguments of Stewart and my replies. He also advanced three archaeological arguments. Pyramids must have been disturbed by strong earthquakes if there were catastrophes such as I described—but they were not; obelisks are still standing, though "even a moderate jerking of the ground would upset them on their narrow basis." He went on:

> There are many other ancient buildings and monuments surviving undamaged in cities which were flourishing before

* *The New York Times,* April 15, 1951.

> or during the same period—in Greece, Sumeria, India, and elsewhere.... Tombs dated from the fourth millennium B.C. were not destroyed by ocean floods in Ur (of the Chaldees), close as it was to the Persian Gulf, nor in Byblus, on the Mediterranean.

For these arguments I needed only to quote from authorities in the field.

Although the pyramid is the most stable of all forms—and in my planned history of earlier catastrophes I shall show that these structures were not tombs but royal shelters—earthquakes have been "extremely severe in wrenching, as all the deep beams of granite over the King's Chamber in the Great Pyramid are snapped through at the south end, or else dragged out.... The whole roof hangs now by merely catching contact."* I also wrote:

> Only one obelisk of the Middle Kingdom remains standing—in Heliopolis. It is built into an immense base, a cube of 10 cubits (15 feet) on each side, covered now with earth (Budge, *Cleopatra's Needles*). The statement that buildings in Greece and elsewhere from before the seventh century survive undamaged is unfounded and contradicts the facts. Every excavation has disclosed marks of violent slidings. No building survived. Professor Stewart says that Ur in Chaldea was not overwhelmed by water. Sir Leonard Woolley, who excavated Ur, says:
>
> "Eight feet of sediment imply a very great depth of water and the flood which deposited it must have been of a magnitude unparalleled in local history. That it was so is further proved by the fact that the clay bank marks a definite break in the continuity of the local culture; a whole civilization which existed before it is lacking above it and seems to have been submerged by the waters. (*Ur of the Chaldees,* 8th ed., 1935, pp. 28 f.)"

In my rebuttal I asked: "What is left of all the arguments? Enough to justify suppression of the book? Or solely the metaphor about the sparrow?"

Did Stewart demonstrate the "severe and powerful way of thinking" of the scientists and "the old wives' " methods of the humanists, or verbalists, as he calls them?

* Flinders Petrie, *Egyptian Architecture* (1938), p. 67.

In the opening part of his article Stewart was apologetic for his colleagues who attempted to suppress my book and was critical of Macmillan for reasoning that "the Homeric sweep of battling planets would attract readers and justify publication." But at the end of his article he was more forgiving and wrote of me: "The prediction is safe that fruitful developments may be anticipated from some of the many irritants which this indefatigable comber-over of forgotten and difficult texts has tossed into the illiterate scientific scene."

But in view of his condescending approach to the humanities, I indulged in irony:

> Are the humanistic and scientific approaches different? Scientists can calculate the torsion of a skyscraper at the wing-beat of a bird, or 155 motions of the Moon and 500 smaller ones in addition. They move in academic garb and sing logarithms. They say, "The sky is ours," like priests in charge of heaven. We poor humanists cannot even think clearly, or write a sentence without a blunder, commoners of "common sense." We never take a step without stumbling; they move solemnly, ever unerringly, never a step back, and carry bell, book, and candle.

I defended the ancients from undeserved contempt. Seneca did not know Young's modulus (which has no application in astronomy), but he knew the real nature of comets, the inertia of their motion, and their periodicity. For 1,500 years after his time science clung to the dogma that comets are apparitions in the atmosphere, like rainbows. Copernicus thought so, too. It was Tycho de Brahe who rediscovered the fact that they are celestial bodies; Halley rediscovered their periodicity.

Humble were the ancients, too. In his tractate *De cometis,* Seneca wrote:

> Many discoveries are reserved for the ages still to be, when our memory shall have perished. The world is a poor affair if it does not contain matter for investigation for the whole world in every age. . . . Nature does not reveal all her secrets at once. We imagine we are initiated in her mysteries. We are as yet but hanging around her outer courts.

THE AAAS IS ALERTED TO ACT

THE DEBATE BETWEEN Stewart and me caused real consternation in scientific circles. Everyone expected that when the scene was changed and, instead of Larrabee singing panegyrics, an astronomer took the stand, Velikovsky would be exposed as ignorant and his book as untruth. The opposite happened. In the opinion of many of the readers of *Harper's*, my lance discovered more than one Achilles' heel in my opponent. Gloom fell on the ranks of my adversaries. Every one of them could write a book to disprove *Worlds in Collision*, every one of them shrank from entering the lists when *Harper's* offered the chance, and the fairest among them who had finally picked up the glove showed the public how unwarranted were their loud proclamations of inevitable victory.

Now certainly something had to be done. No scientific magazine referred to the debate. Instead, voices were heard clamoring for another round. John Pfeiffer, in *Science* of July 13, 1951, questioned:

> Why haven't the astronomers, linguists, geologists, or anthropologists—speaking through their societies—come out with their feelings about *Worlds in Collision?* Or should that be the function of AAAS [American Association for the Advancement of Science]? If not, is there an organization that represents the body of American science in such matters?

As described previously, the AAAS had six months earlier deliberated on the issue and planned the introduction of censorship or of a reviewing board of "peers," and proposals had been made to employ ghostwriters who would assist scientists in expressing their ideas in clear language. The self-appointed censors and self-elevated peers waited for a signal to act, but no new heretic came their way to set them in motion.

When the next yearly meeting of the AAAS was about to convene, *Science,* its organ, carried in the issue of November 23, 1951, under the heading "Articulate Science," a piece by Samuel A. Miles, of the technical literature division in a commercial firm (Hagstrom Company, Inc.), who declared: "There appears to be a need for a new organization" to combat *Worlds in Collision* and similar books. He went on to say: "An attempt to develop such an approach will be made at the AAAS meeting on December 30, at the symposium 'Operation Knowledge.' The author of this note will present a paper. . . ."

In the next issue of *Science* another belligerent writer threw his deadly weapon against my book. He came to the conclusion that *Worlds in Collision* and "the DDT Scandal" have everything in common.

The entire body of a great organization was called to enter the arena, crusaders were summoned, and "Operation Knowledge" was on its way.

After the experience Stewart had in the pages of *Harper's,* it was even more difficult to find a scientist who felt willing and able to defend the honor of his colleagues accused of oppression and obscurantism. Yet the matter could not be ignored and left unanswered because the loss of face was too great. The American Association for the Advancement of Science was repeatedly prodded to produce an opponent. He was finally found in an associate professor of philosophy at Florida State University, Dr. Laurence Lafleur, a name little known in science.

The November 1951 issue of *Scientific Monthly* carried a fourteen-column article by Lafleur. There he quoted the note with which the editors of *Harper's* introduced my debate with Stewart: ". . . A theory so revolutionary ought to be met by careful appraisal rather than by denunciation and boycott." And he picked up the pen dropped by Stewart. He wrote:

> The general public as represented by the editors and many of the readers of *Harper's* has failed to grasp the reasons for the

> scientific rejection of Velikovsky's hypothesis, and many of them may therefore be led to think of scientists as a dogmatic crew, blindly maintaining their own unverified doctrines; intolerant of opposition, and suppressing it by denying free expression to their adversaries.

But he would stand and protect them all from the "tempest."

He called his article "Cranks and Scientists." He gave a picture of a crank. The crank is "ignorant of the principles and facts of the field [he] write[s] about." He "will ignore all facts and deny all theories that stand in his way." To impress the reader with the extent to which a crank forces his theory upon nature, he presented an example.

> The biological crank has the intrinsically harmless theory, for example, that there are winged elephants. Where? For convenience, let us say that they are in the next room. If we do not see them, then perhaps we have a curious physical fact, that light rays bend around winged elephants, thus making them invisible; or a curious psychological fact that winged elephants are good hypnotists and hypnotically persuade us that they are not there.

Thus a reader unfamiliar with *Worlds in Collision* is prepared to evaluate it.

Lafleur explained that "not once in a generation is there an innovation so important that it changes many laws," and therefore, "naturally enough, the odds favor the assumption that anyone proposing a revolutionary doctrine is a crank rather than a scientist." By the odds I lost.

In order to solve the problem whether Velikovsky's is "a revolutionary theory" or the product of a crank, Lafleur established seven criteria for the diagnosis of a crank.

Test 1: "Is the proposer of the hypothesis aware of the theory he proposes to supersede?" Applying this test to me, he found: "In one sense Velikovsky is clearly aware of the laws he proposes to replace, and prepared to quote names, dates, and page numbers without end," yet "he does not understand Newton's law," and "Darwin fails to receive more than a few passing mentions in his book." (This is a sign of heresy.)

Test 2: "Is the new hypothesis in accord with currently held theories in the field of the hypothesis, or, if not, is there adequate reason for making the changes. . . ?" Applying this test to me, he discovered that the "collision theory is in fundamental contradiction with practically every tenet of mechanics. . . . Is there a sufficient counterweight to this? The only evidence adduced is a farrago of legends, myths, and opinions." (Is mechanics the field of my book? And where is mechanics violated?)

Test 3: "Is the new hypothesis in accord with the currently held theories in other fields? If not, is the proposer aware that he is challenging an established body of knowledge. . . ?" Applied to me, the test indicated: "In addition to challenging physics and biology, it is clear that Velikovsky is out of step with astronomy and geology," also anthropology, sociology, and history. (I believed I was aware of this, and so was Kallen.)

Test 4: "In every case where the new hypothesis is in contradiction with an established theory, does the hypothesis include or imply a suitable substitute?" With this test Lafleur found: "The collision hypothesis offers no substitute for the challenged laws of motion, nor for challenged laws in other fields of science." (Such a short statement and so sweeping. I have not challenged the laws of motion, and I do not know what to do with the generality of the second half of the sentence.)

Test 5: "Does the new hypothesis fit in with the existing theories in all fields, or with substitutes proposed for them, to form a world view?" According to Lafleur, it does not fit in with existing theories in "all fields," but it forms a "world view."

Test 6: "If the new hypothesis is at variance with theories capable of prediction . . . is the new theory itself capable of such prediction?" Thus tested, "Velikovsky's theory" again did not measure up: "Its predictions, if capable of any, would certainly be so vague as to be scientifically unverifiable." (I made a number of predictions in my book and elsewhere which are not vague at all; a number of them have been verified, such as the presence of petroleum in rocks of very recent origin.*)

Test 7: "Does the proposer show a disposition to accept minority opinions. . . ?" Lafleur detected that I do: "Velikovsky does show a disposition to accept minority opinions . . . even to quote such opinions when they have been discredited to the point that they are

* [Other predictions which have since been verified include the high heat of Venus, Jupiter's radio noises, the existence of terrestrial magnetosphere, a thermal gradient in the lunar crust, and radiocarbon analyses pointing to a late dating for the Egyptian New Kingdom. See the Epilogue.]

no longer held as minority views. For examples we may cite the notion that the earth's axis has changed considerably. . . ." (The foremost modern authority on the subject, Harold Jeffreys, asked in his book *The Earth* (1924): "Has the inclination of the earth's axis to the plane of its orbit varied during its history?" and proceeded: "The answer to [this] question is a definite Yes!" Similarly, W. B. Wright, author of *The Quaternary Ice Age* (1937): "The earth's axis of rotation has not always had the same position.")

The seven tests were made, and the verdict was: "He qualifies as a crank by almost every one of these tests, perhaps by every one."

Since the purpose of these tests was to show how to discriminate between a revolutionary theory and the idea of a crank, it follows that revolutionary theory is one which is "in accord with currently held theories in the field of the hypothesis" and "in accord with the currently held theories in other fields" and "fits in with existing theories in all fields" (tests 2, 3, and 5).

Accordingly, if *Worlds in Collision* agreed with all accepted theories and disagreed with none, then it would justly be regarded as a "revolutionary theory."

The tests are not from a textbook on sociology or psychology but were prepared by Lafleur *ad hoc.* Name-calling cannot substitute for an argument, nor does it excuse the suppression of a book. And Lafleur acceded: "We must still deal with the feeling, first, that scientists should have attempted to refute Velikovsky's position" and "that they should not have attempted to suppress it." On the last point he said that "it would be surprising if more than a small minority felt that they would be justified in trying to suppress it: free speech is essential, not only to democracy, but also to science." And having paid lip service to freedom of expression, he justified the boycott of the publisher's textbooks as a matter of keeping the camp clean. Done with this, he repeated: "And now we come to the last objection to the attitude of scientists: should they not point out to Velikovsky and his public where the collision theory breaks down?" He takes it upon himself to accomplish this.

By so doing, Lafleur acknowledged that in all the opposition and in all the refutations, in all the numerous reviews, in all the meetings and debates, in the faculties, in the astronomical and other conventions, this very elementary thing was not done: Either it was not attempted, or it failed, as in the case of Payne-Gaposchkin and Stewart.

* * *

The first "difficulty" in refuting Velikovsky, according to Lafleur, lies "in the volume of material required to do so"; nobody is erudite in all the fields that *Worlds in Collision* covers, and such a reply "would require the cooperation of many scientists" and "considerable time in preparation." The second reason for not answering Velikovsky lies in the fact that in order to disprove him even on one point, a full book of fundamentals would have to be written, and existing textbooks serve the purpose and need not be duplicated. In order to demonstrate this, Lafleur chose the field he says he knows the best—celestial mechanics. His third reason why scientists were reluctant to cross pens with me will be stated below.

Lafleur correctly observed that in *Worlds in Collision* "collision" evidently means a "close approach, and not necessarily contact." Then he made this statement: According to celestial mechanics, "after the last collision, whatever it was, the two planets involved would be left with intersecting orbits." And since only the orbits of Neptune and Pluto intersect, there could have been, at some time in the remote past, a collision there, but not between other planets. Apparently Lafleur did not know what he was trying to explain. Intersecting orbits may be a cause of a collision, but they do not necessarily result from collision or near contact.*

When next Lafleur said that Velikovsky asserted that the earth stopped within half an hour, we became suspicious of his familiarity with what I wrote. Nowhere have I put forth or discussed this half hour. It was Lafleur's surmise.

At this point Lafleur selected the target for his major attack. Velikovsky made the suggestion "that magnetic or electrostatic forces are responsible for the hypothetical phenomena, and it is this suggestion that we have chosen to deal with in particular." Here he would show where "the collision theory breaks down." But he has to explain the fundamentals. So he starts with the information that there are two kinds of charges, positive and negative, and what all this means.

> We should explain that it takes energy to separate ordinary matter into its constituent charges, and that, unless there is a continued flow of adequate energy or isolation in space, these

* [Mechanisms by which the last near collision between Earth and Mars might have led eventually to the nonintersecting orbits that we see today have been discussed by Ralph Juergens, *Pensée* II, pp. 6, 12; by Robert Bass, *Pensée* VIII, pp. 9 ff., 21 ff.; and by Lynn Rose and Raymond Vaughan, *Pensée* VIII, pp. 32–34.]

> constituents will recombine. As a result large electrostatic charges are possible in highly dispersed matter such as galactic nebulae, comets' tails, coronae, and stellar prominences; and a smaller electrostatic charge is reasonable for massive hot bodies such as the sun, but large cold bodies will necessarily be close to electrostatic neutrality.

In this passage are two of the most amazing statements I have come across during the entire controversy. If it is admitted that comets' tails have large electrostatic charges, then, of course, Lafleur has proved what he intended to disprove and the earth, which is a magnet, on entering an electromagnetic field of sufficient strength (a moving charged comet will create an electromagnetic field) would have its rotation disturbed, even stopped, and its axis inclined, even reversed.

All the heresy for which I have been attacked so vehemently appears on page 387 of *Worlds in Collision:*

> The accepted celestial mechanics, notwithstanding the many calculations that have been carried out to many decimal places, or verified by celestial motions, stands only *if* the sun, the source of light, warmth, and other radiation produced by fusion and fission of atoms, *is as a whole an electrically neutral body,* and also if the planets, in their usual orbits, are neutral bodies. . . . In the Newtonian celestial mechanics, based on the theory of gravitation, electricity and magnetism play no role.

This is the entire problem. Now, after all the refutations by Stewart and others of charges in celestial bodies, came Lafleur, who affirmed what I offered only for discussion and said that comets' tails and the solar corona can possess large electrostatic charges. He did not realize his blunder or the consequences of his statement for celestial mechanics. Thus he fits perfectly into his own definition under tests 1, 2, and 3 above.

Still more astonishing is his second statement in the same passage; that planets, being "large cold bodies," must be neutral or physically can have no surplus of a positive or negative charge.

This is not merely a blunder; it is ignorance of fundamentals. A large cold body can be charged, and a planet can be charged, and to say differently is to assert that there are flying elephants invisible because of bending rays of light.

To make his point even stronger, Lafleur stated that to assume that planets can be charged proves "scientific ignorance" and "bad logic," and this can be seen from the fact that "even relatively small charges can be detected with an electroscope, and the earth's surface is not charged." Again he said: "If a charge is so slight that it cannot move two pieces of silver foil in contact with each other, what effect can it have on astronomical bodies at a nonnegligible distance?"

The earth may be charged to many billions of volts, and the electroscope will not show it. This is also a rudiment of science. Scientists like Nikola Tesla sought to find the charge of the terrestrial globe; had they thought that the electroscope would provide them with the answer by revealing the neutrality of the earth, they would not have wasted time and effort. Every engineer knows that our assumption of the neutrality of the earth is entirely arbitrary.

Next Lafleur stated that planets are not magnetic bodies, for if they were, spectroscopic observation would show it. How many fundamental errors can be made on one page? It is elementary that spectroscopic investigation of magnetic fields (by means of the Zeeman effect) is possible only on illuminating bodies, not on cold illuminated bodies like the planets. Besides, Earth, one of the planets, is a magnet, as all of us know.

Lafleur wrote: "Objects moving under electrostatic forces, or electrostatic and gravitational forces combined, would obey the same laws of motion as those acting under gravitational forces alone." This is an argument in favor of planets being charged: the action of their charges may not be distinguished from gravitational action. However, Lafleur followed the quoted sentence with this statement: "This is not only a matter of theory: the successful and accurate prediction of astronomical events must either prove *this* or prove the absence of electromagnetic forces." Who can make heads or tails of this?

Lafleur then admitted that magnetic fields around two bodies "at a sufficiently close approach could alter the inclination of the axes of both bodies." Nothing beyond this was needed to explain the effects I have described in my book. But here he made an abrupt and final statement: "We might go on to show that an approach close enough to do that would also cause the collision, evaporation, and amalgamation of the two bodies." Nothing but words. Two interacting magnetic fields may cause all degrees of disturbance not necessarily amounting to collision, evaporation, and amalgamation.

The correct formulation is this: If we assume that the celestial bodies are charged, there would also be a magnetic effect in addition to the electrostatic effect since the celestial bodies are in motion, each in relation to the others. The magnetic effect would be rather small at the usual distances between the planets. If, however, one planet or comet should come close to another, the magnetic fields would cause shifting of the axes and other disturbances.

Concluding his article, Lafleur displayed evident pride in his having met the challenge. Referring to me, he wrote:

> He is a highly intelligent, scholarly, and able man; his facility in writing makes him delightfully readable, and suggests a third reason why scientists may hesitate to cross pens with him. Even the present critic finds him convincing whenever the material dealt with lies in a field in which he is ignorant. . . .

Celestial mechanics Lafleur thinks he knows thoroughly and admits his ignorance in other fields.

Unlike his colleagues, Lafleur did not hesitate to cross pens with me. Of course, he did all the dueling, his opponent not having been invited to answer on the spot, as was the case in the debate between Stewart and myself.

"AFRAID TO THINK"

NOBODY PROTESTED the misrepresentation of the rudiments of science and the parade of nonsense in physics and logic, or nobody's protest was printed, but a letter-feuilleton by Alan O. Kelly of Carlsbad, California, was printed in the February 1952 issue of *Scientific Monthly.* It offered the "crank's-eye view":

> It is our observation that the great majority of people who deliberately decide to be scientists, and so educate themselves, are those who are psychologically unfitted to be real creative thinkers. They go into science because they are afraid to think for themselves. They lack self-confidence; they want to lean on the orthodox, great authorities. The average scientist never dreams of questioning an authority. He takes for granted what he reads in his textbooks and rarely looks up their source material. . . .
>
> The average scientist fears to be different; he fears to be called a crackpot or a crank. He may claim that he cannot afford to jeopardize his job or his professional standing, but actually he knows that he hasn't got what it takes. . . . Living by authority himself, he cannot understand one who does not. . . . He considers himself a thinker or as belonging to a class of outstanding individuals who are thinkers. He has been trained to believe that conservatism and book knowledge are thinking and will somehow lead to the advancement of science without imagination.

> Lafleur argues that we cannot afford to discard accepted theory for new, when the great body of scientists agrees with the old; that we cannot ignore this great weight of scientific opinion. We should like to inquire how, if they refuse to think for themselves, they can be said to have an opinion or how it can carry much weight?

The crank, on the other hand, "has no fear of making mistakes," yet "this is a major requirement for anyone who would propound a new theory or do creative work. Edison, as everyone knows, was the outstanding example of a crank who made thousands of mistakes and cared not a whit what anyone else thought or said."

A LAWYER'S ADVICE

WHEN I HAVE BEEN in need of advice, I have sought the counsel of two men: Professor Horace M. Kallen, who has been my mentor in many a step I have taken since my first year in America and whose kindness, human interest, philosophical attitude, and ethical standards I value; and John J. O'Neill, on whose almost intuitive thinking I repeatedly relied, so unerring was his ability to appraise a scientific idea or a human situation. These two men, as far as I know, never met, and their opinions would not necessarily coincide—they might even more often conflict—nor would I blindly follow either one of them. After the defamation attempt in *Scientific Monthly*, long in the making and now accomplished, I saw both of them. Kallen, who once told me that I would have to wait ten years before the emotional attitude of my opponents subsided, and that I should keep myself from becoming involved in the passion of the controversy and work in peace, after seeing Lafleur's article, became grim and said I would have to bring an action for libel: such evil tactics must not go unpunished. And he gave me the names of two attorneys, specialists in literary libel.

At O'Neill's invitation, I went to see him at his home in Long Island. He had prepared a long article that was to serve me as an answer in a daily newspaper, *The Times* or the *Herald Tribune*. He also advised me once to give the vicious attacks time to spend themselves, perhaps ten years—both men gave the same figure. Meanwhile, I should take things cheerfully and enjoy myself. Now, however, he had written an emotional piece in reply to this most recent attack. I read it and did not like it. It seemed that I was the only one who remained calm in the face of the organized attempt to discredit my theory and myself. O'Neill had written the piece as a ghostwriter for me. For this reason alone I would not have used it: I would not sign my name to anything that someone else had written.

O'Neill advised me to see Professor Warren Weaver. He said that Weaver was very critical of the management and editorial policy of the AAAS and, as the head of a planning committee, advocated reorganization. I decided to explore Kallen's and O'Neill's advice and started with the peaceful approach, calling for an appointment with Weaver, who was the head of the Natural Science section of the Rockefeller Foundation.

This was the first time I had made a complaint to a scientist. I left him with a few pages containing a factual reply I had written and asked him to contact the editor of the magazine in Washington and request space for it in the forthcoming issue.

I waited a while to hear from Mr. Weaver, and when a few weeks passed without any results, I decided to get the opinion of a lawyer. I was advised to see Arthur Garfield Hays, who had served as one of the counsel at the Sacco and Vanzetti trial, and the Scopes trial. In early December 1951 I went to see him in his downtown office. I made my story short and precise, presenting it in a broad perspective, with the real culprits in the forefront and hired writers in the background, and he grasped the situation splendidly.

Libel suits are disagreeable, Hays said. The higher the position a person occupies, the more unpleasant are the things that may be said about him without their constituting actionable statements. The same thing spoken by one neighbor about another would constitute libel or defamation. What, Hays asked, was left unsaid about Roosevelt? This is the price of arriving at a position of political, literary, artistic, or scientific importance.

"Would you advise me to publish the material in my hands with all the compromising letters? What is the legal situation?"

Hays answered that he would certainly advise it. Formally publication is an invasion of copyright since the letters written by a person are his property; but these letters spoke of me as an author and of my book, not of intimate affairs of their writers. Therefore, I could go ahead.

"And if some letters are marked 'Confidential,' what then?" I asked.

Hays thought for a few seconds and said that if he were in my place, he would publish them because they spoke of me and of my book.

He gave me a book of his own, inscribed it, and asked me to send him an inscribed copy of *Worlds in Collision.*

I was relieved. In all my life I have never summoned a man to court, not even to arbitration, and I have lived in various countries and have had contact with many people. Hays's opinion made me think that this time my personal aversion to litigation was not in conflict with the professional advice of an attorney who had spent half a century in the public forum.

I became inclined to make the people of America my jury. In accordance with Hays's advice, I began to consider writing a book that I would call *Stargazers and Gravediggers,* devoting to it the hours when I did not feel like working on my scientific books. The title was suggested by my wife, Elisheva. Yet though she gave the book its title, she was for a long time a silent adversary of the publication of this material.

A CLIENT OF NO IMPORTANCE

THE STORY ABOUT Macmillan's having dropped *Worlds in Collision* made the rounds of magazines and newspapers in Europe and other parts of the world, but here and there in some countries people interested in my work remained unaware of what had taken place in America. In January 1952 a clerk in a suburb of Antwerp, Belgium, wrote to Macmillan in New York, in English:

> In 1950 you have published a book, entitled "Worlds in Collision" by Dr. Immanuel Velikovsky. I bought that book through the intermediary of an Antwerp publishing house. I read it with an ever-waxing interest. The author announced a second work, "Ages in Chaos," which, as he explained, would follow his "Worlds in Collision" soon. I had this second book "Ages in Chaos" ordered by the same Antwerp bookseller who gets his books from your house in London. All this happened about a year ago. However, a few days ago, after repeatedly insisting, I learned that your House in London answered: "That book does not exist"! After consulting your catalogue, it appeared also that neither of Mr. Velikovsky's books were mentioned!
>
> Dear Sirs, I am to you a perfect stranger, and moreover I am a client of no importance at all, since in all my life I bought only one single book of yours. However, I badly want to read that "Ages in Chaos," which is said to be the extension . . . of that first book "Worlds in Collision" which was to me the big-

> gest revelation that ever struck me! So, I am determined to try about everything humanly possible to lay hands upon that same "Ages in Chaos."

He asked to be told whether the book had been published. By them? ". . . and do you mind telling me by whom?" And would they forward a letter he wrote to the author: "I do not know his address but I suppose that you do." In his letter to me he put the same question. Is my new book published? Nobody would tell him. "What else can I do than ask the author himself?"

I informed the correspondent that Macmillan had transferred my first book to Doubleday under pressure by a determined group of American scientists and that Doubleday would publish the second book in six or seven weeks.

In answer to my note, with which I enclosed a reprint of the debate in *Harper's,* June 1951, the Antwerp correspondent wrote in February 1952:

> I was greatly surprised, nay, astonished, to read that "a determined group of scientists" tried to boycott you and your work. But after some moments' reflection I was quite aware of the "why" and "how" of this firm opposition. You see, just like you yourself must have studied and laboured for many years to perform your present achievements (Worlds in Collision, Ages in Chaos, etc.) and to find your present conceptions, all these other men studied and laboured and formed themselves certain ideas. And now you come and tell them all their studying and labouring is [in] vain, or at least falsely directed. Of course they reject your notions. But if I understand this their first movement, which is altogether very human, I must say that I'll never be able to understand their second and following movements. For, if you are wrong, and there may be chances that you are wrong on some points, it is their right to correct your exposals in a scientific way. But I never heard that boycotting is a scientific way of proving anything.

MORE THAN A FAN LETTER

MY BOOK CALLED to its colors those scholars who had revolutionary ideas of their own but were hesitant to publish them, being afraid of the malevolence of their orthodox colleagues. A scholar who worked in the Special Collections at the Butler Library of Columbia University may serve as an example. He began his letter of January 18, 1952, by saying:

> I am not a physicist, nor a geologist or astronomer, but as a historian have been interested in these fields for several decades. I well remember when the Nobel Prize for Physics was awarded to Roentgen [in 1901]. At that time ions and electrons and radium emanation were still vague mysteries, not found in textbooks. . . .

Then he proceeded:

> You have written not only a fascinating book but have supported your contentions and conclusions by strong and indisputable proofs, the almost unanimous rejection and ridicule on the part of the "profession" notwithstanding. Your book has given me the answers to many questions that have puzzled me for years. You have made a fresh approach to old mysteries and have come to startlingly new, even revolutionary, conclusions that a person with an open mind can accept. Your proofs are presented with a clarity worthy of a lawyer's brief. You have

> convinced *this* juror! Allow me to congratulate you on your courage to fly in the face of convention, and to express my admiration for your immense labors.

I answered:

> At present it requires courage of a person employed by an academic institution to express solidarity with the heretical author of *Worlds in Collision.* For this reason a letter of appreciation is more than just a fan letter. You are right in regarding yourself as a member of a jury. My unorthodox procedure was to offer a novel theory to the jury of common sense, and not to the court of the closed chamber.

I added that in a few months, with the publication of the first volume of *Ages in Chaos,* I would antagonize the historians, too. At about the publication date of the new book the historian at the Columbia University library wrote once more:

> Your remark about "offending the historians" strikes a responsive chord in me. I am about to do the same—and it *does* take some courage to stake one's professional reputation on theories that will upset the applecarts of orthodox science. It is only a small phase of history that I am dealing with, but one hotly debated for three centuries. . . . Somehow your *Worlds in Collision* has encouraged me to give vent to my feelings, stored up for many years. I must thank you for stimulating me to action!

DE PROFUNDIS

MY BOOK BECAME a matter for discussion and debate on university campuses, in drawing rooms, even in prisons. A Lutheran chaplain at the Illinois State Penitentiary transmitted to me a letter from one of the inmates, of whom he wrote that he "is well educated and delights in spending very much of his time in research work." After making a few remarks pertinent to some issues in the book, as, for instance, that colorful sunrises were observed in Natal and Trinidad even *prior* to the eruption of Krakatoa, the prisoner went on:

> I am much hesitant about asking you to settle a discussion concerning yourself which has arisen in connection with the reading of your book in here. It is simply this: Does Dr. V. believe in God or is he an atheist? I have held, after reading your book a number of times, that you do believe in the God of Creation, and in Him as the Great Architect of the Universe, which you call him in your book on p. 84. Several fine minds have taken a decisive stand against me on this matter and hold that you have intentionally destroyed all reason to believe in the Miraculous and also in God. They have said that if you were to admit any belief in God, it would only be because of public opinion or because you felt it to be expedient to do so. If you would tell me, by writing to my chaplain, when you find the time, if you do believe in God, and if it is a firm conviction because of your scientific research, it will assist me in no small

> way. I would like to have the very truth whichever way the chips may fall if you care to give it. I hold that . . . there is no real difference of basic opinion between true science and religion.

This was the only time I answered this question, posed by many inquirers. The plight of the man in prison obliged me to give him a reply, and I did it in a few pages in longhand as a sign of my earnestness and respect for this man in trouble. In other instances, as, for example, when a professor at New England College, Henniker, New Hampshire, asked me: "Do you regard the catastrophic occurrences of the past as caused by nature or by some Supreme Being leading us somewhere?" I answered:

> They were caused by nature, and it is a matter of faith whether behind the acts of nature was the will of the Supreme Being. I have written a book of historical research; and I deliberately have left the problem open, because otherwise my work would be regarded as a theological or anti-theological discourse. The same question could be put to Roentgen: Does he regard the x-rays as caused by nature or created by a Supreme Intelligence? The matter of my religious feelings must not be a common domain. An astronomer of Princeton published a book on religious experience, and another book on the solar system; in the latter book he does not say that the planets are moved by the Supreme Being; in the other book he shows himself as a very religious, even very credulous man.

It is true, however, that the single reference to the Great Architect, in the story in which I describe in realistic terms the events at Mount Sinai, could be taken as a hint that I am not an atheist. I remember that Clifton Fadiman marked this place in my manuscript with a sign of wonder since in his opinion it contrasted with my "materialistic" approach to history.

It is my conviction, ever growing with research, that the more knowledge a man acquires and the deeper he penetrates into the plan of the universe, the more sublime for him is the First Cause.

file iii

PURSUING A RAY OF LIGHT

ALL THIS, which looms so important on these pages, occupied only a little of my time—through the winter I was busy in checking and rechecking various references in *Ages in Chaos*, the first volume of which was, after a few delays caused by my slow tempo, scheduled for spring. Dr. Walter Federn was very scrupulous and compelled me to go into endless library work, sometimes opening a hundred volumes to check on one word. Finally I returned the last set of proofs—four or five times I required new proofs—and I went with Elisheva to Arizona and California, traveling by train. We saw the Painted Desert, the Grand Canyon, and the Arizona Crater. In Los Angeles I went to see Professor Walter S. Adams, who had retired from the directorship of the Mount Wilson and Mount Palomar observatories and continued working in the Solar Observatory in Pasadena.

I had started a correspondence with Adams in the summer of 1946, when I asked him for information concerning the spectra of planetary atmospheres. In 1950, after I had sent him a copy of *Worlds in Collision* with a short letter, he wrote me at length:

> I differ from the critics whom you mention in having definitely read your book. Its impression upon me has been mixed. In your introductory chapter you have, I think, made a fairly reasonable statement regarding the origin of the solar system. Astronomers simply do not yet know the full answer to this question, although some progress is being made through the

presentation from time to time of tentative hypotheses for consideration and criticism.

You must have devoted an enormous amount of time and effort to your compilation of the mass of myths, traditions, inscriptions, and quotations you have assembled. I feel that you have done a real service to scholars and the public as well in bringing together in one place material which is difficult of access and requires research to find. On the other hand I cannot help feeling that you have overestimated the value of this material as evidence. Primitive peoples in small countries, with little or no means of outside communication, are, like children, prone to exaggeration. A volcanic eruption is an earthshaking event, and no doubt the inhabitants of Pompeii thought the entire world was coming to an end. Similarly with great storms, fires, and tidal waves.

Then, too, many of the myths and traditions may have been imaginative writing, and should be considered as such. . . .

Your quotations tending to show that Venus was not seen by primitive peoples are interesting, but at the same time constitute only negative evidence. I find it much easier to believe that Venus for some unknown reason was not enumerated than that the planet did not exist at that time. . . .

He continued to offer constructive criticism from the point of view of present-day astronomy. Then, toward the end, he wrote: "I have tried to be quite objective in this letter since I dislike some of the almost abusive criticisms which have been written about your book. They are uncalled for no matter how strongly their writers feel on the subject."

I quote parts of my answer:

I carefully read, then reread your letter of July 28th. It was the first letter of an astronomer in this country who read and sincerely debated the problems of my book. For this, I thank you.

Your arguments raised questions; however, I believe that these questions can be answered. The first argument is the belief that our ancestors were much more easily impressed by phenomena of nature so that they, like children, would exaggerate the extent and the measure of such disturbances. I believe that this comparing of the ancients with children is not warranted. From the study of history I am prone to think that, if anything, they were more stoical than we are. You give the example of Pompeii. The best document of the catastrophe is its description by an eyewitness, Pliny the Younger, in his letters to Tacitus. Although the catastrophe of eruption was accompanied by a strong earthquake and by a great tidal wave with cinders and pumice falling from the sky in a profound darkness, the eye-witness did not regard what was before him as a worldwide catastrophe.

It is not just a tidal wave or an earthquake or the eruption of a volcano that we have carried over from old traditions, historical inscriptions and legends. It is the story of the sun changing its place and the world burning, or the polar star changing its place, or Venus joining the family of planets. . . .

Perhaps I delude myself, but the idea crosses my mind that this correspondence of ours will not be lost in the wastebasket of history.

I do not know how to express my gratitude to you better than by writing a detailed answer to your letter.

Pleasant in correspondence (I received several long letters, some in his careful handwriting), Adams was pleasant also in personal contact.

Adams shared his studio with Harold Babcock, whose son, Horace, had not long before discovered in a star an intermittent 7,000 gauss magnetic polarity—reappearing every so many hours. Babcock, the father, asked me what it could be; I answered that the polar magnetic axis of the star turns its two poles toward us. This was the explanation at which the Babcocks had just arrived, and he showed his pleasure.

On the way back east via San Francisco and after traveling over the Rockies in a sight-seeing car, in the station in Chicago I found a copy of *Ages in Chaos,* which I had not yet seen—it was the beginning of March.

ELEVATED TO UNORTHODOXY: THE AMERICAN PHILOSOPHICAL SOCIETY

About the time of the publication date of *Ages in Chaos,* past the middle of April 1952, John O'Neill called to tell me that the annual meeting of the American Philosophical Society would hold a symposium, "Some Unorthodoxies of Modern Science," and that it would take place in a few days. One of the papers scheduled to be read was by Cecilia Payne-Gaposchkin of Harvard University on "the Velikovsky hypothesis." O'Neill advised me to be present. I agreed with him that we should travel together, and my wife and I met him at Pennsylvania Station in New York.

The very fact that the oldest scientific society in America—founded by Benjamin Franklin in 1743 and often regarded as a counterpart of the Academie Française or the Royal Society—twenty-four months after the publication of *Worlds in Collision,* was to debate the book at its annual meeting was recognition of the importance of my theory or hypothesis. If my work was a hoax or the product of a crank, as it had repeatedly been declared to be, why should the illustrious company of the "immortals" travel from all parts of the United States, their fares being paid by the society, to listen to another disposal of the theory embodied in *Worlds in Collision?* The other two "unorthodoxies" were telepathy and dowsing, both problems of very long standing. With an introductory paper and a concluding one, altogether five papers were on the symposium program for the afternoon session of April 24, the first day of the annual meeting. This symposium was arranged as the main event.

In Philadelphia we found the society building humming with

people. The members and their spouses were in a reception hall partaking of a buffet lunch. In an antechamber O'Neill introduced me to the president of the society, Professor Edwin G. Conklin, an octogenarian who scarcely took an active part in the proceedings. Elisheva and I retreated to the empty conference hall and chose a place at a side wall close to a bust of Benjamin Franklin. From this point I could observe the audience; they, however, had to turn their heads to the right in order to observe me.

One of the early birds in the room was Professor Albright, a member of the society. When he saw me, he was obviously amused and excitedly passed on the word to his neighbors, who looked curiously at the man by the wall. Albright was very lively, and he acted like a boy in grammar school who whispers news to his classmates.

When the hall was filled and the meeting was about to start, I went over to the chairman on the podium, identified myself, and asked to be given a chance to answer after the papers were read. He promised me this.

The opening address was by I. Bernard Cohen, professor of the history of science at Harvard and a collaborator of Dr. Conant's. This young man of ability had taken over the editorship of *Isis* from Professor Sarton.

The paper that Cohen prepared, judged by the mimeographed abstract that was distributed, sounded rather encouraging for the future of my theory. I reproduce this abstract in its entirety.

ABSTRACT

ORTHODOXY AND SCIENTIFIC PROCESSES

I. Bernard Cohen

> The history of science shows that most of the great revolutionary scientific theories, hypotheses, and even announcements of new effects have met with hostility on the part of those who preferred to cling to artificial modes of thought. This phenomenon seems to be part of a more general trait of the human species, namely, an inertia of the mind, or a resistance to change, or a kind of "scientific orthodoxy." A number of case histories illustrate varying patterns. For example, what is orthodox at one time may be unorthodox at another; at first astrology was scorned by the astronomers (ancient Babylonia), later it became orthodox (Ptolemy), but today it is beyond the

pale. Even the greatest of scientific revolutionaries cling to orthodoxies; e.g., Galileo, despite his attack on ancient scientific doctrines, clung steadfastly to the doctrine that all planetary motions must be explained by combinations of circular movements (as taught by Plato, Aristotle, Ptolemy) and he rejected the theory of elliptical orbits advanced by Kepler. Varying degrees of orthodoxy prevent scientists from accepting the "logical" consequences of their own discoveries, e.g., Planck and the Einstein theory of photons, Dalton and Avogadro's hypothesis, Baer and the theory of evolution.

Two general conclusions may be noted. (1) It is difficult to tell at any given time whether or not any given unorthodoxy actually may contain seeds for further scientific progress. One of the reasons for rejecting Velikovsky is that his ideas imply a revision of much of orthodox physical theory; yet it is difficult to predict just how much of present physical theory will still seem valid three centuries from now; Einstein, for example, cannot bring himself to accept the conclusions and premises of present quantum mechanics. Yet we must note that Velikovsky's ideas imply that gross phenomena did not in the past occur as they do now (e.g., those connected with the principle of inertia*). An eminent group of scientists condemned Mesmerism, yet that practice contained seeds of important scientific knowledge when seen in a new light.

(2) The inertia of scientific orthodoxy is not entirely inimical to scientific progress. Had scientists to test every new idea ever proposed, they would have no time for research. The hurdle of orthodoxy acts as a screen permitting only useful and well substantiated ideas to pass. Hence, even though we may point to a number of delays in the acceptance of new ideas, we would have difficulty in conceiving the true progress of the sciences without the restraining bond of orthodoxy.

This was certainly a radical change in approach. Discussing my theory in a historical perspective and saying as much as he did, Cohen must have had in mind the judgment of future years. Otherwise, it would have been very foolish of him even to mention my name among the illustrious names of former and present genera-

* This statement by Cohen is erroneous. I do not question the validity of mechanical laws, and certainly not of inertia. But in celestial motion I do not discount the role of electromagnetic fields of force, in addition to that of gravitation and inertia.

tions and to discuss the possibility of my theory's proving itself right. To join the choir of detractors is more secure today, but what about the verdict of tomorrow? In the paper he read, he said, according to O'Neill's report in the *Herald Tribune* on May 4:

> I do not know of any scientist who was not antagonistic to, or who welcomed, a change that wholly replaced and rendered useless his own work. It would thus be a perversion of the facts to say that all scientists welcome all changes. . . . There exists in science a general resistance to changes in fundamental concepts and theories and this constitues a kind of scientific orthodoxy. The degree of violence with which a new idea is rejected by scientific orthodoxy may prove to be an index of its importance.

But the general tone and content of Cohen's speech was less favorable than his abstract.

The second and the fourth papers had for their subjects "An Evaluation of Extra-sensory Perception," the experiments in telepathy of Dr. Joseph Banks Rhine at Duke University being chosen as representing this field of research, and "Dowsing," or the practice of finding water with the help of a divining rod. The problem dealt with in the first paper on telepathy had interested me years past; in 1931 I published a paper, with a Preface by Professor Eugen Bleuler, the leading European psychiatrist of his time, "The Physical Existence of the World of Thought,"* in which I discussed this topic. Sigmund Freud, in correspondence with me, claimed that he had "very similar, in some parts identical ideas," then not yet published, on the subject.†

As for the divining rod, I do not know the explanation of the phenomenon. However, its practice is very old. The story of Moses who struck a rock with his rod and caused water to flow shows that it was already known in ancient times. In modern times governmental agencies employ the services of the diviners with their rods. I wondered why under the heading of "Some Unorthodoxies in Modern Science" my theory found a place with two ancient beliefs and practices.

* *"Über die Energetik der Psyche und die physikalische Existenz der Gedankenwelt," Zeitschrift für die Gesamte Neurologie und Psychiatrie,* vol. 133 (1931).

† See my article "Very Similar, Almost Identical" in *Psychoanalysis and the Future* (1957), pp. 14–17, 152–153.

"WE ARE SHAKING IN OUR SHOES"

THE THIRD PAPER was by Cecilia Payne-Gaposchkin. She herself was on her way to Europe, but before boarding the ship, she addressed a letter to the meeting of the American Philosophical Society in which she stated that on her journey she would read my *Ages in Chaos* and that certainly she would find it as erroneous as *Worlds in Collision.*

According to the printed program of the annual meeting her paper, "The Velikovsky Hypothesis" (time: thirty minutes), was to be read by Donald Menzel, professor of astrophysics at Harvard University, but it was read by Dr. Karl K. Darrow, physicist at the Bell Telephone Laboratories. Menzel did not come, for he was preparing a paper for the annual meeting of the American Physical Society to be held in Washington a few days later.

Professor Payne-Gaposchkin specialized in disproving Velikovsky. She had already published a number of articles, starting with the piece "Nonsense, Dr. Velikovsky!" the story of which I told previously, followed by "Retort to Velikovsky" in *Science News Letter* and *Science Digest* and a longer article in *Popular Astronomy* (June 1950).

Once more she tried to show that I was wrong in quoting my sources. She started with this instance: Was it an angel that destroyed the army of Sennacherib, as related in one place in the Scriptures, or a blast, as related in another place? Preferring the first version, she proved me wrong for quoting the second, too. I shall analyze this part of her paper on subsequent pages on the basis of a written version, published half a year later.

Listening there, in an audience with several Nobel prizewinners, to a discussion of whether it was an angel or a natural phenomenon that destroyed the Assyrian host, I thought of the scholastic debates of five or six centuries ago, when theologians quarreled over how many angels could stand on the head of a pin. In such an assembly I would have thought that the astronomical, physical, archaeological, and geological problems of my theory would come to the fore.

With regard to these scientific problems, Payne-Gaposchkin confined herself largely to saying in the concluding paragraphs of her paper that astronomers were not afraid of catastrophes, and indeed had only recently accepted a theory of great collisions, but they would not agree to catastrophes so recent. She wrote:

> Since the publication of *Worlds in Collision* I have noted, with some amusement, the progress and publication of several researches in the realm of astronomy that put the fireworks of *Worlds in Collision* quite in the shade. One is the demonstration that the distribution and motions of the asteroids, or minor planets, can be interpreted as the result of not one but several collisions between small planets. The result was not a mere change in orientation of axis or rate of rotation: the planets were smashed to fragments.

Against these "spectacular findings" Velikovsky's suggestions were "far milder." Then what was so impossible in Velikovsky's theory? He placed the catastrophic events too close in time—in a historical age.

The reason for the acceptance of an astronomer's theory of catastrophes in the solar system was that it is "based on known facts—careful measurements of the motions of hundreds of asteroids, laborious calculations of their orbits, and the discovery that these orbits are closely related to one another in a way that suggests an origin by explosion. There have been catastrophic events within the solar system, though not within the past three thousand years."

Payne-Gaposchkin did not name the author of the theory she described. Since the publication of my book two theories on catastrophic events in the solar system involving the asteroids had been presented, one by Kuiper, the other by Whipple. Kuiper computed that planets collided at an early time somewhere between the orbits of Jupiter and Mars. Whipple calculated the orbits and the motion of the asteroids and announced that a comet collided with the swarms of asteroids between the orbits of Jupiter and Mars, throwing these asteroids off their orbits, for the first time 4,700 years ago and for the second time 1,500 years ago, the latter being even more recent than the dates of catastrophes described in *Worlds in Collision.*

Payne-Gaposchkin must have known of the theory of Whipple, director of her observatory, a position he had taken over from Shapley. She must have known that he ascribed "these spectacular findings" to a historical age well *within* the past 3,000 years.

In the same paper she said: "Every scientific man, every man who devotes his life sincerely to the advancement of knowledge, commits himself to certain loyalties. His loyalties are to principles, not to dogmas; to respect for evidence—all the evidence, not merely such as fulfils his expectations. . . ."

Payne-Gaposchkin did not follow her principle of loyalty; nor did Whipple find it necessary to correct her paper where it concerned his theory, after it had been read or printed.

Payne-Gaposchkin quoted from my interview with Harvey Breit of *The New York Times,* given on the publication date of *Worlds in Collision,* in which I said:

> Science . . . has become dogmatic. . . . A scientist must swear loyalty to the established dogmas. The first rule of the scientific attitude is to study, then to think, and then to express an opinion. A reverse of this . . . is exactly what has been done by a group of scientists who have expressed opinions about my work! (Omissions by Gaposchkin.)

And she proceeded to say: "That a considerable number of intelligent people [who] share this view ought to make the man of science take stock of himself. To what extent is it true? and, whether it is true or not, why is it so generally held?" She did not recognize that these words of mine referred to the author of "Nonsense, Dr. Velikovsky!," who admitted, four weeks after the publication of that piece, that she had not read the book when she wrote it, though she discussed its content, its sources, and even its language.

She went on:

> We who are engaged in research are not concerned in preserving the existing framework of theories. We spent our lives

> searching for the wherewithal to modify and supplant them. The discovery of discordant facts is cause for rejoicing, not consternation. If Velikovsky had adduced any real evidence that compelled a revision of the laws of celestial mechanics, astronomers would have accepted the facts, and the challenge, with delight. His supporters imagine that we are shaking in our shoes. This is partly true: we *are* shaking, but with laughter.

But why should the entire scientific collegium shake in its shoes because of a book? If it shook with laughter, all the worse, for ridicule is the argument of the mob, and this argument alone, plus suppression, was employed by the professors.

There must have been a worm eating inside: Is the new theory perchance right, if only in part, and very many accepted notions wrong? Payne-Gaposchkin declared:

> There have, admittedly, been many ideas that were rejected at first, but, like the heliocentric [Copernican] theory of the solar system, have survived to become the headstone in the corner. We try to remember, in the face of unorthodox views, that "some true thought might also occur to another man. . . ."
>
> But to accuse scientific men of dogmatism, as a reaction against the results of what is perhaps the most amazing example of a shattering of accepted concepts on record, seems to be a non-sequitur of the first order.

Is it a non sequitur? Only one hour earlier her colleague Professor Cohen, in his paper in which he spoke of *Worlds in Collision,* had said: "There exists in science a general resistance to changes in fundamental concepts and theories and this constitutes a kind of scientific orthodoxy. The degree of violence with which a new idea is rejected by scientific orthodoxy may prove to be an index of its importance."

For the third time the audience was occupied with my theory when Professor Edwin G. Boring, a psychologist, also from Harvard (like Cohen and Payne-Gaposchkin), read the concluding address of the symposium, "The Validation of Scientific Belief." He addressed his words, or, better, his barbs, to me. According to the prepared abstract, he was as sharply opposed to Payne-Gaposchkin as he was to me. But in the paper he read he made me the sole target of his humor. His remarks evoked laughs and cheered up the audience. In one of the first rows a man turned his face to me at every gibe and laughed with a grotesque grimace. This he did many times in full view of the audience. He was certainly ill-mannered, his behavior only showing the depth of the hatred engendered by my book. If such a scene had appeared in a motion picture, the antics of the person playing the grimacing member of the American Philosophical Society would be regarded as bad acting, so exaggerated and overdone it would seem. He was shaking in his shoes.

"SIT DOWN BEFORE A FACT AS A LITTLE CHILD"

The Lutheran magazine a few days later described me as a silent figure seated in the midst of a jeering audience. But I kept silent only as long as my opponents spoke. The chairman announced that after a short intermission following the five papers, Dr. Velikovsky, who was present, would have a chance to reply, and he offered me half an hour. As I listened, I made some notes. When I stood before the audience with my papers before me, I started by thanking this illustrious 200-year-old society for devoting an afternoon to my theory. Then I said:

> When my theory first came out, scientists called it nonsense. Later they called it a hoax, then heresy. Today it is promoted to an "unorthodoxy in science." I hope that it will not become a dogma in the days to come. As for Mrs. Gaposchkin, who has spent the last two years combating my theory in numerous articles, she deserves that her chair at Harvard should be called the "Velikovsky Chair of Astronomy."

There were laughs, and I had already won the audience a little. At this point I noticed that the few notes I had jotted down as leads in my reply were lost among the papers I had with me, and evaluating the poor impression that fumbling among papers would make, I decided to proceed without their help.

Our daughter Shulamit arrived from Princeton just in time to listen to me, and I was glad that she was there. There were also three or four friends and followers, who came as guests.

My answer was directed to astronomers, geologists, and historians, the first group receiving the main attention. I made it clear that the conflict is not between my theory and astronomical facts, but between astronomical facts and the teachings of astronomers. "You [the scientists] don't believe in facts—you only believe in theories you created yourself," quoted the Associated Press in its report of the meeting.*

I vividly described the cometary tails which, like rigid rods, revolve at terrific velocities when circling the sun; the behavior of solar protuberances; and many other similar conflicts of theory and fact. I spoke of the great fear of admitting electrical charges and magnetic fields, existing as they do, into the field of celestial mechanics, as if there could be sterile electricity or impotent magnetism. I saw the attentively listening face of Arthur Compton, winner of the Nobel Prize in physics, in the back of the very quiet auditorium, and felt generally that the audience was following me closely. I referred to the work of Joseph Prestwich, professor at Oxford in the eighties of the last century, on the great cataclysm that had left its marks all over Western Europe and on the islands of the Mediterranean, with splintered animal bones filling the fissures of many rocks to overflowing.

Turning to the historians, I faced Albright and told of the recent findings of Professor Claude F. A. Schaeffer, renowned archaeologist. In a large volume published by the Oxford University Press, Schaeffer showed that every excavated site of the ancient East, from Troy to Persia and from the Caucasus to Egypt, gave evidence that the entire ancient world had been repeatedly overwhelmed by great catastrophes; that the greatest of them occurred at the very end of the Middle Kingdom in Egypt and actually terminated it—the very time when, according to both my books, such a catastrophe took place.

I finished by quoting from Thomas Huxley: "Sit down before a fact as a little child, be prepared to give up every pre-conceived notion, follow humbly wherever and to whatever abysses nature leads, or you shall learn nothing."

Prolonged applause followed and continued as I walked up the aisle. The chairman followed me and spoke to me, praising the

* As printed in the Palm Beach (Florida) *Post*, April 27, 1952.

tenor of my address. In the hall outside stood Professor Albright, who only a few days earlier had published an attack on my new book, *Ages in Chaos.* With animated expression and hands outstretched to me he said: "I admire your coming and speaking as you did in the camp of your adversaries." Recalling an accusation he had made in his review a few days before, I asked: "Where did I violate historical facts in my book?" He did not give me any instance, but instead, he asked how I would harmonize my synchronization of the catastrophe that ended the Middle Kingdom and the catastrophes of the days of the Exodus with Schaeffer's work, since he adhered to the conventional chronology. To this I could answer that Schaeffer did not insist on his "absolute dating." ("The value of the absolute dates adopted by us depends, of course, on the degree of precision attained in the study of the historical documents which may be used for the purposes of chronology."*) Then Albright asked me how I would explain the presence of letters signed by Assuruballit in the el Amarna correspondence, and one or more questions concerning *Ages in Chaos,* and I gave him my explanations.

Here a gentleman who stood next to Albright showed signs of great displeasure. I asked his name. "Chaney," he said. Turning from the Orientalist to the paleobotanist, whose name was familiar to me,† I asked him a question from his field and concerning his part of the country (he had come from California to attend the meeting): "How do you explain the finding of human bones in the asphalt pit of La Brea under the bones of a vulture of an extinct species?" He was forced to admit: "I don't know." Then he told me that *Harper's* had asked him to write a rebuttal of my theory but that he had refused in order not to give more publicity to my work. As soon as he finished saying this, he repeated it. On leaving, I extended my hand, and he had to make a visible effort to take it.

A man followed me to the cloakroom in the basement and engaged me in conversation. I listened long for what he would produce, and he slowly came to his point. Finally he got it out. It was an anecdote, and he began to giggle and choke as he came to the punch line: "I do not need to eat the entire apple in order to know that it is wormy"—this in defense of scientists who discussed my theory without having read my book. I asked him his name, but he refused to say, and content, he left the room. He had the last word.

The next day the Philadelphia *Evening Bulletin* reported:

* Claude F. A. Schaeffer, *Stratigraphie comparée* (1948), p. 566.
† Ralph W. Chaney

The staid, august American Philosophical Society rocked with controversy yesterday over the theories of Dr. Immanuel Velikovsky expressed in his book *Worlds in Collision.*

Its members, meeting in the society's quarters on Independence Square, heard one of the most violent arguments presented before this scholarly body in many a year.

One member declared that Benjamin Franklin, a founder of the society, who looked down on the gathering from a portrait on the wall, would have relished every minute of it.

"LET THEM THROW THE BRICK"

FROM AUGUST 1942 until the spring of 1952, almost ten years, Professor Robert H. Pfeiffer followed the development and the fate of my reconstruction of ancient history, *Ages in Chaos.* He read its first draft and, as it encompassed ever larger areas, the additional chapters; he was unfailingly benevolent to me and my work through all those years. Repeatedly he expressed the wish to see my work published so that his students at Harvard and Boston universities might deliberate on its merits, taking sides and analyzing it in an earnest endeavor to find the historical truth. On one occasion in 1949 he wrote:

> Dr. Velikovsky discloses immense erudition and extraordinary ingenuity. He writes well and documents all his statements with the original ancient sources.... His conclusions are amazing, unheard of, revolutionary, sensational. If his findings are accepted by historians, all present histories for the period before Alexander the Great (who died in 323 B.C.) must be discarded, and completely rewritten. If Dr. Velikovsky is right, this volume is the greatest contribution to the investigation of ancient times ever written.... I would like my students to read it, being convinced that only out of the discussion of opposite views may the truth, or an approximation thereto, be attained.

These words did not signify that Professor Pfeiffer agreed with me, but he reckoned with the possibility that I had discovered the correct sequence of historical events, though if he had to choose, he would probably think it safer to cast his vote for the old, established, and never-before-challenged order of events. On the other hand, to my request that he point out some intrinsic difficulty or inconsistency in my reconstruction, he answered in a letter that he knew of none; to my request that he explain certain enigmatic matters in conventionally written history, like the use of Greek letters of the fourth century by the pharaoh Ramses III of the twelfth century before the present era, he conceded that he knew of no valid explanation. Altogether he reserved his opinion of the ultimate correctness of my work until after the debate, with all its pros and cons, which he expected to follow the publication of the entire work, the two volumes of *Ages in Chaos.* After the publication of *Worlds in Collision* I had asked his advice regarding the order of publication of my works, and he had expressed the opinion that both volumes of *Ages in Chaos* should be published simultaneously.

When, in the beginning of 1952, the first volume of *Ages in Chaos* was on the press, the text for the dust jacket was being composed. Excerpts from Pfeiffer's letters were selected. They dated from 1942, 1945, 1947, and 1949, thus conveying to the prospective buyer of the book the idea that the work had been long in the making and thoroughly discussed with a scientist of international repute.

I telephoned Pfeiffer at his Cambridge, Massachusetts, home and told him of the publisher's desire to use these excerpts for the jacket. He gave his consent. I read him the excerpts. He again agreed. Then I voiced a warning: "Please think it over again. A brick will be thrown into your window, too."

"Let them throw the brick," was his reply.

An American born in Florence, married to a Florentine woman of unusual charm, Pfeiffer had taken on the aura of the Renaissance that still filled that city, and it could be felt in his generous turn of mind. A scholar who spent his life on the Old Testament and its prophets, he had also acquired, in his search for truth, the adamant streak of the ancient seers.

Upon my explanation of Pfeiffer's position, the publisher printed in the blurb: "Without identifying himself with its conclusions, he [Pfeiffer] recognized their great significance." In the acknowledgments I stated: "Neither subscribing to my thesis nor rejecting it, he kept an open mind, believing that only objective and free discussion could clarify the issue." Thus Pfeiffer's attitude was correctly presented.

In order that there be no misunderstanding, Pfeiffer, on his own initiative, put in writing his authorization to use excerpts from his letters.

One can imagine the consternation that must have been felt on the Harvard University campus when *Ages in Chaos* was published carrying four quotations from Pfeiffer on the back of the jacket, and the passage "If Dr. Velikovsky is right, etc.," repeated on the front. The word "if" should have immediately conveyed Pfeiffer's stand.

Two weeks after the publication of *Ages in Chaos* Pfeiffer received a letter from Shapley:

> At a meeting next week a considerable group composed of Harvard Faculty plus the Nieman Fellows, I am asked to speak on Velikovsky, the dowsers, and the wave of credulity. This is an off-record comment on a number of current unorthodoxies. Dr. [William F.] Albright [Orientalist and archaeologist] has sent me a copy of his review of "Ages in Chaos," published ten days ago in the Herald-Tribune, and I have a considerable report on the meeting of the American Philosophical Society in Philadelphia last week when Dr. Velikovsky was present for Mrs. Gaposchkin's paper.
>
> Naturally in commenting on "Ages in Chaos" I shall want to comment also on the jacket, and the statement credited to you on the top of the front cover page. The statement is pretty obviously out-of-context. It occurred to me that you might like to give me the whole of the context, just so that unfair conclusions will not be drawn. And also we should be very happy to know what your reaction is to this use of your correct statement of the facts concerning "Ages in Chaos." I and others would naturally like to know whether the quotation has been used with your permission; and if not, whether you are inclined to protest.
>
> Please do not take these inquiries of mine as criticisms, or as invading your privacies and freedoms. I shall want to present to my Faculty colleagues the actual facts of the case.
>
> Incidentally, Dr. Walter S. Adams, former Director of the Mount Wilson Observatory, wrote a kind letter to Velikovsky with respect to "Worlds in Collision" and he is unfortunately

used extensively by the publishers to sell and vindicate that volume.

As for the last statement, to my knowledge the publisher did not quote Adams or even mention him in any ad or any other public announcement; the only reference to him that was made was in my debate with Stewart in *Harper's* of June 1951.

It is not surprising that among the members of the faculties at Harvard there was wonder. For two and a half years a man regarded as a great authority in the field of science had done everything in his power to destroy the reputation of *Worlds in Collision* and of its author, and at the end of that time the windows of the bookstores were displaying a new book by the same author bearing the momentous words of Pfeiffer, from their university, a recognized authority in ancient history and an international authority on the Old Testament. So Shapley summoned the meeting, or was summoned to the meeting, to speak before the members of the faculties and the intelligentsia of the campus.

Pfeiffer's answer I have not read, but he said he was entitled to have his opinion as Albright had his. Certainly he wrote that the excerpts had been approved by him for use by Doubleday.

For a while I feared that Pfeiffer might lose his position as curator of the Semitic Museum at Harvard University and his other academic positions there, as had happened with Putnam and with Atwater.

A few weeks later Pfeiffer received a letter from the director of the observatory of the University of Arizona, Edwin F. Carpenter. He inquired of Pfeiffer whether he really intended to support the new book with the weight of his own professional judgment: "Or is the publishing industry continuing to live down to the same standard of ethics which characterized its promotion of the same author's preceding book?" Carpenter spoke of the "ethical nadir" to which the publishing world had descended, being blind to the fact that it was not the publishing world, but the behavior of the scientists, that was at its "ethical nadir."

Good and bad books have been printed; good and bad books have been advertised. And nobody protested. But scientific dogma was questioned, and cries of indignation erupted from observatories and were repeated when my purely historical book was published.

A LETTER FROM AN EGYPTOLOGIST

ON MAY 29, 1952—the same day that the director of the Steward Observatory at Tucson protested to Pfeiffer about his support of my *Ages in Chaos,* a work in the fields of archaeology, history, and chronology—Professor Etienne Drioton, historian and world authority on Egyptology, wrote me a most delightful letter from Cairo. At the time Drioton held the position of *directeur général du service des antiquités,* once occupied by G. Maspero. In this capacity he had under his care all the antiquities—monuments in the field and in the museum, the famous Cairo Museum included—and every excavation made in Egypt, by whatever agency or learned society, was under his supervision. Following the national revolution in Egypt Drioton returned to his other post as chief curator of the Egyptian Department of the Louvre Museum in Paris. I had never before corresponded with him, but in Cairo he received a complimentary copy of *Ages in Chaos.*

Cairo, May 29, 1952

Dear Doctor,

You have so kindly sent me a copy of your fine book, *Ages in Chaos,* which I received this morning, and which I have already read almost in its entirety, so stirring and fascinating is it.

You certainly overturn, and with what zest!, many of our historical assumptions, which we have considered established. But you do it with total absence of prejudice and with impar-

> tial and complete documentation, all of which is most gratifying. One might dispute point by point your conclusions: whether one admits them or not, they will have posed the problems anew and made it necessary to discuss them in depth in the light of your new hypotheses. Your fine book will have been in every way of great use to science.
>
> I thank you warmly for having sent it to me and I beg you to accept, dear Doctor, the assurance of my sentiments of cordial devotion.
>
> Etienne Drioton
> General Director
> Department of Antiquities*

What I cherish most in his reaction is not his praise of the readability of the book, which kept him tied to it from the moment he received the book until later that same day when, already close to the end, he wrote me his letter. Nor is it even his admission that many doctrines with respect to history, thought to be firmly established, have now been unsettled. Rather, it is in his statement that I have given a complete, fully objective, unbiased presentation of the facts. Egyptian history and antiquities are the main subject of *Ages in Chaos* (especially the first volume); to write it, I consulted and took notes from many thousands of books and articles. Drioton, who knows the facts of Egyptian history and archaeology as probably nobody else, attested in his letter that on no point did I suppress any evidence. Ignorant reviewers, who had never before heard the name of Thutmose III or Amenhotep III, conducted a short trial and condemned the book as "farrago."

* *"Cher Docteur, Vous avez eu la bonté de me faire envoyer votre beau livre "Ages in Chaos," que j'ai reçu ce matin, et que j'ai déjà lu presque en entier, tellement il est passionnant et attachant.*

Certes vous bousculez, et avec quel entrain!, beaucoup de nos positions historiques que nous pensions acquises. Mais vous le faites avec une absence totale de préjugés et une information impartiale et complète, qui sont des plus sympathiques. On pourra discuter pied à pied vos conclusions: qu'on les admette ou ne les admette pas, elles auront posé à nouveau les problèmes et obligé à les discuter à fond à la lumière de vos nouvelles hypothèses. Votre beau livre aura été, de toutes façons, très utile à la science.

Je vous remercie chaleureusement de me l'avoir envoyé et je vous prie d'agréer, cher Docteur, l'assurance de mes sentiments de cordial dévouement. Etienne Drioton."

A BOY FROM TEXAS

IN THOSE DAYS when I observed with regret that even new evidence would not compel the scientific groups to reconsider their stand, I enjoyed several letters of a high school boy:

> I am 17 years old and a senior in high school. When I first moved to Waco (Texas), I decided to visit the Public Library. The first book I checked out was your "Ages in Chaos." I have read it several times and I finally bought it. I also have "Earth in Upheaval" and have read "Worlds in Collision." I was interested in your theory on historical catastrophes but I was most interested in your revised chronology of ancient history.
>
> After I had finished Volume I of Ages in Chaos, I tried to reconstruct the last volume. While I can't get the inscriptions themselves, I think that I have done fairly well.

He described his own library—the books he had received from his elder brother, like John B. Bury's *History of Greece* and George Rawlinson's translations of Herodotus and Thucydides—and the books he had consulted in the public library, like the *Cambridge Ancient History* or *Egypt from the Records* by M. E. Jones, and wrote:

> I have made these points: Herodotus tells of Necho at Cadytis supposed to be Carchemish (city of Chemosh?) where he fought Nebuchadnezzar. [This battle] is the same as Ramses

> II's so-called victory over the Hittites at Kadesh. Seti I equals Psamtik I, and the 26th Dynasty is the 19th and 20th. I think that Merneptah is the Pharaoh Hophra.

He wrote me that he would read Manetho as quoted by Josephus ("from a 1832 edition of my brother Robert who has an oversupply of books") and "try to get all the information I can out of the *Cambridge Ancient History* about the Egyptians, Hittites, Assyrians, Babylonians, Hebrews, Phoenicians, Greeks, and Persians. . . . I don't know when the second volume of 'Ages in Chaos' will be published so I would like very much if you would help me by giving me some hint as to how I can finish this reconstruction. The end of the first volume left me dangling and I wanted to find out the rest."

I wrote him that his letter was a pleasure to me. Since the publication of the first volume many readers had written me concerning the sequel of *Ages.* I told him:

> But nobody of all these who corresponded with me came by himself upon the main clue, in your words: "the 26th Dynasty is the 19th and 20th." Omit "the 20th," and you are right! I congratulate you; and I firmly believe that should you dedicate yourself to historical studies you will be someday a great historian.

I gave him some clues. I advised him to compare the record of Ramses III about his war with intruding Pereset with Diodorus's account of the wars of the pharaoh of the Thirtieth Dynasty, Nectanebo I, with the Persians. I also advised him to contemplate these questions: Why did Homer, who lived in Asia Minor and who mentioned in the *Iliad* every small tribe of that area, know nothing of the Hittites, and why did no other Greek author know anything of their empire or late kingdoms? And why were the remains of the empire always found *above* the Phrygian level (of the seventh century)? Or why were no Chaldean scripts ever found, though the ancient authors mentioned their secret knowledge and separate language? "Should you progress with your work with the help of these clues write me again."

Only a short time passed, and his second letter was on its way. He explained the motives that brought him to identify Ramses I with Necho I, Psammetichos I with Seti I, Merneptah with

Hophrah, and Ramses II with Necho II (he also noticed that the building of the canal connecting the Mediterranean through the Nile with the Red Sea was ascribed to both of them).

He came up with original ideas concerning the languages of the archives of Hattusas, in which the Lydian, the Phrygian, the Carian, and the Median, and the Chaldean, too, figure in modern books under names of nonexisting races ascribed to wrong centuries in the distorted scheme of ancient history.

In his third letter my correspondent from Waco let me know that he had obtained the information from the archaeological societies about the selection of archaeologist and historian as a profession and of his decision to follow my advice. Since a truth discovered on one's own has a much stronger evidential value than a truth indoctrinated, I felt secure that the reconstructed scheme of history would not wither in an all too long academic winter. Whatever the reception of the present generation, there will be among the coming generation young men and women who will continue my work and advance it, not allowing it to stagnate or become a dogma. Thus, when many thought me discouraged and even disgraced, I carried an inner smile, thinking of the kindled light.

THE "HERCULEAN LABOR" OF CECILIA GAPOSCHKIN

HALF A YEAR AFTER its annual meeting the American Philosophical Society published in its *Proceedings* the papers "Some Unorthodoxies of Modern Science." This time, instead of three professors from Harvard University, there were four of them who dealt with *Worlds in Collision* and its author: a historian of science, two astronomers, and a psychologist—Professor Donald Menzel joining his three colleagues whose papers had actually been read at the meeting.

When Bernard Cohen spoke at the meeting, he reckoned—according to the abstract distributed at that time and reproduced on pages 247–248—with the possibility that my ideas might win out in the end. His repeated references to my theory in this abstract almost gave the impression that this theory was one of the main subjects of his paper, yet in its printed form half a year later in the space of sixteen columns he refers to it only in these words: "Velikovsky's theories are admittedly unorthodox, but their utter rejection is not based on their unorthodoxy, but on the palpable fact that they are unsupported by a body of reliable data such as is demanded of every new conceptual scheme." Reference is made in a footnote to the paper by Payne-Gaposchkin, which purportedly demonstrates this lack of reliable evidence.

Presented now in print, Payne-Gaposchkin's method of proving that my work was built on spurious evidence can be properly analyzed. She started with a few quotations from my Epilogue and proceeded: "Scarcely a man, woman or child can have escaped one of the adroitly-placed versions of these daring conclusions during the past two years. Their author himself was not unaware of the implied collision with most of modern science. . . . The thesis of the book is scientific, but the evidence is drawn from an immense mass" of ancient literature and tradition. And she complained of the "Herculean labor of laying a finger on the flaws in an argument that ranges over the greater part of ancient literature."

Readers found the book "very impressive" only because they could not check on the sources. "If all readers had complete classical libraries, and could read them; if every man were his own Assyriologist and habitually studied the Bible in the Hebrew and Septuagint versions, Dr. Velikovsky would have had short shrift. For when one examines his sources, his argument falls to pieces."

Cecilia Payne-Gaposchkin gave five instances where I invented my sources or distorted them. This is a grave accusation; it was the result of the difficult labor of checking my sources. These five cases must presumably be the most blatant found in my book, and here are the five cases.

First case. Payne-Gaposchkin quoted me: "One of the places of the heavenly combat . . . was on the way from Egypt to Syria. According to Herodotus, the final act of the fight between Zeus and Typhon took place at Lake Serbon on the coastal route from Egypt to Palestine." She proceeded to state: *"But Herodotus says nothing about the battle, or even about Zeus, in the passage quoted* (History, III, 5)." She reproduced and translated two lines from Herodotus: "Egypt begins at the Serbonian shore, where, they say, Typhon is hidden." The case is complete; everyone will agree that Velikovsky used his source in a cavalier manner.

What can I say in my defense? I shall fill in the dots Payne-Gaposchkin inserted in the quotation from my book. The sentences read thus:

> One of the places of the heavenly combat between elementary forces of nature—as narrated by Apollodorus and Strabo—was on the way from Egypt to Syria. According to Herodotus the final act of the fight between Zeus and Typhon took place at Lake Serbon on the coastal route from Egypt to Palestine. [Footnote: Herodotus III.5. Also Apollonius Rhodius in the *Argonautica* Bk. ii, says that Typhon "smitten by the bolt of Zeus . . . lies whelmed beneath the waters of the Serbonian lake."]

Payne-Gaposchkin, by omitting the words "as narrated by Apollodorus and Strabo" and the quotation from Apollonius, made it appear that I had invented the battle between Zeus and Typhon because Herodotus speaks only of Typhon's place of burial, not of the battle itself. Preceding this sentence on page 81 in my book is a full page of quotations, page 79, from Apollodorus about the furious battle between Zeus and Typhon.

My reference to Herodotus is to the Loeb Classical Library edition of that author, which I use throughout my book; Harvard University is the publisher of that standard series. A. D. Godley, translator and editor of Herodotus in that edition, makes this note to verse III.5 to which I referred in my footnote: "Hot winds and volcanic agency were attributed by Greek mythology to Typhon, cast down from heaven by Zeus and 'buried' in hot or volcanic regions . . . and the legend grew that he was buried in the Serbonian marsh."

I have not invented the battle; I have not invented the participants in the battle; I have not invented the place of the battle. Lake Serbon is on the way from Egypt to Palestine. The cavalier method of using sources is not mine.

Second case. Payne-Gaposchkin stated:

> A cosmic encounter, we read, was responsible for the destruction of the army of Sennacherib by a "blast of fire." But none of the three biblical accounts of the event mentions a *blast:* each one ascribes the defeat of the enemy to an angel (II Kings, xx, 35; II Chronicles, xxxii, 21; Isaiah, xxvii, 36). We do find a blast in the prophecy made by Isaiah *before* the event: "Behold, I will send a blast upon him, and he shall hear a rumor, and shall return to his own land" (II Kings, xix, 7). But the Hebrew word used here means "wind or spirit" rather than "fire."

(In the footnote she said: "I am indebted to Professor Robert Pfeiffer for this information. The Septuagint has the word *pneuma,* wind or air.")

The Payne-Gaposchkin statements amounted to an accusation that I suppressed the "angel" in the story of Sennacherib's debacle; that I incorrectly quoted "blast" in Isaiah 37:7; and that I invented "blast of fire," making it appear that it is a biblical expression in this story about Sennacherib. Three grave offenses crowded into one single episode in my book.

So let us quote pages 230–31 of *Worlds in Collision:*

> The destruction of the army of Sennacherib is described laconically in the Book of Kings: "And it came to pass that night, that the angel of the Lord went out, and smote in the camp of the Assyrians a "hundred fourscore and five thousand; and when the people arose early in the morning, behold, they were all dead corpses. So Sennacherib king of Assyria departed, and went and returned, and dwelt in Nineveh." It is similarly described in the Book of Chronicles: "And the prophet Isaiah, the son of Amoz, prayed and cried to heaven. And the Lord sent an angel which cut off all the mighty men of valor, and the leaders and captains in the camp of the king of Assyria. So he [Sennacherib] returned with shame of face to his own land."

I continued:

> What kind of destruction was this? *Malach,* translated as "angel," means in Hebrew "one who is sent to execute an order," supposed to be an order of the Lord. It is explained in the texts of the Books of Kings and Isaiah that it was a "blast" sent upon the army of Sennacherib (II Kings 19:7; Isaiah 37:7). "I will send a blast upon him . . . and [he] shall return to his own land," was the prophecy immediately preceding the catastrophe. The simultaneous death of tens of thousands of warriors could not be due to a plague, as it is usually supposed, because a plague does not strike so suddenly; it develops through contagion, if rapidly, in a few days, and may infect a large camp, but it does not affect great multitudes without showing a curve of cases mounting from day to day.
>
> The Talmud and Midrash sources, which are numerous, all agree on the manner in which the Assyrian host was destroyed: a blast fell from the sky on the camp of Sennacherib. It was not a flame but a consuming blast: "Their souls were burnt, though their garments remained intact." The phenomenon was accompanied by a terrific noise (Tractate Shabbat 113b; Sanhedrin 94a; Jerome on Isaiah 10:16; Ginzberg, *Legends of the Jews,* VI, 363).

I did not suppress the "angel" in the story; I did not invent "blast" in Isaiah 37:7 or in II Kings 19:7; I did not ascribe "blast of fire" to any biblical text; I gave talmudic sources for the words, "It was not a flame, but a consuming blast." There was no reason to refer to Pfeiffer's opinion that the Hebrew word used in the Scriptures means "wind or spirit" rather than "fire" because I did not quote "a blast of fire" in my account of the scriptural story.

Third case. Payne-Gaposchkin accused me of suppressing not only the "angel" but also the version of Herodotus because, she wrote, "Herodotus gives a very different account of the defeat of Sennacherib's army, which does not suggest any catastrophe on a cosmic scale." She reproduced Herodotus in Greek and gave a translation (by Rawlinson) of the passage II, 141:

> Afterwards . . . Sennacherib, king of the Arabians and Assyrians, marched his vast army into Egypt. . . . As the two armies lay here opposite one another, there came in the night a multitude of field-mice, which devoured all the quivers and bowstrings of the enemy, and ate the thongs by which they managed their shield. Next morning they commenced their flight and great multitudes fell, as they had no arms with which to defend themselves.

What do I have on this account in my book? From page 231:

> Another version of the destruction of the army of Sennacherib is given by Herodotus. During his visit in Egypt, he heard from the Egyptian priests or guides to the antiquities that the army of Sennacherib, while threatening the borders of Egypt, was destroyed in a single night. According to this story, an image of a deity holding in his palm the figure of a mouse was erected in an Egyptian temple to commemorate the miraculous event. In explanation of the symbolic figure, Herodotus was told that myriads of mice descended upon the Assyrian camp and gnawed away the cords of their bows and other weapons; deprived of their arms, the troops fled in panic.

Payne-Gaposchkin made it appear as though I had deliberately omitted Herodotus's version.

Fourth case. Payne-Gaposchkin wrote: "Or we may take the references to the myth of Phaëthon, which our author also identifies with the invading 'comet,' Venus. 'The earliest writer,' he says, 'who refers to the transformation of Phaëthon into a planet is Hesiod,' and he cites the *Theogony*. But Hesiod says nothing of the kind."

My text on pages 159–60 states:

> Phaëthon, which means "the blazing star" (Cicero, *De natura deorum,* transl. H. Rackham, II. 52), became the Morning Star. The earliest writer who refers to the transformation of Phaëthon into a planet is Hesiod (*Theogony,* II., 989 ff.). This transformation is related by Hyginus in his *Astronomy* (ii, 42), where he tells how Phaëthon, who caused the conflagration of the world, was struck by a thunderbolt of Jupiter and was placed by the sun among the stars (planets). It was the general belief that Phaëthon changed into the Morning Star. (See "Phaëthon" in Roscher's *Lexikon der griechischen und römischen Mythologie,* Col. 2182.)

W. H. Roscher, the greatest authority on the subject, refers to "Hesiod's myth of Phaëthon . . . who as the Morning-Evening Star was placed in the sky."* Also, Hesiod's passage in *Collection des Universités de France* has the following note by Paul Mazon of L'Institut de France: "Phaëthon . . . is here the name of the Evening Star, that is of Venus."†

Gaposchkin led the reader to believe that it was **I** who placed Phaëthon among the planets (*inter sidera*).

Fifth—and last—case. Payne-Gaposchkin stated: "Although Mr. Velikovsky cites the results of excavations at Ur in support of his contention that the deluge was universal, the findings of the archaeologists do not bear him out." And she quoted from Sir Leonard Woolley, *Ur of the Chaldees:*

> The annalists . . . made mention of it as an event which interrupted the course of history . . . but . . . so far from the disaster being universal some at least of the local centers of civilization survived it. . . . This deluge was not universal, but a local disaster confined to the lower valley of the Tigris and Euphrates affecting an area perhaps 400 miles long and 100 miles

* *"Hesiodischer Mythus von Phaëthon . . .* [*der*] *als Morgen-Abendstern an den Himmel versetzt wurde"* (Vol. III, ii, Col. 2523).

† *"Phaëthon . . . est ici le nom de l'Etoile du Soir, c'est-à-dire de Venus."*

> across. . . . According to Sumerian annals, some of the cities did survive [Payne-Gaposchkin's omissions].

Thus Payne-Gaposchkin said that I sought to establish that the Deluge "was universal" by a reference to Sir Leonard Woolley, excavator of Ur of the Chaldees, whereas Woolley stated that the Deluge had been local in the Euphrates Valley and some cities had survived it.

What can I answer to this last grave charge that I fabricated my sources? In the first place, in *Worlds in Collision* I mentioned neither Ur of the Chaldees nor Sir Leonard Woolley. From what, then, does my accuser quote me without revealing the source and leaving the reader to think that it is from *Worlds in Collision?* It is from my debate with Professor Stewart in *Harper's.* Did I refer to the city of Ur and to Woolley to prove the universality of the Deluge? I did not discuss the Deluge, much less try to prove its universality. So what are the facts?

Stewart wrote that if the earth had been disturbed in its rotation, the sea would have erupted, and added: "Tombs dated from the fourth millennium B.C. were not destroyed by ocean floods in Ur of the Chaldees, close as it was to the Persian Gulf, nor in Byblus, on the Mediterranean."

In my reply to Stewart in *Harper's* I wrote:

> . . . Professor Stewart says that Ur in Chaldea was not overwhelmed by water. Sir Leonard Woolley, who excavated Ur, says:
>
> "Eight feet of sediment imply a very great depth of water and the flood which deposited it must have been of a magnitude unparalleled in local history. That it was so is further proved by the fact that the clay bank marks a definite break in the continuity of the local culture; a whole civilization which existed before it is lacking above it and seems to have been submerged by the waters" (*Ur of the Chaldees,* 8th ed., 1935, p. 28 f.).
>
> Woolley thinks that "we have thus found . . . evidence [of] the flood of Sumarian history and legend."

This was my restrained answer to Stewart, who took the chance, without reading the report of excavations in Ur, to affirm that no sign was found of tidal water's having submerged that city; I only confronted him with the actual findings in Ur. There was neither intention nor need to show at that point that the findings in Ur could serve me to prove the Noachian Deluge. I quote once more the accusation of Payne-Gaposchkin: "Although Velikovsky cites the results of excavations at Ur in support of his contention that the deluge was universal, the findings of the archaeologists do not bear him out." She called this an "example of [the] liberties" I took. The liberties were hers.

If all readers had complete classical libraries and could read them; if every man were his own Assyriologist and habitually studied the Bible in the Hebrew and Septuagint versions, Dr. Payne-Gaposchkin would have had short shrift. Only by suppressing texts and by misquoting evidence could the astronomer, who was described as "being also a classicist," prove her point.

Now if, after years of work, during which she wrote many articles on *Worlds in Collision,* after the "Herculean labor of laying a finger on the flaws in an argument that ranges over the greater part of ancient literature," after she announced, "I did examine all the original sources that I was able to obtain and competent to read," if after all this, the five cases cited above are the worst misrepresentations of my sources—and *Worlds in Collision* contains thousands of references and quotations—then Professor Payne-Gaposchkin demonstrated only that all my other quotations and references are at least as unassailable as these five cases. If the sources and references are genuine and true, then there is no way to escape accepting the conclusions of *Worlds in Collision* in full or at least to the extent of reexamining many of the current beliefs in science.

I wrote a short factual reply to Payne-Gaposchkin and mailed it to L. P. Eisenhart, editor of the *Proceedings of the American Philosophical Society.* I received the answer that the Committee on Publications "decided not to publish it." Then I finally decided to write these memoirs. I remained silent in the face of the suppression of my book; I held my peace when I was called a crank and deluded, though I certainly had the weapons and the ability to take a stand. I have made no claim of being infallible; I may have made errors, and my conclusions may be vulnerable. But one point I could not afford to pass in silence.

> I felt that I cannot . . . indulge my earnest desire to be silent on the matter, without incurring the risk of being charged with

> something opposed to an *honest* character. This I dare not risk; but in answering for myself, I trust it will be understood that I have been driven unwillingly into utterance.

So wrote Michael Faraday to R. Phillips on May 10, 1836.

"EXAMINE ALL THE EVIDENCE YOURSELF AT FIRST HAND"

HERE IS AN EXAMPLE of how distortion and defamation travel. Eighteen months after Payne-Gaposchkin's paper had been published in the *Proceedings of the American Philosophical Society,* an article by L. Sprague de Camp (May 1954) entitled "Orthodoxy in Science" was printed in *Astounding Science Fiction.* In it he brought together a gleaming galaxy of names. He spoke of Copernicus and Newton and told how Louis Agassiz had been called a "quack." But with the progress of science there remains hardly any room for great scientific revolutions such as took place in the past. "As a science grows up, the complete revolutionary overturns, like those effected by Copernicus and Darwin and Pasteur, become rarer and rarer." He told also of experiences of Freud and Einstein, as well as of Planck, whom he quotes as having said: "New scientific truth does not triumph by convincing its opponents and making them see the light but rather because its opponents eventually die."

Sprague de Camp called Galileo and Freud "aggressive, combative, peppery" types who fought their own battles; of Newton and Darwin he said they were "fortunate in having belligerent friends to do their fighting for them: Halley who bullied Newton into completing his work on physics and astronomy, and Huxley and Haeckel, who rushed about proclaiming the Darwinian revelation. A mousy scientist without such help may have his discoveries buried for decades, as happened to Gregor Mendel's findings in genetics." He continued:

> Then how should you, as a reader, go about judging between new and old theories, between the orthodox and the heterodox?
>
> The only sure way—and even not too sure—is to examine all the evidence yourself at first hand. That means you actually look at the specimens, even if you have to cross oceans to do so. Any experiments you repeat, under adequate controls and safeguards. Any calculations and measurements you run over yourself to be sure they are accurate. Any assertions that cast doubt on previous beliefs you analyze by checking the evidence and the reasoning on which doubt is cast, and any objections to the new theory you investigate and weigh with equal thoroughness and judicious impartiality.

After all these illustrious names and proclaimed lofty principles came my turn.

> If I undertook to write a book refuting Velikovsky, there would be no difficulty in finding the fallacies in Velikovsky's arguments and the errors in his assertions. But he dips into so many sciences, and cites so many sources, that to do the job properly would require a book at least as big as the original. And then who would buy it? For one of mankind's less endearing traits is that they [*sic*] will pay fortunes to be gulled, humbugged and chicaned, but very little to be debunked and undeceived.
>
> If, then, you cannot examine all the evidence and repeat all the experiments yourself, you can still save yourself from being misled to some extent by checking the theorist's assertions as far as you can. Thus when Velikovsky quotes Herodotus about a battle between Zeus and Typhon, and Hesiod on Phaëthon's becoming a planet, and Isaiah on the destruction of Sennacherib's army by fire, you have only to turn to the books cited to learn that Herodotus and Hesiod and Isaiah said nothing of the sort.

De Camp obviously did not follow his own advice "to examine all the evidence yourself at first hand" with "thoroughness and judicious impartiality," although all that was necessary was to check a few sentences in *Worlds in Collision* with a few standard books; there was no need to cross the ocean. But he made his job even easier: He copied from Payne-Gaposchkin.

Looking through this piece by De Camp, I was reminded of a story about a fellow who stole counterfeit money and, not knowing its nature, passed it in good faith all over the market, telling people how good it is to work hard in order to earn this kind of money. When finally apprehended, he was tied to a post in the marketplace and horsewhipped for stealing, for passing counterfeit money, but, above all, for preaching falsely.

CAN ONE BURN AT TWO STAKES?

"CHURCH PEOPLE ACCUSED Dr. Velikovsky of being a rationalist—in explaining miracles as natural phenomena; and scientists accused him of reliance on literary sources, ancient traditions, Scriptures, etc., and giving a rational meaning to things they regarded as mythical."*

In Germany it was the church that performed the work of the astronomers in America. I have paid almost no attention to the matter, but it is worth telling.

When *Worlds in Collision* was published by Macmillan, several offers from publishers in Germany came daily, and before long there were about forty, all of them very persistent. The blood of martyred Jews was still crying from the soil of Germany, and I objected to giving the rights for a German translation to any German firm; I signed a contract with Europa Verlag in Zurich. This publishing house was headed by Dr. Emil Oprecht, member of a prominent socialist family in Switzerland. But Swiss firms cooperate with German firms, and the question arose: With whom should Dr. Oprecht cooperate in Germany in publishing my book? Again German firms wrote me persistently, each asking that it be selected for that purpose, and some of the famous publishers wrote me long personal accounts of their experiences with the Gestapo and the sufferings they had gone through. Dr. Oprecht, however, thought

* The editors of a posthumous collection of essays by Fulton Oursler, *Lights Along the Shore.*

that Kohlhammer Verlag in Stuttgart had not cooperated with the Nazis as the other houses had done, and its catalog had been free of Nazi titles the whole time. I inquired of Dr. Oprecht whether Kohlhammer Verlag would have the steadfastness to go ahead with my book when the attack came or would they follow Macmillan's example. I was assured that the Macmillan story would not be repeated. So Kohlhammer got the German market from Europa Verlag as well as the printing job for both publishing houses. It presented a fine translation, every paragraph of which I read in proofs, correcting where necessary.

The controversy in Germany was almost as violent as that in the United States, and it had many reverberations. In the spring of 1950 several articles had already been published, partly by correspondents from America. In the February 1951 issue of *Der Monat* a fourteen-column article by Gerald Wilk had sharpened the expectation for the German edition of *Worlds in Collision. Kristall,* an illustrated magazine of large circulation, obtained serialization rights from Kohlhammer and carried excerpts from my book in thirteen consecutive issues, bringing broad circles into the discussion.

Soon after *Ages in Chaos* had been published in the United States, Kohlhammer Verlag sent me a cable asking for a contract for this book, either directly or through Europa Verlag, our previous intermediary. Generally speaking, I was no longer eager to see my books translated. In cases in which I could not check the translation—as with the Japanese translation (by the Hosei University Press, Tokyo) and the Afrikaans translation (by Dr. A. H. Jonker, member of the South African Parliament), I could not know if and how far the translator had digressed from the original. And in languages in which I could check the translation, it required much of my time, but without such checking, the translation might easily contain some inaccuracies that could become indefensible targets for attack. Consequently, I was in no hurry to satisfy Kohlhammer's request for the rights to *Ages in Chaos.*

After a burst of communications Kohlhammer stopped writing me. Thereafter I received letters from readers telling me that Kohlhammer had informed them that it would not publish my book. I did not intervene and did not react. Then came a letter from a reader saying that in answer to an inquiry about the German edition of *Ages in Chaos,* Kohlhammer said that it would not publish the book, having been compelled to this decision by its main patrons (*Hauptauftraggeber*) because of the ideas contained in it. I asked my correspondent for more details. On May 17, 1954, she wrote that the above answer had been given orally at the Kohlhammer office, and it meant that the ecclesiastical groups (*kirchliche Kreise*) had applied strong pressure on that firm not to publish another book of mine (*"starken Druck ausgeuebt hätten, um den Verlag davon abzuhalten, weitere Bücher von Ihnen zu verlegen."*)

And have not Condon, Herget, and other academicians in the United States and Haldane in England called the attention of the church to the fact that my book is blasphemous from the theologians' point of view?

There is one thing of which science and religion are equally afraid, the questioning of fundamentals.

> And so you think that Newton told a lie;
> Where do you hope to go to when you die?

These two lines from a famous book* are illustrative of the mental bent of the primates, prelates, and vicars of the scientific collegium.

"I abjure, curse, and detest the said errors and heresies . . . and I swear that I will never more in the future say or assert anything, orally or in writing, which may give rise to a similar suspicion of me." Publicly and on his knees Galileo recited this formula drawn up by the Inquisition; he was further sentenced to repeat for the next three years the seven penitential psalms. Thus he saved himself from the stake.

Were it possible to burn my books and their author publicly, then most probably the councils of the church and of the scientific collegium would have fought for the privilege of taking hold of me and would have dragged me, each out of the grasp of the other, to its own stake.

* Augustus de Morgan, *Essays on the Life and Works of Newton* (1914), p. 188.

"NEARER THE GODS NO MORTAL MAY APPROACH"

IN MODERN SOCIETY the scientist takes the place of the priest of ancient times. He won this place after difficult battles with the clergy only a few hundred years ago, in the days of Galileo, and in the time of Darwin he clinched the victory. The priest is not omniscient; he cannot foretell what will be tomorrow. All his prophesying has to do with the Day of Judgment, and this day is so far off that nobody can ever know if there is any truth to his prophecy. But a scientist can foretell the weather of the coming weekend and the eclipse 100 years from now. Therefore, he, not the priest, is the prophet.

Among the general public, even among otherwise progressive and independent thinkers, one may often observe an absolute faith in science or, more properly, in what is uttered by scientists. Karl Menninger, the psychiatrist, had this to say:

> Many put the same faith in science that others put in religion, the same faith that we all once put in the comforting arms of mother and father; they cannot let themselves conceive of any inadequacy of science, just as the deeply religious man cannot conceive of defects in his God. Today one may laugh at magic and express doubts about a Supreme Being with impunity, but it is worse than heretical to cast suspicion upon science: it is impious, blasphemous.*

* K. Menninger, *Love Against Hate* (1942), p. 200.

The scientist exploits his position as the clergyman exploited his: He allows people to think that he is in some way in communion with the First Cause and that he is in possession of the Ultimate Truth.

Among scientists the astronomers have abrogated to themselves the topmost place, that of the high priests, and nobody challenges them. All agree that no natural science is as exact as astronomy. The astronomers, with few exceptions, jealously guard this privileged position and look down on geologists, chemists, and biologists as class B scientists. The object of their investigation is heaven itself. In this, too, they have superseded the high priests, who claimed for themselves the keys to heaven.

In the astronomers' view there can be no greater effrontery than the questioning of their truths, and nothing enrages them more than to challenge such a perfect science by recourse, *horribile dictu*, to the Scriptures as a historical document. That *Worlds in Collision* contains much folklore, or "old wives' tales," was not so ludicrous as the fact that it brought the Old Testament back into the debate. The citation of passages from the Vedas, the Koran, and Mexican holy books was not so insulting as quotation from the Hebrew Bible. It is irrelevant that this book is among the most ancient of written literary documents in existence. As the theologian believes with blind faith that the Scriptures contain only truth, that their authorship is from God, and therefore, that every verse in them can be quoted as an irresistible argument, so the astronomer believes that where a passage is reproduced from the Scriptures, there must be a blunder, a softening of the brain tissue, or an attempt to hoax the credulous, as if the Scriptures were written by the devil.

To my way of thinking, these books of the Old Testament are of human origin; though inspired, they are not infallible and must be handled in a scientific manner as other literary documents of great antiquity. Yet I must admit that I had a share of satisfaction upon discovering that the so-called miracles of the Hebrew Bible were physical phenomena, and like the disturbance in the movement of the sun, being of a nature that made them visible to other peoples of great antiquity in different parts of the world, they are also found preserved in the ancient literature of other nations. Once again I was gratified when, in *Ages in Chaos*, upon synchronizing the histories of the ancient East, I found substantiation and often verification of events in the political life of the Israelite nation from the days of the Exodus to the days of the Exile, as they are narrated in the Scriptures.

The new keepers of the heavens, like the old ones, claim to be infallible and omniscient.

> But now, behold,
> Admitted to the banquets of the gods,
> We contemplate the polities of heaven;
> And spelling out the secrets of the earth,
> Discern the changeless order of the world
> And all the aeons of its history.

So wrote Halley about the guild of astronomers for whom Newton "unlocked the hidden treasures of Truth." Of Newton he said: "Nearer the gods no mortal may approach," and this holds good for those who are Newton's heirs in science.

Professor Horace M. Kallen, being by nature a philosopher, not a fighter, for many months merely observed the goings-on in American science. Then he wrote for the July 28, 1951, issue of the *Saturday Review of Literature* its leading article, "Democracy's True Religion." There he said:

> There is a widespread and dangerous disposition to consider science as in some sense holy and to attribute to it that assurance of salvation greater than any other which defines the supernatural. In the life of the mind the communicants of such a religion of science figure as so many more dogmatists of another intolerant cult, with observatories or laboratories for churches and with their formulas as infallible revelations ordaining the rites and liturgies of their respective specialties. Such religions of science insist on their own orthodoxies, exercise their own censorships, maintain their own Index, and impose their own Imprimatur.
>
> A current instance of this traditional religionism of scientists is the aggression against the original publishers of Velikovsky's "Worlds in Collision." Instead of acknowledging the inquirer's right to be wrong or right at his own risk and treating the claims of the imaginative adventure into history, physics, and astronomy on its own merits, certain vested interests of scientific enterprise first threatened a boycott of other books brought out by the publishers of this one and then apparently made good the threat to the point where this best seller was transferred to another house.

He continued:

> The realm of knowledge is an open realm. It has neither boundaries nor frontier guards. All sorts of ideas, speculations, hypotheses, and theories may enter it freely on equal terms and present themselves . . . with their rival claims to the truth. The method of science is the way in which the rivalry is brought to a decision. Its essence is what is called sportsmanship or fair play. It requires that the works and the ways of the field, the laboratory, the observatory, and the study shall be . . . [put] to the test without fear, favor, or privilege; that the experiment shall invalidate [the] hypothesis on its own deficiencies or validate it on its own merits. It requires that every idea shall receive an equally free opportunity to do the same job better than its rivals. . . .
>
> [An idea, when victorious,] cannot, like some champions in sport, retire unbeaten. Perforce, [the idea] remains in the open field, ever confronted with the challenge of rivals new and old and is relied on as truth only so long as it continues to do the same job better than ever.
>
> This is why the history of science is the history of ideas first developed into truths, then abandoned as errors. Those ideas were . . . set down in books, later to be displaced . . . by choices from among old and new competing alternatives.
>
> [It is] the self-altering, self-correcting process of the scientific enterprise, whose ever-renewed beginnings come first in the happy hunch, the spontaneous observation, the imaginative response to the challenge of a problem; then, in its searching and seeking among old solutions, its inventing and elaborating of still newer alternative solutions; finally, in its planning, organization, and betting on one such, chosen from many alternatives.

This process makes of science a continuously reshaping body of knowledge "whose stuff is ever not quite this-and-nothing-else and whose form is ever not final."

The true science in democracy is "this alternative enterprise of free, open inquiry, whose springs are curiosity, whose protection is doubt, whose security is experiment. . . ."

BEFORE THE CHAIR OF JUPITER

ON NOVEMBER 8, 1953 we were invited by Einstein to visit with him. The story of my relations and debates with Albert Einstein, from his first reading of the manuscript of *Worlds in Collision* until his death, is related in a separate book, *Before the Day Breaks.** On that evening he greeted my wife and me—his long hair well groomed, his face lighted with a friendly smile—and started to move a chair with a very high back, which had already drawn my attention in the modestly furnished living room. As I helped him, he said: "This is my Jupiter chair."

During our conversation I took this lead and remarked: "If one evening I should stop every passing student and professor on the campus and should ask which of the stars is Jupiter, it is possible that not even one would be able to point to the planet. How is it, then, that Jupiter was the highest deity in Rome, and likewise Zeus in Greece, Marduk in Babylonia, Amon in Egypt, and Mazda in Persia—all of them represented the planet Jupiter. Would you know why this planet was worshiped by the peoples of antiquity and its name was in the mouth of everyone? Its movement is not spectacular; once in twelve years it circles the sky. It is a brilliant planet, but it does not dominate the heavens. Yet Apollo—the sun—the dispenser of light and warmth, was only a secondary deity." After explaining that Marduk was the Babylonian name of the planet Jupiter and Mazda its Persian name, Einstein expressed his wonder. Then I told him that in the *Iliad* it is said that Zeus can

* *Before the Day Breaks* is being readied for publication.

pull all the other gods and the Earth with his chain, being stronger than all of them together; and that an old commentary (by Eustathius, a Byzantine scholar) states that this means the planet Jupiter is stronger in its pull than all the other planets combined, the Earth included. Einstein admitted that it was really very strange that the ancients should have known this.

When, after three quarters of an hour during which we were served tea, we rose to go, Einstein kept us, saying, "We have only started." In order not to appear a bore or a fanatic of one idea, I repeatedly changed the theme of conversation as is so easy with Einstein, whose associations are rich and whose interests are many. The conversation was vivid. We spoke again of the problem of time, which apparently occupied his mind then, and of coincidence and accident. He observed that it was an accident of unusual rarity that his chair should occupy its very position in space, but that it was no accident that we two were sitting together, because *meshugoim* (Hebrew for "crazy people") are attracted to one another.

In the following weeks I put my lecture before the Princeton Graduate Forum in writing, and discussed it with Professor Motz of Columbia University. Then I sent a copy of it to Einstein. After a few days he invited Elisheva and me to come and discuss it.

The problem he selected for discussion that evening, from a series of problems mentioned in my lecture, was the round shape of the sun. Because of rotation it should be somewhat flattened; and, in addition, the sun rotates at a greater velocity at its equator than at higher latitudes. We spent the evening talking about this and a few other points in my lecture.

In the morning I thought of calling Helen Dukas, Einstein's secretary, to say a few words of apology for our too long conversation, when the phone rang and Miss Dukas said: "The professor would like to talk to you." His voice sounded resonant and clear and, I thought, if one does not see Einstein but only hears him, he might imagine that he's speaking with a young man. Einstein said:

"After our conversation last night I could not fall asleep. For the greater part of the night, I turned over in my mind the problem of the spherical form of the sun. Then before morning I put on the light and calculated the form the sun must have under the influence of rotation, and I would like to report to you." I mention this episode only to emphasize Einstein's attitude toward a scientific problem that intrigued him and, even more, his behavior toward a fellow man.

EVENINGS WITH EINSTEIN

EINSTEIN MADE NO SECRET of his interest in my ideas and his good personal feelings toward me; often he asked me not to go away when it was late, but to spend more time in discussion. He was surrounded by much love but was a lonely man. Not once and not twice he called me to follow his example and be content in isolation. "Don't you feel fine being alone? I feel unconcerned being alone." The fact was that most physicists of the younger generation, including those connected with the Institute for Advanced Study, opposed his later stand in physics that conflicted with the quantum theory, which requires the principle of chance or indeterminacy in natural events. On one occasion I answered to his monition: "Yes, there are two heretics in Princeton. Only one is glorified; the other, vilified."

His theory increased immensely the regard the general public has for science: If a scientist's theory can be understood only by a very few in the entire world, as it was in the beginning with Einstein's theory, what a supreme race are the scientists! But if one comes with a theory which, if true, would let many reputed scholars appear in error before the public, what should he expect from them?

One evening in May 1954, sitting with Einstein in his study, a few days after another ugly attack on me and my theory, I referred for the first time to the behavior of the scientists against me, and I showed him a file with some letters quoted earlier in this book. He read them with very great interest, and he was obviously impressed.

He thought that the letters and other material must be put into a readable form, as a story, and that somebody with a talent for dramatic writing should be entrusted with the composition; he was already concerned with the success of my defense. He wished to read more of the letters, but I was interested in taking up the problem that really occupied my mind: my theories.

The same evening I left with Einstein Chapters VIII to XII of *Earth in Upheaval* in typescript, and we parted close to midnight. Upon reading these chapters, he wrote me a long handwritten letter with criticism. In this letter he also inserted a few passages concerning the letters he had seen. He thought that Shapley's behavior could be *explained* but in no way *excused* ("*erklären* aber keineswegs *entschuldigen*"), and he added:

> One must, however, give him credit that in the political arena he conducted himself courageously and independently, and just about carried his hide to the marketplace.
>
> Therefore it is to some extent justified if we spread the mantle of Jewish neighborly love over him, however difficult that is.*

Yet Einstein did not change his opinion that the material pertinent to the suppression of my book must be made public.

At the conclusion of my letter written several weeks later as the next step in our debate, I returned to that issue:

> Too early you have thrown the mantle of Jewish compassion over Shapley: you have seen only the beginning of the file of the documents concerning the "Stargazers and Gravediggers" and their leader. His being a liberal is not an excuse but an aggravating circumstance.

In the summer and fall of 1954 I wrote most of *Stargazers and Gravediggers.* Its first reader was Professor Salvador de Madariaga of Oxford University, who visited me while he was a guest lecturer in Princeton. A few months later I gave the manuscript to Einstein; it was in March 1955, fully ten months after he had first read a few letters quoted in it. It was almost finished, the section "Before

* *"Man muss es ihm aber zugute halten, dass er sich auf politischem Gebiete mutig und selbständig verhalten hat und geradezu seine Haut zu Markte getragen hat. Also ist es einigermassen berechtigt, wenn wir den Mantel jüdischer Nächstenliebe ihn ausbreiten, wenn es auch schwer fällt"* [Einstein to Velikovsky, May 22, 1954].

the Chair of Jupiter" included. He supplied some of the pages of *Stargazers and Gravediggers* with handwritten marginal notes; some of the notes were very emphatic: "mean" and "miserable" to some letters, and "bravo" to others, and which side commanded his sympathy is clearly discernible.

Upon reading the first of the three ring files of *Stargazers* Einstein wrote me on March 17, 1955:

> I have already read with care the first volume of Memoirs to "Worlds in Collision" and have supplied it with a few marginal notes in pencil that can be easily erased. I admire your dramatic talent and also the art and the straightforwardness of Thackrey who has compelled the roaring astronomical lion to pull in to some extent his royal tail without fully respecting the truth. I would be happy if you, too, could enjoy the whole episode from its humorous side.*

Interesting is his note on the back of the page on which I tell about Larrabee's article in *Harper's*, which broke the story of *Worlds in Collision* to the public in 1950. He wrote:

> I would have written to you: The historical arguments for violent events in the crust of the earth are quite convincing. The attempt to explain them is, however, adventurous and should have been offered only as tentative. Otherwise the well-oriented reader loses confidence also in what is solidly established by you.

This came very close to Atwater's judgment, in his capacity as a reader for Macmillan, and it sealed his fate.

But this was a great stride away, on Einstein's part, from the view he once took that the events I have described could not have happened. Einstein said, not once and not twice, also in the presence of his secretary: "The scientists make a grave mistake in not studying your book (*Worlds in Collision*) because of the exceedingly important material it contains."

In our debate, which spread over eighteen months, I drove ever

* *"Den ersten Band der Memoiren zu 'Worlds in Collision' habe ich bereits aufmerksam gelesen und mit einigen leicht zu radierenden Randbemerkungen versehen. Ich bewundere Ihr dramatisches Talent und auch die Kunst und Geradheit von Thackeray, der den brüllenden astronomischen Löwen dazu gebracht hat, einigermassen den königlichen Schwanz einzuziehen unter nicht völliger Respektierung der Wahrheit. Ich würde glücklich sein, wenn auch Sie die ganze Episode von der drolligen Seite geniessen könnten"* [Einstein to Velikovsky, March 17, 1955].

closer to a point not necessary for the validation of *Worlds in Collision,* but of prime importance per se: the revision of celestial mechanics in the face of the accumulated data pointing to the charged state of celestial bodies. When I wrote: "The real cause of indignation against my theory of global catastrophes is the implication that celestial bodies may be charged," he wrote in the margin: "*Ja*" ("Yes").

JOVE'S THUNDERBOLTS

MY UNDERSTANDING OF THE NATURE of the sun and planets made me assume that these bodies are charged, or that, at least, their atmospheres are strongly ionized. I wished for several years that a check could be made on Jupiter. I took the opportunity of my lecture before the Graduate College Forum of Princeton University on October 14, 1953, and after presenting many reasons for believing that the members of the solar system—the sun, the planets, the satellites, the comets, the meteorites—are not electrically or magnetically neutral, made the following statement:

> In Jupiter and its moons we have a system not unlike the solar family. The planet is cold, yet its gases are in motion. It appears probable to me that it sends out radio noises as do the sun and the stars. I suggest that this be investigated.

The lecture was a discussion of my theory of 1950 "in the light of new discoveries in the fields of astronomy, geology, and archaeology"; I presented a considerable collection of recent findings that support the theory given in *Worlds in Collision.* It was natural to offer, at the end of that register, some new tests. And this I did by asserting that Jupiter sends out radio noises. The radio noises coming from the sun were explained as the effect of its great heat, but Jupiter is a cold planet and, therefore, nobody expected radio noises coming from it or from any other planet. In conventional astronomy Jupiter is an inert body, neutral in charge; in my understanding it is the center of a powerful electromagnetic system.

The summer of 1954, in a letter that I wrote to Einstein, I included these sentences: ". . . I question the neutral state of celestial bodies. There are various tests that could be made. For instance, does Jupiter send radio noises or not? This can easily be found, if you should wish."

It was a plea to help me convince others that this test should be performed. I did not doubt the result of such a test. Einstein did not respond in that instance. I have the original of my letter with many of Einstein's marginal notes.

Eighteen months after my lecture and nine months after my letter to Einstein (written June 16, 1954), strong radio noises coming from Jupiter were discovered. They were detected entirely by chance, yet the discovery appeared of such importance that it was immediately reported to the scientific world in a dramatic manner.

The spring 1955 semiannual meeting of the Astronomical Society met in Princeton. A very long list of papers was scheduled. The new discovery was presented to the meeting because of its importance, though it was not scheduled, having been made only a few weeks earlier. The next day the newspapers displayed the sensational discovery. *The New York Times* (April 6, 1955) in a column-long story from Princeton reported the news: "SOUND" ON JUPITER IS PICKED UP IN U.S.

> Radio waves from the giant planet Jupiter have been detected by astronomers at the Carnegie Institution in Washington. . . . No radio sounds from the planets in our solar system have been reported previously. . . . The existence of the mysterious Jovian waves was disclosed by Dr. Bernard F. Burke and Dr. Kenneth L. Franklin. . . . The two scientists said that they did not have an explanation for the observed radio emission.*

The press reported that the discovery was made entirely by chance, when the Carnegie Institution astronomers scanned the sky for radio noises from faraway galaxies. The noises were so strong that the discoverers thought they were caused by some experiments in a neighboring radio station. It was only after they found out that the noises were repeated every third day for six minutes, when the receiving antenna was directed toward the spot crossed at these minutes by Jupiter, that the astronomers came to the correct conclusion, unexpected and surprising as it was.

* W. Kaempffert, *The New York Times*, April 10, 1955.

In November 1955, Harlow Shapley, reviewing the field of astronomy for the year that was coming to a close, selected a few "highlights" as the most important events of the year. At the top of the discoveries he placed:

> Detection of "thunderbolts of Jove" or some similar strong electric effect in the atmosphere of the planet Jupiter, . . . the first to be found from another planet in the solar system. . . ."*

Shapley did not know the true significance of his metaphor. Of the thunderbolts of Jupiter the classical literature and the religious beliefs of the races of the Earth speak without end. My own treatment of the subject will be resumed when I present the story of earlier cataclysms.

When I brought Einstein the news he was obviously much taken by what he learned. He was also embarrassed, for not only had he disregarded my request for this test, but also at our previous meeting he had stressed the great importance for the acceptance of a theory that it be able to generate correct predictions.

He stood up and asked: "Which experiment would you like to have performed now?" I asked him to help me obtain radiocarbon tests to check on my reconstruction of ancient history. He was very emphatic in his desire to help me in this. This was our last meeting; he died a few days later. In fulfillment of his wish, a letter went from his home after his death to the Metropolitan Museum of Art with the request that some of the relics of Egypt be submitted for radiocarbon analysis.

* *Science*, November 28, 1955.

IN KEPLER'S COMPANY

As I reported earlier, I. Bernard Cohen, the historian of science at Harvard, took a vacillating position in relation to me and my work at the 1952 symposium of the American Philosophical Society. In the abstract of his paper he took an objective stance regarding the ultimate value of my work, but in his oral delivery and especially in the subsequent published paper he relied on Payne-Gaposchkin and put me down in one short sentence.

Two and one-half months after Einstein's death the July 1955 issue of *Scientific American* carried an article by Bernard Cohen describing his visit and interview with Einstein on April 3, two weeks before the latter's death. It was Cohen's first and only meeting with Einstein. The recentness of Einstein's death made the interview appear like a testament, utterances of a now dead person spoken to a witness. Illustrated with pictures of Einstein's home and of the street he used to walk on his way to the Institute for Advanced Studies, the piece attracted much attention.

Einstein and Cohen talked about "the history of scientific thought and great men in the physics of the past." As Cohen reported it, Einstein started by saying: "There are so many unsolved problems of physics. There is much that we do not know; our theories are far from adequate."

They spoke of Newton, whom Einstein had "always admired," and of the fact that Newton would not give Hooke any credit for his priority in the discovery of the law of the inverse square in gravitation, to the extent that Newton had expressed his preference not to publish the third and most important part of the *Principia* at all rather than give credit to Hooke in the Introduction to the volume. In his feud with Leibniz over the precedence of the invention of the calculus, Newton had secretly directed the activity of the committee that had to decide between the two savants in order to have it declare Leibniz a plagiarist.

According to Cohen's report, Einstein was dismayed by Newton's conduct and "did not appear too much impressed when I asserted that it was the nature of the age to have violent controversies, that the standards of scientific behavior had changed greatly since Newton's day."

Then the conversation turned to Benjamin Franklin, who had prided himself for not engaging in polemics in defense of his ideas, believing that they must make their own way by proving their vitality. Cohen professed his admiration for this behavior. Einstein, however, disagreed. "It was well to avoid personal fights," he said, "but it was also important for a man to stand up for his own ideas. He should not simply let them go by default, as if he did not really believe in them."

Then, almost inescapably, Einstein talked about me and my work. Though my name was not mentioned, it was obvious about what book and author he spoke. His opinion of the standards of scientific behavior and the obligation of a man to stand up for his ideas in science was a good introduction to my case. The fact that Einstein spoke of me and my work after talking about Benjamin Franklin and discussing Isaac Newton did not surprise me. He was then very much taken by my work. He was reading the second and third files of *Stargazers and Gravediggers* and was reading *Worlds in Collision* once again, this time in German translation. However, in Cohen's presentation Einstein's comments went thus:

> The subject of controversies over scientific work led Einstein to take up the subject of unorthodox ideas. He mentioned a fairly recent and controversial book, of which he had found the nonscientific part—dealing with comparative mythology and folklore—interesting. "You know," he said to me, "it is not a bad book. No, it really isn't a bad book. The only trouble with it is, it is crazy." This was followed by a loud burst of laughter. He then went on to explain what he meant by this distinction.

According to Cohen, Einstein said:

> The author had thought he was basing some of his ideas upon modern science, but found the scientists did not agree with him at all. In order to defend his ideas of what he conceived modern science to be, he had to turn around and attack the scientists.

I knew that Einstein could never have expressed himself this way about my work. In his report of the interview Cohen made Einstein appear as my opponent, while Cohen allowed himself to seem open-minded and sympathetic—the reverse of the actual attitudes of the two men. Cohen continued:

> I replied that the historian often encountered this problem: Can a scientist's contemporaries tell whether he is a crank or a genius when the only evident fact is his unorthodoxy? A radical like Kepler, for example, challenged accepted ideas; it must have been difficult for his contemporaries to tell whether he was a genius or a crank. "There is no objective test," replied Einstein.
>
> Einstein was sorry that scientists in the U.S. had protested to publishers about the publication of such a book. He thought that bringing pressure to bear on a publisher to suppress a book was an evil thing to do. Such a book really could not do any harm, and was therefore not really bad. Left to itself, it would have its moment, public interest would die away and that would be the end of it. The author of such a book might be "crazy" but not "bad," just as the book was not "bad." Einstein expressed himself on this point with great passion.

The rest of the conversation turned around Newton.

That he was speaking "with great passion" on the subject was true: Before that interview and also at my last meeting with Einstein five days after he spoke with Cohen, I heard him speak on the subject with great passion. But there was a wrong twist in Cohen's story: It appeared as if Einstein spoke with great passion against my book.

The word "crazy" may have various connotations—one meaning "most unusual," the way Einstein used the word *meshugoim* in referring to himself and myself in one of our conversations. Thus he likened himself to me. (*Meshuga* is a Hebrew word; it means "crazy," in both senses—like the English word—and more often in its milder meaning. *Meshugoim* is the plural form.)

It appeared in Cohen's report as if Einstein thought that suppression of a book was evil because a bad book left alone would not survive anyway. This is true, but this was meant by Einstein, if he said it, in defense of my book, which he was reading again and again. Opposing the ways my book was suppressed, he could have said that *if worthless* and left alone, it would have died by itself—but the "if worthless" fell out. Einstein, five days later, in his last conversation with me, said, and with passion, that the book contained much of importance; five days earlier he could not have said that the book would have died a quiet death if not suppressed.

I was deeply hurt. In the five and a half years of vilification, distortion, and abuse I had usually remained unperturbed; all the attacks that had taken place until then had not really stung. This time I was angered: Einstein, who obviously in the last weeks of his life was occupied with my case and my book—it was he who raised the subject with Cohen—was made to appear my antagonist. Several years earlier, under the influence of the agitation among the scientists, Einstein may have felt hostile toward me, as so many other scientists did. But at the time of the interview with Cohen his relation to me was at its highest and closest point. The manuscript of *Stargazers and Gravediggers* was on his desk when he spoke to Cohen—he finished reading its almost 400 pages—and his marginal notes there better than anything else spoke of his feeling at that time. I could not bring together the attitude and the words Cohen ascribed to Einstein with the feelings Einstein had displayed during the hours he and I had sat side by side discussing my work; with his encircling my letters and pages of my manuscripts with numerous notes all around the margins; with his writing me by hand—a distinction he reserved for only a few select; with his saying to me before parting on March 11 that he thought it a great mistake on the part of the scientists that they did not study my book for the useful information and fruitful problems it contains; with his writing me on March 17 the letter from which I quoted above, and my meeting with him on April 8, after his talk with Cohen; with his saying words of praise and offering to explain all in my book in the frame of accepted principles in science; and with his offering to help me with his authority so that a test of my theories could be performed.

During his lifetime the scientific establishment could not make Einstein express himself publicly against my work or myself, though it must have tried. Now, as soon as he died, his name was used to combat me and my work.

I wrote Einstein's secretary, Miss Dukas, who knew of our meetings and correspondence, a letter for the record.

Was it worthwhile to write a rebuttal to Cohen's article? The reader would have to decide where the truth was, and how could he know?

I went for three days to the ocean shore to regain my peace of mind, watching the surf and the great expanse of water. I decided how to act. The only one who could revise what had been printed was Bernard Cohen himself.

I wrote him this letter:

July 18, 1955

Dear Professor Cohen:

In your published interview with the late Einstein you refer to the great passion with which he spoke of my book. The reader may conclude that with great passion he opposed my work.

In the last eighteen months of his life, Einstein spent not a few long evenings with me discussing my work, exchanged long handwritten letters with me, read repeatedly my book and also several, some of them extensive, manuscripts, supplied them with marginal notes, in short, showed great interest in my ideas and gave me very much of his time. On a manuscript containing the history of my first book, he wrote what he exactly thinks of "Worlds in Collision"—he wrote it in the very week you have seen him; it is in great disagreement with what I read in your interview. In a letter of March 17, 1955 he made very clear what he thought of my adversaries and their methods of combatting my book; and on margins of the pages containing copies of letters confidentially written by some scientists to my publishers with expressions similar to those you ascribe to him, he marked: "miserable."

I assume that with great passion he spoke against my opponents and their campaign. This does not mean that he agreed with my theories on all points: after many gradual agreements, there remained between us a large area of disagreement, but our debate, orally and in writing, was carried on in the spirit of mutual respect and friendliness. Our last long conversation took place on April 8th, five days after your interview, and nine days before his death. He was rereading my "Worlds in Collision" and he said some encouraging sentences—demonstrating the evolution of his opinion in the space of 18 months.

I assume that the expressions that you mention were not used by Einstein in the meaning you have unintentionally given to them. I think that upon searching your memory you will find that the predominant feature of his in speaking of my book was positive and not negative, sympathetic and not hostile. Would you like to write down a more complete version of that part of your conversation? I believe you would like to have a chance to rectify yourself.

Einstein appears from the portion of your interview dealing with me as unkind and cynical—and these features were very far from him. And certainly he was not two-faced. It appears to me that the scene you describe is in a final count more damaging to Einstein's memory than to me.

Is not an historian of science, even more than any other scientist, kept under scrutiny by future members of his guild? There can be no greater mishap to an historian of science as when he unwittingly becomes the cause of a distortion of history at its source.

If I understand right, you have not yet made up your mind conclusively as to my position in science as it will find its evaluation by a future generation (see also the advance abstract of your lecture before the Amer. Philos. Soc., April 1952). So why not to learn about a dissident from close? When in Princeton, you are welcome to visit me and read the letters Einstein exchanged with me, his notes on my manuscripts, or any other material that may interest you. You are really welcome.

I did not hear directly from Cohen. Dr. Otto Nathan, executor of Einstein's estate, protested the fact that the interview had not been submitted to him before being printed, as it would have been submitted to Einstein for approval if he had been alive; Nathan's letter, the first part of which I quote here, was printed two months later in the September issue of *Scientific American.* He began:

> In "An Interview with Einstein," published in the July issue of your magazine, I. Bernard Cohen quotes remarks which Albert Einstein allegedly made about a recently published book and its author. Professor Cohen represents Einstein as having said that both the book and its author were "crazy," but not "bad."
>
> As executor of Einstein's estate and as one who has the responsibility to protect his scientific and literary interests, I feel compelled to say that I deeply regret Professor Cohen's statements. The article was not submitted to me before publication. If it had been, I should have made every effort to prevent it from being published in its present form. Professor Cohen would certainly not have published it without Einstein's approval had he been alive. Similarly, after Einstein's death, it was Professor Cohen's duty to seek permission for publication. . . .

Bernard Cohen answered in the same issue and offered what was actually his response to my letter to him, though he did not mention it:

> The immediate cause of Dr. Nathan's concern is my reporting of the remarks made in my presence by Professor Einstein about a book. The remarks were evidently intended to illustrate two main points: (1) that any acts toward suppressing a book which contains heretical or unorthodox ideas (even in science) is evil; (2) that there is no objective test of whether notions that contravene accepted scientific ideas and theories are the work of a crank or a genius, nor whether such ideas will forever seem crazy or perhaps become the orthodoxy of the future. As an illustration there was a reference to Kepler and to a book which Professor Einstein had read and had found in part interesting. Professor Einstein did not mention the author's name because he was speaking in general terms about the above-mentioned issue and was using the book only as an example of work that was sufficiently unorthodox to appear "crazy" to a scientist. Thus on the basis of the few words said, and reported by me in full, there is no basis for concluding that Professor Einstein might not have had a friendly feeling for the author in question or that he might not have had some interest in his work. As is plain from my article, Professor Einstein

sympathized with the author when he was attacked and disliked the methods used by some of his attackers.*

Although Bernard Cohen, under pressure, wrote the above letter, I could only hear Einstein's words: "Don't let the abuse discourage you; are you not happy in your isolation?"

* Twenty years later Walter Sullivan quoted in *Continents in Motion* (1974) from the original article by Cohen but remained ignorant of Cohen's subsequent qualifying remarks.

EARTH IN UPHEAVAL

WHEN *Worlds in Collision* was published, numerous scientists repeatedly claimed that events of such magnitude and at such comparatively recent dates must have left vestiges not only in folklore, but even more so in geology and archaeology.* Actually in the Epilogue to *Worlds in Collision* I wrote: "Geological, paleontological and anthropological material related to the problem of cosmic catastrophes is vast and may give a complete picture of past events no less than historical material." My new book, *Earth in Upheaval*, published in 1955, was a collection of this material, where I brought together evidence from geology, paleontology, and archaeology. I excluded from this new book every reference to ancient literature, traditions, and folklore; and this I did purposely so that careless critics would not decry the entire work as "tales and legends."

I could show—always quoting academic sources—that the level of all oceans dropped suddenly thirty-four centuries ago; that mountains rose in spasmodic movements in the time of advanced man, who developed advanced cultures and built cities. Abandoned cities like Tiahuanacu, and agricultural terraces, are now covered with perennial mountain snow. The deserts of Arabia, Sahara, and Gobi were covered by forests and pastures, and man's neolithic relics and rock drawings show how recently these wastes were richly watered and were inhabited. The remains of whales are found on mountains; fig trees and corals are found in polar regions, and signs of ice in Equatorial Africa. Widespread ex-

* See below, section "A Master of Fieldwork."

tinctions in America occurred "virtually within the last few thousand years."*

I gave the history of the theory of catastrophism versus the theory of gradualism and evolution. The Agassiz theory of the ice ages was originally also a catastrophist theory. Agassiz spoke of the sudden arrival of the ice cover seizing the mammoths in Siberia. The north Siberian islands consist of trunks of uprooted trees and bones of mammoths, rhinoceroses, horses, and buffaloes—when today only lichen and moss show themselves for two months in a year—and the sea is fettered in ice from September to July. In Alaska, too, gold-digging machines, slicing the ground by the mile, disclosed all over the peninsula immense heaps of animals of species both extinct and extant, forms that do not belong together, in a melee with millions of broken and uprooted trees.

The fissures of rocks of Britain, France, Spain, and also the Mediterranean islands are filled with bones of animals—and their state and position suggest that the land and the sea repeatedly changed places. Also on the American continent, North and South, caverns in the hills are found filled with animals of various habitats, entombed in conditions of catastrophes. Actually Darwin could be quoted from his *Journal of the Voyage of the* Beagle. After observing the immense heaps of fossil bones in South America, he wrote:

> The greater number, if not all, of these extinct quadrupeds lived at a late period.... Since they lived, no very great change in the form of the land can have taken place. What, then, has exterminated so many species and whole genera? The mind at first is irresistibly hurried into the belief of some great catastrophe; but thus to destroy animals, both large and small, in Southern Patagonia, in Brazil, on the Cordillera of Peru, in North America up to Behring's Straits, we must shake the entire framework of the globe.†

No lesser physical event could have brought about this wholesale destruction, not only in the Americas but in the entire world. And such an event being beyond consideration, Darwin did not know the answer.

* Flint, *Glacial Geology in the Pleistocene Epoch*, p. 523.

† Charles Darwin, *Journal of Researches into the Natural History and Geology of the Countries Visited During the Voyage of the H.M.S.* Beagle *Round the World*, under date of January 9, 1834 (New York, London: Appleton & Co.), pp. 169–70.

Actually, poles *were* displaced and the terrestrial axis did shift under violent conditions. In this connection, in Chapter IX—"Axis Shifted"—of *Earth in Upheaval* (published in November), it was possible to quote a very recent article, "The Earth's Magnetism," by Professor S. K. Runcorn of Cambridge, which appeared in the September 1955 issue of *Scientific American* (the same issue in which Otto Nathan's and Bernard Cohen's letters were published). In it he wrote that the lavas and igneous rocks in various parts of the world disclose that during the Tertiary period "the North and South geomagnetic poles reversed places several times. . . ." After long periods of stability "the field would suddenly break up and re-form with opposite polarity." The unavoidable conclusion, according to Runcorn, is that "the earth's axis of rotation has changed also. In other words, the planet has rolled about, changing the location of its geographical poles."

PHYSICIST, HISTORIAN, AND CRITIC CONVERSE

ON JANUARY 5, 1956, three gentlemen discussed my new book, *Earth in Upheaval,* and former books, *Worlds in Collision* and *Ages in Chaos,* on the radio program of the NBC network called *Conversation.* Besides the host of the program, the literary critic Clifton Fadiman, the participants were: Professor Jacques Barzun, a cultural historian, who only a short time before had been appointed to serve as dean of the graduate faculties of Columbia University, and Professor Alfred Goldsmith, one of the most prominent electrophysicists of America, vice-president of RCA in charge of research.

Barzun said: "I've read only the last, the third of the three books. I haven't the advantage of knowing Dr. Velikovsky personally, and I have no scientific competence whatever to judge his hypothesis; but I was impressed by the firmness of what might be called his scholarly polemical method."

"As a humanist I find him very convincing," said Fadiman. But since the theory is scientific, he offered to hear what Dr. Goldsmith had to say.

Goldsmith spoke slowly and impressively with emphasis on every word. The scientist said: "Well, I feel strongly that he has done a most thoughtful, careful, and apparently sincere job and that his proposals should be approached with an open mind." He continued: "Velikovsky is certainly to be commended for very careful assembly of data from all available sources. He has drawn his conclusions most painstakingly on the basis of these data. His tenacity of purpose is commendable; he sticks to his guns; he has insisted properly on an open-minded attitude by those who consider his theories and he is entitled to that interest which most thinking men would have in any theory such as his which is so fundamental in its implications." Not being versed in all the fields in which the theory is ramified, he would not regard himself qualified to decide whether the theory is right or wrong. "I've, however, noticed a rather frightening silence in some cases on the part of these gentlemen who might perhaps demolish theories by analyzing them rather than keeping silent concerning them."

Here Goldsmith was asked by Barzun whether assembling information from all available sources, Velikovsky did omit taking important matters into account.

Goldsmith: "It would be almost impossible to imagine an assembly of data that stretched more widely between solar theories, geological theories, theories of the atmosphere, theories of the shift of the axis of the earth, theories of the motions of oceans and of glaciers, theories of magnetism and magnetic effects, and any number of other geological and astronomical theories."

Barzun concurred and said: "I suppose that the difficulty is that since no one has attempted what he has attempted, no one is in a position to judge his correctness in each of the fields." Fadiman noted: "Isn't his method—I'm not talking about his results—isn't the method fairly similar to that which Darwin used in *The Origin of Species?*" Goldsmith agreed. Fadiman continued: "Darwin drew his proofs from at least seven or eight sciences as they were constituted in his day and always drew upon the material which seemed to prove his thesis." To this Barzun remarked that in Darwin's days the natural philosopher was more likely to be familiar with half a dozen fields than he is today and that there were also plenty of people to tell him where he went wrong. Fadiman: "True enough. It's only fair to Dr. Velikovsky to state that he does seem to have a mind unusual in our time. To judge from the evidence in these three books, he possesses far more than a mere smattering of knowledge in at least a dozen scientific fields."

Finally Goldsmith answered the question previously posed to him: "Judging from the reading of these books, he has made no deliberate attempt to exclude data which might be prejudicial to his own theories. He appears to have included things that seemed on their face to be ineffective toward his theory, but he has developed highly ingenious explanations as to why they're not actually so. There does not seem to be any deliberate exclusion of negative data."

Barzun agreed with this. And when they discussed the implications of my theory for the origin and disappearance of the species, he observed: "As a cultural historian not competent to judge the scientific data I am most interested by the cultural implications of such a book." The nineteenth century with its ideas of gradualism in everything, with its love of stability and slow change, produced scientific theories based on these principles, but with the turn of the century and the work of Hugo de Vries there were "the first growlings against gradualism." When Barzun admitted that cataclysmic evolution is no less agreeable to him than the gradualism of Darwin, Fadiman said: "You know all scientists who may be listening to you, Mr. Barzun, are condemning you at this moment."

Barzun answered: "No, I would say to them that they're habituated to one thing rather than another. . . ."

Goldsmith concurred: "I must come to Mr. Barzun's help here because this is in full agreement with my own views of scientists. I might say that science could almost be defined as that which is accepted as valid or truthful at a given time by a great majority of trained thinkers and observers in a field and which is obviously not out of accord with the observed facts so that therefore by definition science is necessarily in a state of flux and is not absolute or permanent, and that is well worth remembering."

Fadiman asked: "But is it not the fact historically that the vastest and most useful new theories when they first appeared were greeted with criticism by the best scientific authorities? I need hardly remind you of the classic example of Galileo."

Barzun injected: "And even before that, Copernicus. And the odd thing was that in the instance of Copernicus's theory, about which I know more than I do about more recent science, there were very good reasons for denying the validity of his views."

"Excellent reasons," said Goldsmith. "And also the Ptolemaic theory was a more satisfying theory because it ministers to the egocentricity of man."

They all agreed that records cannot be read with such finality as to exclude new interpretation, especially when new data—unaccounted for by the old theory—come to light. Goldsmith was asked: "How do you account for the fact that a great many of your colleagues have attacked Dr. Velikovsky's theory with an ire and impatience, and I may add with discourtesy, all of which are quite unscientific?"

Barzun added: "Wasn't there more than that, wasn't there even a deliberate boycotting attempt which led to difficulties with publishers?"

Fadiman said: "Yes, indeed. I see no reason why that scandal shouldn't be aired. . . . Just because a certain number of scientists didn't like the book [*Worlds in Collision*] is no reason for not permitting the American public to read it."

Barzun observed: "One would have thought that the scientists would have been the first to say: 'Well, now let's thrash this one out and get rid of it as soon as we can by the usual methods of disproof,' if disproof was possible." He went on: "One of the things that struck me particularly in reading this book of Dr. Velikovsky was a thing which is one of the attractions and beauties of science—namely, how from one inference to the next one can erect a structure of tenable ideas which leads to a result far from the point of origin."

For half an hour they discussed the theory, and unusual was the fact that in this instance the three disputants did not present opposing views; all three of them expressed themselves favorably and sympathetically about my heretical books.

MASTER OF INNUENDO

THE SCIENTIFIC PRESS, it seemed, intended to remain silent about my new book and not to repeat the error made when scientific circles had reacted with violent emotions to my earlier books. Before *Earth in Upheaval* was published, Doubleday asked to reserve space in *Scientific American* for an advertisement. At the time the order went out, the book had not yet been printed and could not be judged on its merits, nor, as far as I know, was an advertisement copy composed; but *Scientific American* refused room for an ad. On November 1, 1955, the advertising manager of *Scientific American,* Martin M. Davidson, wrote: "We are turning down your order to publish your advertisement for Velikovsky's *Earth in Upheaval.* This is a decision made by our publisher. . . ."

Less than two months after Professors Barzun and Goldsmith debated my book, a seven-column review of *Earth in Upheaval,* written by Harrison Brown, was printed in the March 1956 issue of *Scientific American.* Brown had written a review of my first book six years earlier in the *Saturday Review of Literature.* The new review was for the most part a repetition of his old review about my first book, whole passages being repeated with slight changes in wording; only in 1950 Brown had been presented as an "atomic scientist," while this time a banner over three columns said: "A geochemist views Immanuel Velikovsky's unconventional theory of the earth's history." Brown was not a geologist; his field was the origin of atmospheres on planets, and therefore, most facts discussed in my new book, as in the old, must have been unfamiliar to him. His review was not opposed to the book—he did not mention a single datum from it. Nor did he assail or refute a single statement. He was still in the emotional state created by my *Worlds in Collision,* published six years earlier; the new review was written in opposition to that book, and he frankly admitted that he "boils." Nor did he offer an argument against that first book. In his review he wrote: "When I first read *Worlds in Collision* I, like many of my colleagues, put Velikovsky's theory to the foregoing test. I made an itemized list of contradictions and errors. The list quickly grew to unwieldy proportions, and it became amply clear that the theory was nonsense. I stated this emphatically in a published review." He did not mention now that he had not brought a single one of the alleged errors to the knowledge of his readers.

Brown composed a declaration of principles—a seven-point manifesto "concerning the ethical principles involved in Velikovsky's affair," each of which starts with "I believe": "I believe that Velikovsky has behaved badly in that he has not really answered his critics in a way that befits a true scholar." He omitted to inform his readers that I had published an answer to my critics in my debate with Professor J. Q. Stewart in *Harper's* in June 1951.

Of the new book all that Brown offered was an unsupported statement: "He [Velikovsky] quotes some data which we know to be true, some which we know to be dubious and some which we know to be false." He did not support this by a single example, and probably he was not able to do so: I was very careful in selecting my data and my quotations.

Brown wrote his piece not against my theories and my data and my arguments, leaving the reader in ignorance what they are about, but against their author and, even more, their publisher, Doubleday. He dwelt only on prefaces and on dust jacket texts. He called me "master of innuendo" and he supported this by quotes from the preface to *Ages in Chaos* and the acknowledgments in *Earth in Upheaval:*

> Velikovsky wrote in the foreword to *Ages in Chaos:* "Should I have heeded the abuse with which a group of scientists condemned *Worlds in Collision* and its author? Unable to prove the book or any part of it wrong or any quoted document spurious, the members of that group indulged in outbursts of unscientific fury. . . . The guardians of the dogma were, and still are, alert to stamp out the new teaching by exorcism and not by argument, degrading the learned guild in the eyes of the

> broad public, which does not believe that censorship and suppression are necessary to defend the truth."

Brown omitted to quote the middle part of the passage and went on:

> Velikovsky apparently looks upon himself as an original thinker whose truths so contradict "orthodox" scientific thought that the members of the scientific community are taking every possible measure to keep the new heretical ideas from spreading. The scientists, he believes, have organized themselves into a sort of anti-Velikovsky club which is extremely powerful and which cajoles or threatens all persons who look favorably upon Velikovsky's theories. They [Brown quoted me] "thus drove many members of academic faculties into clandestine reading of *Worlds in Collision* and correspondence with its author," he [Velikovsky] says.

The sentences omitted by Brown and supplanted by ellipses read thus:

> They suppressed the book in the hands of its first publisher by the threat of a boycott of all the company's textbooks, despite the fact that when the book was already on the presses the publisher agreed to submit it to the censorship of three prominent scientists and it passed that censorship. When a new publisher took the book over, the group tried to suppress it there, too, by threats. They forced the dismissal of a scientist [Gordon Atwater] and an editor [James Putnam] who openly took an objective stand, and thus drove many members of academic faculties into clandestine reading of *Worlds in Collision* and correspondence with its author. The guardians of dogma were, and still are, alert to stamp out the new teaching by exorcism and not by argument. . . .

When the omitted part of the passage is reinstituted where it belongs, Brown's allegations become baseless. He wrote further:

> Perhaps the most flagrant use of innuendo is revealed in the "Acknowledgments" section of *Earth in Upheaval.* Here Velikovsky implies strongly that Albert Einstein was beginning to understand Velikovsky's views and that the two men were

> close to agreement: "The late Dr. Albert Einstein during the last eighteen months of his life (November, 1953–April, 1955), gave me much of his time and thought. . . . We started at opposite points; the area of disagreement, as reflected in our correspondence, grew ever smaller, and though at his death (our last meeting was nine days before his passing) there remained clearly defined points of disagreement, his stand then demonstrated the evolution of his opinion in the space of eighteen months."
>
> This carefully worded statement, upon close analysis, cleverly says nothing definite or significant—but it creates an impression upon the casual reader.

Brown omitted to quote the middle of the passage and supplanted it with ellipses—namely:

> He [Einstein] read several of my manuscripts and supplied them with marginal notes. Of *Earth in Upheaval* he read chapters VIII through XII; he made handwritten comments on this and other manuscripts and spent not a few long afternoons and evenings, often till midnight, discussing and debating with me the implications of my theories. In the last weeks of his life he reread *Worlds in Collision* and read also three files of "memoirs" [*Stargazers and Gravediggers*] on that book and its reception, and he expressed his thoughts in writing. We started at opposite points. . . .

When the omitted part of the passage is restored where it belongs in the text, Brown's allegation becomes baseless. The reader of the omitted paragraph realizes the serious attitude of Einstein toward my work; the reader of Brown's review is denied this realization and is asked to believe that there is an innuendo.

Doubleday did not react, but before the year was over, it signed, as a gesture of confidence, a contract for two books.

Eric Larrabee of the editorial board of *Harper's*, who had opened the debate in January 1950 with his preview of *Worlds in Collision*, wrote a letter to *Scientific American* (May 1956) in which he said:

> The question at issue here is how to handle iconoclasm—how the iconoclast is to behave. As one who has participated in this affair from an early stage, I am of the opinion that Dr. Veli-

kovsky has behaved better than his detractors, and Dr. Brown does not convince me otherwise. His account of the Macmillan Company's action in abandoning *Worlds in Collision* is disingenuous in the extreme, since he does not mention the main reason for it—the threat of boycott, clearly expressed both in word and act by individual scientists. He later describes this pressure as "unfortunate," which is an inadequate term. It was a disgrace to American science, and will so remain long after the substance of the dispute has been contained and dissolved in the flow of the scientific process.

I also find evasive his statement that the major reason for the over-emotionalism of scientists about Velikovsky is the amount and nature of the publicity received, since highly adverse opinions were fully publicized before the book appeared in journals that scientists could be expected to read, such as *Time* or *The Reporter.* A more illuminating reason seems to me to lie in the nature of the challenge Velikovsky offered—in the fact that, unlike the run-of-the-mill heretic, he was scholarly, and in earnest.

I was shocked to discover how slender is the faith of many scientists in the open testing of ideas and how many of them tend to suppose their own beliefs and "science" to be identical. Respect for scientific method unfortunately does not require blanket acceptance of all the current orthodoxies.

Despite their repeated assertions that he will soon be forgotten, scientists seem unable to leave Velikovsky alone; and each new position they take is a retreat from the previous one.

Larrabee ended by stressing that Brown "does not review the new Velikovsky book, *Earth in Upheaval;* instead he offers us a description of his own mental processes plus a tendentious account of events he knows only at hearsay. If this is science, you are welcome to it."

Brown answered, and spread his answer over 500 words: "As to our being unable to leave Velikovsky alone—he continues to write books, and this in effect compels us not to leave him alone." Since Velikovsky offers his theories "*which can be proved wrong* [Brown's italics], I am compelled to speak up." He spoke up for the third time, but he again kept to himself the secret of what is wrong in my books.

In four out of eleven issues in the space of eleven months, *Scientific American* had dedicated its columns to me. Nobody kicks a dead dog, says the proverb. I thought it worthwhile to clarify Einstein's stand, and I wrote a precise factual statement. Dennis Flanagan, the editor of *Scientific American,* knew before I mailed it to him that Einstein and I had exchanged letters on my theory, that he had read several of my manuscripts and supplied them with numerous marginal notes, *Earth in Upheaval* included; it was after *Scientific American* had published B. Cohen's interview with Einstein in the July 1955 issue that I went to see Flanagan and showed him this material. It was now *Scientific American*'s second innuendo on the same subject, and it needed a reply.

I did not enter a discussion concerning the review and clarified one point only: Einstein's stand on the issue of a heretical book.

> For the second time in less than a year *Scientific American* printed articles that threw a shadow on me not only as a scholar but as a human being as well. I like to believe that you will give room to this factual description which also lifts a little the veil of mystery from an episode in the last 18 months of Einstein's life; you will agree that I was provoked into divulging this material before I actually intended to do so.

Walter Bradbury of Doubleday wrote me: "It is a wonderful answer and I hope it is printed exactly as written. It is particularly wise and valid in its final sentence: '. . . it isn't at all important whether Einstein felt it right or wrong. Important was his attitude toward a new idea.' "

It took a month before Flanagan replied, declining to publish my answer. He did not believe that Brown had made a moral accusation: "Brown has made it quite clear that he does not doubt your sincerity." And why prolong the debate—"to the point of boredom"? Thus I was not given a chance to answer where it mattered—in the magazine that published the accusations.

Then I mailed to Flanagan a copy of *Earth in Upheaval* and wrote him that the accusation made by Harrison Brown against Macmillan was that it had not examined the book carefully before it published it. Since Flanagan acceded to me that he had not read my books, I wrote him: "I mail you a copy of *Earth in Upheaval.* If, upon reading it, you will find that you were misled and have failed in your duty as an editor, then I presume that you will look for a chance to correct the wrong. The wrong is . . . to your magazine and its readers more than to me and my book."

Flanagan answered five weeks later. He did not say that he read my last book or any of my books. He laid his cards out: "I think you should know my position once and for all. I think your books have done incalculable harm to the public understanding of what science is and what scientists do. There is no danger whatever that your arguments will not be heard; on the contrary they have received huge circulation by scientific standards. Thus I feel that we have no further obligation in the matter."

I did not react. Flanagan had admitted in conversation with me a year earlier that he was not a scientist, only a magazine writer. He, I believe, by his statements provided some material for his publisher in the future, for the column "Fifty Years Ago." However, possibly loyalty will keep the future editor from divulging the errors of his predecessor, just as Flanagan omitted including in "Fifty Years Ago" the references *Scientific American* made to the flights by Wilbur and Orville Wright.

Fifty years earlier almost to the day, on January 16, 1906, *Scientific American* printed an editorial comment on the "alleged" flights by a "mysterious aeroplane" that covered a "reputed" distance of 38 kilometers. The brothers Wright were presented as two shadowy persons with fantastic claims, unfounded because unheard of.

> If such sensational and tremendously important experiments are being conducted in a not very remote part of the country, on a subject in which almost everybody feels the most profound interest, is it possible to believe that the enterprising American reporter, who, it is well known, comes down the chimney when the door is locked in his face—even if he has to scale a fifteen-storey skyscraper to do so—would not have ascertained all about them and published the broadcast long ago?

The Wright brothers appear even as two crooks: "Why particularly, as is further alleged, should the Wrights desire to sell their invention to the French government for a 'million' francs?"

The Wrights made their first successful flight in December 1903 and in 1904 and 1905 performed many more flights; the above was printed in 1906; fifty years later, almost to a day, the issue with Brown's article went to the press.

MASTER OF FIELDWORK: COME SEE FOR YOURSELF

> I hope you will go on with your research. You are working in the right direction and time will help to show the reality of global or near global catastrophes. Already continental or near continental catastrophes cannot be doubted as I showed in my stratigraphical work in the Near East. It will take time for your findings and mine to be acknowledged. This may make us sometimes impatient. But it will stir us to more work and more research.

SO ENDED THE ten-page handwritten letter of one of the most eminent archaeologists of our time, Claude F. A. Schaeffer, member of the Institut, professor at the Collège de France. He wrote it from the Côte d'Azur on July 23, 1956, after reading *Earth in Upheaval.*

> I took it with me to the South where at the Mediterranean shore I find some time for reading and writing before I shall go out again to further archaeological and stratigraphical research in Syria (Ras Shamra) and Cyprus (Enkomi-Alasia), in September. I finished reading your book with the greatest interest and much profit.

So he started his letter.

No discovery made a revolution in biblical studies comparable with that which was caused by Schaeffer's findings in Ras Shamra-Ugarit. Seventy years of biblical criticism that had found its main mouthpiece in Julius Wellhausen and that was finally taught in all universities and preached from most of the pulpits was largely annulled by Schaeffer's finds. This story is given in *Ages in Chaos,* in the chapter entitled "Ras Shamra." In Ras Shamra Schaeffer had conducted yearly excavations since 1929, and the results appeared in large volumes. During World War II, "mainly between 1942 and 1945," as he wrote me, he worked on his *Stratigraphie comparée,* which was published by the Oxford University Press in 1948. It all started with his visit to Troy, where Professor Carl Blegen of Cincinnati University was digging. Troy was repeatedly destroyed by natural causes at the very same times that Ugarit (Ras Shamra) on the Syrian coast, more than 500 miles away, was laid waste, also in natural crises. Schaeffer studied the excavated places and the reports of their archaeologists all over the lands of the ancient East, from Persia to the Caucasus to Egypt, and in each place found vestiges of synchronical catastrophes.

Schaeffer described the different archaeological findings: Troy II, or the city which was built second on the same place, was covered by a layer of ashes fifty feet thick; no burning city could by itself leave such a deposit of ashes. Troy II was destroyed at the very time when the Old Kingdom of Egypt went down under the blows of nature. In this catastrophe cities were ruined one and all, empires ceased to exist, trade stopped entirely, civilizations were entombed, populations decimated—by earthquakes, ubiquitous fire, and epidemics—and the climate suddenly changed. Schaeffer found that there were six or seven crises during the history of the ancient East caused by catastrophes in nature; the cause of these great convulsions of nature remained unknown to Schaeffer. He realized that the area of destruction must have been much larger than the Middle East.

I came into possession of *Stratigraphie comparée* soon after the publication of *Ages in Chaos,* volume I, and I described it on pages 193–99 in *Earth in Upheaval.* Like myself, Schaeffer discerned several all-embracing catastrophes that ruined the ancient East during human history; like myself, he ascribed the fall of the Middle Kingdom in Egypt to the action of a catastrophe; and in migrations and the invasion of Egypt by the Hyksos, again like myself, he saw a consequence of that catastrophe. Thus the starting point of my research was proved on archaeological grounds.

In February 1946 I had published the *Theses for the Reconstruction of Ancient History.** There I wrote:

* Published as a scientific report in the series *Scripta Academica Hierosolymitana.*

> The literal meaning of many passages in the Scriptures which relate to the time of the Exodus, imply that there was a great natural cataclysm of enormous dimensions.
>
> The synchronous moment between the Egyptian and Jewish histories can be established if the same catastrophe can also be traced in Egyptian literature.
>
> The Papyrus Ipuwer describes a natural catastrophe and not merely a social revolution, as is supposed. A juxtaposition of many passages of this papyrus . . . with passages from the scriptures dealing with the story of the plagues and the escape from Egypt, proves that both sources describe the same events.
>
> The Papyrus Ipuwer comprises a text which originated shortly after the close of the Middle Kingdom; the original text was written by an eyewitness to the plagues and the Exodus. . . .
>
> The Exodus took place at the close of the Middle Kingdom; the natural catastrophe caused the end of this period in the history of Egypt. (Theses 5, 6, 7, 8, 14)

I established from literary sources what Schaeffer arrived at on archaeological grounds. One is complementary to the other: If such catastrophes as Schaeffer discovered took place in the third and second millennia before the present era, where is the human memory of them? Or if the human memory retained these events, where is the archaeological evidence? We worked independently of each other, on materials of different natures, and we came to identical results. Schaeffer first found out about my work upon reading *Earth in Upheaval,* which I mailed to his château near Paris.

Although Schaeffer's position as archaeologist is second to none—and as presiding officer of the Commission des Fouilles, he dominates the field of archaeology in France—he, too, felt the odium of being a trailblazer and an innovator or a discoverer of a truth unscheduled by the conservative standards.

Since the publication of *Stratigraphie comparée,* as he wrote me,

> . . . further study and research in several near eastern archaeological sites have disclosed new confirmations of the reality of these crises on a continental scale which I have tried to analyze. I would be glad if I could write now immediately the contemplated second edition of *Stratigraphie Comparée* in two volumes, for with the new confirmations these crises could no

longer be questioned . . . so striking are the proofs and so accurate the dates established by the new discoveries. . . . It will take some more time until the new idea has taken roots, but it will ultimately take roots, for the truth always in the end prevails.

He continued:

. . . Perhaps it is good, at present, to establish only the reality of these crises and tremendous upheavals during the last millennia before our time, or B.C., and leave the study of the causes to later research. For the historians and the general public are not yet ready to accept the thought that the earth is a much less safe place than they are accustomed to believe. . . .

Here Schaeffer entered into a discussion of numerous points in *Earth in Upheaval.* So he wrote about page 77:

I have excavated neolithic tombs and settlements in the Alsatian loess region. But I did not think this loess formation could be contemporary with the neolithic sites. I would like to reinvestigate the matter. You should come over to do yourself effective research. For with the great knowledge you have collected by studying the results of other scientists, you should now take a hand in firsthand research. I would gladly give you all the support in my power. There are many possibilities where you could increase your knowledge and verify your conclusions. Your own feeling of security for the conclusions to be made from the results by other research workers would thus increase. Also the critical approach is facilitated by investigating on the spot. . . .

About page 78 he wrote that he discovered signs of *Klimasturz* and inundation in Alasia, capital of Cyprus: "I left the deposit *in situ* to be shown and should like to show it to you if you can come over there. I shall be in Cyprus again next November. . . . These layers are contemporary with upheavals we know of in prehistoric Europe."*

And the most important portion of the letter for my work was in his note to page 278:

* Europe was still in its prehistoric stage when the Near East was far into its history.

> You wish that radiocarbon analyses be made of objects dating from the New Kingdom. I offer you gladly the material I have from dated Ras Shamra levels of the time of Amenophis III, IV (Akhnaton), and Ramses II. I could send it over to you for analysis by radiocarbon, or better, you come to collect it in Paris. Your dating could thus be proved or disproved. The lowering of the accepted chronology by 5 to 7 centuries is perhaps not impossible, but seems at the present state of our knowledge improbable. But tests made as you suggest (p. 278) would decide.*

I answered that if his departure from the East would still permit a meeting, I would come; but he was already sending off the members of the expedition, and we decided that I would come choose the material in the spring upon his return from the Orient. He asked me for my earlier books and mailed me his latest book on the Cyprus expedition. My *Worlds in Collision* he read on board the ship that took him to Syria, and the same evening he wrote me he was to start *Ages in Chaos.* I wrote advising him to pay special attention to unexpected combinations in the graves of Cyprus which had already caused much wondering in the past when A. S. Murray of the British Museum dug there; the story is told in *The Dark Age of Greece*† in the section called "The Scandal of Enkomi."

In the summer of 1957 Elisheva and I traveled to Europe, and at Lake Lucerne in Switzerland we met Schaeffer and spent a week with him. We were charmed by his personality. He was immersed in reading *Ages in Chaos* and was inseparable from the volume. Schaeffer and I became friends.

* Schaeffer adhered to the conventional chronology, yet on the fact that catastrophes ended the Old and Middle Bronze Age and on their relative datings we were in complete agreement.

† [Velikovsky's *The Dark Age of Greece* is being prepared for publication. "The Scandal of Enkomi" was published in *Pensée,* IVR X (winter 1974–1975).]

MONA LISA AND THE ANTARCTIC

ONE AFTERNOON, several months after we had moved to Princeton in 1952, while working in the library of Guyot Hall (Geology Department of the university), I was approached by a friendly gentleman, a professor of the department, who asked me if my name was Velikovsky. I confirmed that it was. The gentleman was Glenn L. Jepsen: he had heard me speaking at the American Philosophical Society. The members of the faculty must have wondered at my invasion of their library.

When the manuscript of *Earth in Upheaval* was complete, I asked Professor Jepsen to read it; he pleasantly consented, but after a while he called me back and asked to be excused from the task since there was opposition in the department. However, in Professor Jepsen's paleontology course at Princeton, *Earth in Upheaval* was required reading for the next two decades, from its publication on.

Almost a year had passed since the publication of *Earth in Upheaval,* and I had not heard of any reaction by the faculty or the student body in Princeton. Then, in October 1956, a graduate student came to ask me to speak before the students and the faculty of the geology department. I saw a good augury in the fact that the visitor brought with him an issue of the *Journal of Geology* with an article on the Columbia Plateau. "Your description of the catastrophic origin of this plateau is surpassed by the finds of the survey by the authors of the article," he said. It was not easy to overshadow my description of that catastrophe. I actually indulged in poetry when I wrote on page 88 in *Earth in Upheaval:*

> Only a few thousand years ago lava flowed there over an area larger than France, Switzerland and Belgium combined; it flowed not as a creek, not as a river, not even as an overflowing stream, but as a flood, deluging horizon after horizon, filling all the valleys, devouring all the forests and habitations, steaming large lakes out of existence as though they were little potholes filled with water, swelling ever higher and overtopping mountains and burying them deep beneath molten stone, boiling and bubbling, thousands of feet thick, billions of tons heavy.

I agreed to speak but stipulated that my listeners should read my book first. On November 30, 1956, I spoke in Guyot Hall to the graduate students, the seniors, and their professors of the Geology Department on the subject "The Common Frontier of Geology with Astronomy, Archaeology and Folklore." The atmosphere was friendly. During the question period Professor Harry H. Hess, head of the department, participated, too. When the talk was over, he asked me to walk with him in the dark to our homes and continue the discussion. Parting, he gave me his paper on submarine formations in the Pacific (guyots) and the isostatic submersion of the oceanic floor, written in 1946. I asked if he would agree to submit several suggestions for inclusion into the program of the International Geophysical Year, since coming directly from me, they would be disregarded. He agreed.

Upon reading Hess's paper I wrote a constructive, in parts unsparing, criticism and sent it to him "for whatever it is worth" together with a list of measurements and tests for inclusion into the program of the IGY, which was to start seven months later.*

I mailed my letter on December 5, 1956. Professor Hess proved to be a man who could take criticism even from an outsider. On January 2 he wrote me: "Your comments on guyots are acute. You have put your finger on most of the deficiencies of my hypothesis as it stood in 1946. Perhaps you would like some further explanation." He compiled for me a page of figures and measurements pertinent to the problem of his paper. When he wrote me that he would pass my list of problems for testing to the person in charge of the program of the International Geophysical Year, he added:

> I take a rather gloomy view of IGY and doubt if anything of much interest will come of it. Fifty-six million dollars will pro-

* The list is reproduced in "H. H. Hess and My Memoranda," *Pensée*, vol. II (Fall 1972); reprinted in *Velikovsky Reconsidered.*

> duce a lot of scurrying back and forth to the South Pole and an indigestible mass of random observations on everything. Scientific discoveries and ideas are produced by the intuition, creativeness and genius of a man. Dollars of themselves don't produce this, any more than they could be expected to produce another Mona Lisa. This is something which I believe you can readily understand.

Hess forwarded my list of proposals to the IGY committee.* The first of the suggested projects—to investigate the Earth's magnetic field above the ionosphere—had been, according to Edward Hulburt, one of the scientists in charge of the program, considered by the planning committee. In my Forum lecture of October 14, 1953, I had already claimed the existence of a magnetosphere above the ionosphere.†

Although Hulburt referred to the plan of measuring the strength of the magnetic field above the ionosphere as considered for the program, the fact is that the discovery of the Van Allen belts, the main achievement of IGY, was not anticipated or considered: When no charged particles were registered at a certain altitude, James van Allen of the University of Iowa was startled, but one of his co-workers suggested that possibly the recording apparatus was jammed by too many charged particles. The apparatus was modified and the belts were discovered. At the beginning they were featured in the form of two doughnuts; only much later was it recognized that on the anti-solar side the belts are stretched far out. But in my memo, as also in the Forum lecture, I visualized a magnetosphere reaching as far as the lunar orbit.

Another claim made in my Forum lecture of 1953—namely that Jupiter could be a source of radio signals—had been confirmed in the spring of 1955, as told in a preceding section.

Years later Hess took the initiative to organize open discussions about my work. One of these was to be a debate on evolution based on the uniformitarian principle versus evolution based mainly on cataclysmic events. My opponent should have been Princeton professor of biology, Colin Pittendrigh. There was a mutual respect between us (earlier he had visited me and also inscribed to me a biology text that he coauthored with G. G. Simpson, my early antagonist), but Pittendrigh insisted that the problem of extinction in the

* The following is taken from Velikovsky's article "H. H. Hess and My Memoranda," *Pensée* IVR II (1972).

† The lecture was printed as a supplement to *Earth in Upheaval.*

animal kingdom should not be a part of the debate. I could not see how the two parts of the evolutionary problem—the evolution of new species and the extinction of the old—could be separated in a meaningful debate. It appeared that the friendly relations between us were in jeopardy. Hess, without fanfare, offered to be my opponent.

Once, when I exhorted Hess to reread a chapter in *Earth in Upheaval,* he replied that he knew the book by heart.

In debate with me at my occasional lectures at the geology department, Hess ascribed the reversal of magnetic orientation in rocks to a spontaneous process in the minerals. But when he finally realized that such spontaneous reversals could not occur simultaneously in rocks of various compositions, he volunteered to tell me that he was wrong.

When, years after my first memo of December 5, 1956, he read or heard a paper concerning the reversal of the direction of winding in fossil vines and shells from both Southern and Northern hemispheres, he was pleased to let me know that the claims the IGY would not investigate were confirmed by independent research.

Of people who were prominent in their fields and who, since the beginning of my work and through the years showed me more than casual interest and sympathy, I name Robert Pfeiffer, orientalist and biblical scholar; Horace Kallen, philosopher and educator; Walter S. Adams, astronomer; Albert Einstein; and Harry Hess. They were few, but each of them was great as a human being.

ONLY A STONE'S THROW FROM MACMILLAN

HOW IS IT NOW with the textbook department, in the wake of the storm that was unleashed in 1950 from many observatories and laboratories? Are textbooks being discarded or rewritten? Not yet. But changes creep in one by one. In the books on geology new sections appear dealing with sudden drops in the level of the oceans and the sudden uplift of mountains, and these processes are assigned to a time only a few thousand years ago; drastic climatic changes, too, are said to have occurred all over the globe; the ice ages are brought much closer to our time. Many new finds are announced in the records of explorers, but these have not yet penetrated into the textbooks. New great meteoric craters are described, land beaches are found in the depths of the ocean, and the nickel content of the oceanic beds is regarded as a vestige of immense showers of meteorites. The reversed magnetic orientation of rocks and lavas, and the abnormally high remanent magnetic fields in ancient rocks are introduced into science as puzzling phenomena, contradicting scientific theories and even natural laws.

In the vestibule of the textbook department are also gathered many facts from the domain of astronomy that attest to the existence of unlawful phenomena. The sun emits radio noises which by its heat alone it could not produce. The sun has an atmosphere which is much hotter in its corona, or outer envelope, than in its photosphere, under the corona. The sun gives off gases that follow strange trajectories and then fall without acceleration. The planets influence terrestrial radio reception. The solar tides in the upper atmosphere, on the day and on the night sides, are much greater than the lunar tides.

Another crowd of illegal facts comes from the spades of archaeologists and from the desks of decipherers. Several hundred years are unaccounted for in the Helladic past; all the sites of the ancient East disclose signs of great natural catastrophes.

The textbook department buzzes with facts clamoring for admission. Each of them insists, "I am a fact," and each asks to be allowed in. "Wait a little," every one of them is told by a courteous attendant. "First, an explanation of your existence must be found." And here and there, after long waiting, they are granted admission—not all at the same time, only as single individuals, one by one, on condition that they do not make a disturbance, so that the old textbooks can take them between their covers without succumbing to senescence and shock. Often these finds are absorbed into the textbooks with the introductory words "As we have always believed . . ."

Paraphrasing Louis Agassiz, "Every great scientific truth goes through three stages. First, people say it conflicts with science.* Next, they say it has been discovered before. Lastly, they say they have always believed it."

Only daring minds are prepared to correlate enough unexplained phenomena, old and new, in many fields, and thus to recognize that a revolution is mandatory. Daring and imaginative minds, though few, are never entirely lacking.

Only a stone's throw from Macmillan on Fifth Avenue, the house that parted with *Worlds in Collision,* is the School of Education of New York University. The other day I received, enclosed in a letter from a student, the list of required reading on history: H. S. Commager, *The American Mind* (1950); H. G. Wells, *The Outline of History* (1920); Herbert Muller, *The Uses of the Past* (1952); Immanuel Velikovsky, *Ages in Chaos* (1952); Immanuel Velikovsky, *Worlds in Collision* (1950).

The accompanying letter read:

> Dean Ralph S. Pickett is giving this particular course which is called *Integrated Arts and Sciences* and incidentally it is a wonderful course. It is given on an undergraduate level for

* Agassiz has "with the Bible."

> juniors and seniors. Dean Pickett thinks the world of you, in fact he said something to the effect that you are one of the greatest thinkers we have today. This course is given at New York University, School of Education.

The dean of that school was, by basic education, a civil engineer. It is not an insignificant fact that among my supporters, judging by the letters received from many countries, civil engineers constitute a leading group. It is also cause for a little reflection that *Worlds in Collision* and *Ages in Chaos* are required reading in the university whose windows look out on the Macmillan building where, on May 25, 1950, I ventured to predict that such an hour would come.

I CLEAR MY DESK

Is a theory right? Should its publication be suppressed? These are two separate problems. It must be made clear that even if a theory is wrong, it has the right to be presented for public hearing. Science and scholarship progress by trial and error. Scores of theories concerning the cause of the ice ages were published in the last 100 years, yet only one of them, if any, could be right. A theory when made public is debated. If proved wrong, it is rejected; if proved right, it is accepted. It may first be accepted as being right, and later shown to be wrong, or first rejected as being wrong and then, possibly years later, demonstrated to be right.

I wrote these pages to defend my right to publish my books and the right of others to accept or reject my views. I wrote them also to protect the rights of others who may have unconventional views so that they are able to express themselves without fear. To oppose a theory by suppression is a perversion of the natural process of science. Independently of whether my theories are right or wrong, the forms of reaction were—and still are—clearly unreasonable.

As a psychoanalyst I have analyzed the sources of the fury and the roots of the blind opposition to my theories, but I omit to add a psychoanalytical discourse to this book, already larger than contemplated. Security of accepted views and fear of novelty; protection of interests vested in time and efforts spent; articles and books published, positions and names acquired—these are only a few of the motives, rather on the surface. Among the deeper motives may be a mental reservation that the new solution, though radically different from the dominant views, could be right. "We are most likely to get angry and excited in our opposition to some idea when we ourselves are not quite certain of our position, and are inwardly tempted to take the other side" (Thomas Mann).

As I remarked in the Foreword to *Ages in Chaos,* we have a way by which to know whether or not a book is spurious: Never in the history of science has a spurious book aroused a storm of anger among members of scientific bodies. But there has been a storm every time a leaf in the book of knowledge has been turned over.

All this having been said and documented, I clear my desk of these papers and spread there again the material for the next piece of work. The last word and warning are left to Hermann J. Muller, the renowned explorer of mutations in living organisms:*

> Even yet, the very findings of science that are of the greatest significance for a deeper understanding of ourselves and of the universe are the most apt to arouse concerted opposition from powerfully organized groups representing established ideologies and institutions that the new knowledge would upset; hence, even in western civilization, persistent vigilance and endeavor are necessary in the defense of the honest search for truth. . . .

* H. J. Muller, "Science in Bondage," *Science* (January 1951).

EPILOGUE

SINCE 1956, when the first draft of this book was completed, there has been an increasing interest in Velikovsky's work primarily because the space age, which began in 1957, brought a remarkable record of additional confirmations of his advance claims. Wherever the investigators have looked—Earth and Moon, Sun, the planets with their moons—the story has been the same: Their findings were in accord with Velikovsky's concept of the recent history of the solar system, while the conventional views had to be revised, re-evaluated, or supported with *ad-hoc* explanations.

The electromagnetism that astronomers disparaged in 1950 has come to be seen as playing a major role in cosmic processes. Youthful features have been found on Venus and Mars. Jupiter and Saturn have been found to be considerably more active than the cold, dead planets they were thought to be. Recent space data have led some astronomers to consider that Mercury, and the satellites of Saturn underwent major orbital changes. Repeated major faunal extinctions are now thought to have been caused by extraterrestrial impacts. Even in the field of archaeology, where the available evidence grows more slowly than in the space sciences, more and more findings have confirmed Velikovsky's earlier claims.

On the basis of his understanding that Venus is a relative newcomer to the planetary system, Velikovsky claimed that the planet was candescently hot within historical times and that even today "Venus gives off heat" (*Worlds in Collision,* pages 370–71, "Thermal Balance of Venus"). Up to 1959 its ground temperature was estimated (e.g., by V. A. Firsoff) to be an Earth-like 63 degrees Fahrenheit. In 1961, on the basis of radar measurements it was found to be 600 degrees Fahrenheit. F. D. Drake wrote: "We would have expected a temperature only slightly greater than that of earth, whereas the actual temperature is several hundred degrees above the boiling point of water." The finding was "a surprise . . . in a field in which the fewest surprises were expected" (*Physics Today*, Vol. 14, No. 4, 1961). In 1962 Mariner 2 found the temperature to be even higher—800 degrees Fahrenheit; currently Venus's surface temperature is measured at nearly 900 degrees Fahrenheit, some 300 degrees higher than the temperature at which lead melts.

In 1962 radio astronomers discovered that Venus rotates retrogradely (i.e., in the opposite direction from all the other planets). At the meeting of the American Geophysical Union in December 1962 a scientist commented: "Maybe Venus was created apart from the other planets, perhaps as a secondary solar explosion, or perhaps in a collision of planets."

In October 1975 two Soviet probes landed on the sunlit side of Venus. An article in *Aviation Week and Space Technology,* "Data Show Venus Young, Evolving Planet," noted that the results "tend to support the idea that Venus is a planet in an early cooldown phase of evolution rather than in a final stage of suffocation in a thickening atmospheric greenhouse."

In 1979 spokesmen for the research team of Pioneer Venus, John Hoffman and Thomas Donahue, "stunned" their colleagues by reporting that the Pioneer Venus probes had detected in Venus's atmosphere hundreds of times as much Ar-36 as is found in that of the Earth. They were quoted as saying that there was "something unexpected and different about Venus, pointing scientists toward a major discovery." "It means that either Venus was formed from different substances than [sic] the rest of the solar system, or that the formation process was different. . . ." "The cosmogonic implications on the formation of the solar system are staggering."*

As described in the section "Jove's Thunderbolts," Velikovsky claimed that Jupiter sends out radio noises; he stated this on October 14, 1953, in his forum lecture at the Princeton Graduate College. In 1954, in his correspondence with Einstein, Velikovsky

* See *Popular Science,* April 1979.

offered this claim as a crucial test of his theories. In 1955 B. F. Burke and K. L. Franklin discovered Jupiter's radio noises. For weeks neither man could believe the noises were actually emitted by Jupiter.

Velikovsky claimed the existence of a magnetosphere above the terrestrial ionosphere that would sensitively reach as far as the Moon (memorandum of December 5, 1956, submitted by Velikovsky through Professor Harry H. Hess to the committee of the International Geophysical Year). The most significant discovery of the IGY (1958), made by James A. Van Allen, was the existence of a magnetosphere beyond the ionosphere. Its presence at the lunar orbit and beyond was detected by Van Ness in 1964.

In the December 21, 1962, issue of *Science,* V. Bargmann, professor of physics at Princeton University, and Lloyd Motz, professor of astronomy at Columbia University, published a letter in which they documented Velikovsky's correct predictions of the radio noises emitted by Jupiter, the existence of a magnetosphere around Earth, and the very high temperature of Venus (the first and the last Velikovsky claimed as crucial tests; both were regarded as impossible). Bargmann and Motz concluded the letter, without accepting Velikovsky's theories, as follows: "We feel compelled to make this statement to establish Velikovsky's priority of prediction of these [three] points and to urge, in view of these prognostications, that his other conclusions be objectively re-examined."

In 1969 Velikovsky made a number of predictions concerning the Moon, which he listed in a memorandum submitted to the Space Science Board of the National Academy of Sciences more than two months before the first lunar landing. He reiterated his predictions in an article he wrote at the invitation of the editors of *The New York Times,* which appeared on July 21, 1969 the day it was announced that man had first stepped on the Moon. Among his predictions were:

> A few feet under the lunar surface a steep thermal gradient would be found, with heat flowing to the surface.
>
> Remanent magnetism would be discovered in lunar rocks and lavas, though the Moon itself possesses hardly any magnetic field.
>
> Traces of hydrocarbons or their derivatives (carbides) would be discovered.

Thermoluminescence dating of the lunar rocks would show the recentness of the last heating (melting) of the lunar surface.

Frequent moonquakes would be detected.

The Apollo landings soon confirmed all of these prognostications. The lunar findings evoked exclamations of surprise and led to some farfetched *ad-hoc* hypotheses.

In celestial mechanics all new evidence has conjured against the concept—basic in science until very recently—that gravitation and inertia are the only forces in action in the celestial sphere. The new discoveries are the interplanetary magnetic field centered on the sun and rotating with it; the solar plasma; the terrestrial magnetosphere; and the enormously powerful magnetic envelope around Jupiter through which the Galilean satellites plow, themselves influencing the Jovian radio signals. By 1969 Velikovsky could write: "Who is the physicist that would insist that Jupiter, traveling with its powerful magnetosphere through the interplanetary magnetic field, is not affected by it? Or that the Jovian satellites are not influenced in their motions by the magnetic field of their primary?"* (A decade later Voyager would find the Jovian magnetosphere to be even stronger and more extensive than data available in 1969 suggested.) In 1979 Bernard Lovell wrote: "The recognition during the last ten or twenty years that magnetic fields must have a significant role in the Universe has provided an escape from the problem of the mass distribution in the solar system: it is argued that the unusual distribution could result from a magnetic coupling between the sun and the planetary disk."†

In the field of archaeology, two excavations of the 1950's are notable:

Kathleen Kenyon found that the walls of Jericho fell at the end of the Middle Kingdom. Thus the Israelites arriving there after the Exodus would have found no walls, since according to the conventional chronology the Exodus took place some 500 years *after* the end of the Middle Kingdom.‡ However, according to the revised chronology of *Ages in Chaos,* the Exodus took place precisely at the end of the Middle Kingdom.

Yigael Yadin found that Hazor was an important city during the

* *The New York Times,* July 21, 1969.

† Bernard Lovell, *In the Center of Immensities* (New York, 1978). See also the article by Leon Golub, "Solar Magnetism: A New Look," *Astronomy* (March 1981), pp. 66–71.

‡ Kathleen Kenyon, *Digging Up Jericho* (London, 1957).

Hyksos period but hardly existed in the time of the Judges—thus, according to the conventional chronology, the war with Hazor in the time of Deborah could not have taken place.* However, according to the revised chronology, the time of the Judges exactly coincided with the Hyksos period.

These matters are discussed at length in Velikovsky's forthcoming book, *The Test of Time,* which documents how geological, astronomical, and other discoveries subsequent to the initial presentation of Velikovsky's theories have confirmed the predictions that were deduced from those theories and have thus greatly strengthened the case for them.

This successful track record of Velikovsky's work has led to an ever-growing interest in the man and his ideas. In the 1960's and 1970's he received scores of invitations to speak on college and university campuses throughout the United States and Canada.

On February 17, 1972, at the invitation of the Society of Harvard Engineers and Scientists, he addressed an audience of more than 900 graduates, undergraduates, faculty, and alumni at Harvard University. The magazine *Pensée* reported:

> Velikovsky did not take advantage of the occasion by attempting to pay old debts. . . . Characteristically he did not even mention his sometimes libelous Harvard critics, but instead praised the late Robert Pfeiffer, former chairman of the Department of Semitic Languages . . . [who had] retained an open and fair mind.

On August 14, 1972, Velikovsky lectured and consulted at the invitation of NASA's Ames Space Research Center in California, and on December 10, 1973, he spoke before a capacity audience of scientists and engineers of the NASA Langley Space Research Center in Virginia.

As a result of the ever-growing academic and scientific interest in Velikovsky, some members of the scientific establishment made a new effort to discredit his theories and to deny him the priority of his predictions. A symposium, "Velikovsky's Challenge to Science," sponsored by the American Association for the Advancement of Science, was held on February 25, 1974, in San Francisco. There Velikovsky debated four opponents. The complete tapes of the speeches

* Yigael Yadin, "Excavations at Hazor (1955–1958)" in *The Biblical Archaeologist Reader* (New York, 1961).

and of the debates document that the opposing scientists again failed in their effort to refute him.

The critics' arguments, which were published two and a half years later in *Scientists Confront Velikovsky* (1977) (without the debates and without the participation of Velikovsky), were answered in *Velikovsky and Establishment Science* (1977), and in *Scientists Confront Scientists Who Confront Velikovsky* (1978), both published by KRONOS Press.* The complete story of that debate and its continuing aftermath will be discussed in detail in a forthcoming book by Velikovsky and Professor Lynn Rose.

In May of the same year (1974), at a symposium at Lethbridge University, Alberta, Canada, Velikovsky received an honorary doctorate in arts and science. The papers read at this symposium, including Velikovsky's lecture and his acceptance speeches to the faculty and students, were later published in a book, *Recollections of a Fallen Sky: Velikovsky and Cultural Amnesia* (1978). Also in 1974, Velikovsky participated in various symposia on his work at McMaster University in Hamilton, Ontario (June 17–19, 1974) and at Duquesne University in Pittsburgh, Pennsylvania (October 27–29, 1974), as well as at Notre Dame University, South Bend, Indiana (November 2, 1974).

Numerous books have been published on Velikovsky's work and its reception. These include *The Velikovsky Affair* (1966), which grew out of a special issue of the *American Behavioral Scientist* (September 1963); *Velikovsky Reconsidered* (1976), which consists of articles from the ten issues of *Pensée* devoted to a reevaluation of Velikovsky's work (1972–1975); and *The Age of Velikovsky* (1976), a short summary of Velikovsky's books and their impact, written by the physicist Dr. C. J. Ransom.

Many scientists, scholars, and teachers around the world are pursuing research based on Velikovsky's work, with more joining the ranks each year. Many colleges and universities offer courses and seminars on Velikovsky and include his books on required reading lists. Several journals are devoted to discussion of Velikovsky's work—notably *KRONOS*, published at Glassboro State College, New Jersey.

The most exciting scientific controversies of the 1980's appear to be revolving around alternatives to Darwinian evolution (ac-

* See also *The Age of Velikovsky* (1976) by C. J. Ransom, Chapter 8, and *Velikovsky and His Critics* by Shane Mage (1978).

tually a long-overdue discussion of points raised by Velikovsky in *Earth in Upheaval* in 1955); the problem of the cause of mass faunal extinctions in past ages (the most popular current theory invokes collisions between Earth and comets or meteorites*—again, see *Earth in Upheaval*), and the origin of catastrophic features on the bodies of the solar system.

Evidently establishment science is now beginning to accept Velikovsky's main theses: (1) that there were global catastrophes of extraterrestrial origin that caused mass faunal extinctions; (2) that Venus was formed differently from the other planets of the solar system and that it probably suffered some collision;† and (3) that electromagnetic forces must play a role in the solar system. There are some who view these as "new" theories and problems, but there are many who, familiar with Velikovsky's writings, see these developments as merely a stage in the growing acceptance of Velikovsky's work.

Worlds in Collision created one of the great controversies in the history of science. Yet, as Velikovsky explained in the Preface to *The Test of Time,*

> "I was compelled by logic and by evidence to penetrate into so many premises of the house of science. I freely admit to having repeatedly caused fires, though the candle in my hand was carried only for illumination."

* L. W. Alvarez et al., "Extraterrestrial Causes for the Cretaceous-Tertiary Extinctions," *Science*, 208 (1980), p. 1095.

† S. F. Singer, *Science* 170 (1970), p. 1196.

INDEX